Building Databases for Global Science

Building Databases for Global Science

Edited by

Helen Mounsey

Department of Geography,
Birkbeck College, London

General Editor

Roger F Tomlinson

Tomlinson Associates Ltd,
Ottawa, Canada

The Proceedings of the first meeting of the International Geographical Union Global Database Planning Project, held at Tylney Hall, Hampshire, UK, 9-13 May 1988.

Taylor & Francis
London ● New York ● Philadelphia
1988

UK   Taylor & Francis Ltd, 4 John St., London WC1N 2ET

USA   Taylor & Francis Inc., 242 Cherry St., Philadelphia,
PA 19106-1906

Copyright © Taylor & Francis Ltd 1988

British Library Cataloguing in Publication Data

Building databases for global science.
    1. Geography. Information systems. Machine-readable files
    I. Mounsey, Helen   II. Tomlinson, Roger
    F 910′.28′5

    ISBN 0-85066-485-3

Library of Congress Cataloging in Publication Data is available

Cover design by Russell Beach
Printed in Great Britain by Taylor & Francis (Printers) Ltd.,
Basingstoke, Hampshire.

Contents

PREFACE

It is now widely recognised that many processes acting at a global scale have significant local impact; conversely, the summation of many local processes may have significant global impact. This volume records the proceedings of a meeting held to discuss the provision of spatial databases which may help us to examine complex real-world problems on a global scale, studies only possible through the increasing sophistication of today's technology.

This meeting, then, the first of the International Geographical Union's Global Database Planning Project, was convened to examine the provision of databases to the International Geosphere Biosphere Programme. It was held at Tylney Hall, Rotherwick, Hampshire, from May 9th - 13th, 1988, and attended by some 50 participants from North America, Europe, China and the USSR. After a welcome by Lord Shackleton, the meeting was opened by the Chairman of the Organising Committee, Roger Tomlinson: his opening remarks provide a summary of the background to, and aims of, the meeting, and form part one of this volume.

Section two records the day spent reviewing some principles and problems in the design of global databases: seven papers examining data sources, the efficient design of databases, problems of resolution and accuracy, and legal issues, are included. A further day and a half were spent discussing existing and planned databases held by national and international agencies and scientific bodies: these papers form part three of this volume.

Throughout the meeting, a number of rapporteurs were asked to summarize the papers and discussions, and to identify critical issues arising. Their reports were then prepared overnight, and distributed the following day for further discussion. Unfortunately, space does not permit the inclusion of their excellent summaries here; instead, Terry Coppock has drawn together their work and presented an overall conclusion in part four of this volume. Also included in this part is Mike Goodchild's presentation to a wide audience at the Royal Society, on the final day of our meeting.

Preface

A large number of people were involved in the organisation of the meeting; space permits the naming of only a few, but thanks go to them all. Specifically, the meeting would not have taken place without the foresight and imagination of Roger Tomlinson, Chairman of the Organising Committee: many thanks go to him and to his two Vice-Chairmen, Mike Goodchild and David Rhind. That the meeting ran exceptionally smoothly was due to tremendous work behind the scenes by Lila Tomlinson, Sue Stewart and Fiona Goodchild, and prior to the meeting by Geoff Davenport, Lyndan Gray, Merle Abbott and Laurie Becker of Birkbeck College: many thanks.

Single handed, it would not have been possible to deliver this book to the publishers within three weeks of the close of the meeting; thanks go to everyone who made this possible, especially to the contributing authors, and to colleagues at Birkbeck College, for tolerating my endless demands on their time and patience. In particular, thanks to Duane Marble for much of the early work on the papers; to Vince Andrews and Nigel Foster for technical wizardry (especially to the former for deciphering many mysterious electronic mail addresses, a facility of untold benefit throughout the entire organisation of the meeting); to Tina Buckle and George Reeve for production of some of the illustrations; to Louise Sage for some very last minute secretarial assistance; and finally to Robin Mellors, of Taylor and Francis, for staying remarkably calm throughout! Many thanks go to them all.

Helen Mounsey.

Department of Geography,
Birkbeck College,
University of London.

June, 1988.

PARTICIPANTS

Dr. Joe H. ALLEN
ICSU Panel on World Data Centres,
NOAA, 325 Broadway, Boulder, CA 80303, USA.

Mr. F.W.G. BAKER
ICSU Secretariat
Boulevarde de Montmorency 51, 75016 Paris, France.

Dr. Larry BAND
Department of Geography
University of Toronto, Toronto, Ontario, M5S 1A1, Canada.

Dr. Claude BARDINET
CODATA Task Group on Multisatellite Thematic Mapping
Ecole Superieure des Mines, Rue Claude-Daunesse, Sophia-
Antipolis, Valbonne-Cedex, F 06565, France.

Dr. Marion F. BAUMGARDNER
International Society for Soil Science (SOTER)
Department of Agronomy, Purdue University, West Lafayette,
Indiana, 47907-7899, USA.

Dr. David P. BICKMORE
IGU/ICA Joint Working Group on Environmental Atlases & Maps
28 Northmoor Road, Oxford OX2 6UR, UK.

Dr. V.G. BOLDIREV
World Meteorological Organisation
World Climate Programme, 41 Guiseppe-Motta, Case Postale 5,
CH 1211 Geneva 20, Switzerland.

Dr. Joe H. BREDEKAMP
National Aeronautics and Space Administration
Information Systems, 600 Independence Ave SW, Code EC Room
125, Washington DC 20546, USA.

Dr. David J. BRIGGS
Whimbrel Consultants Ltd.
Rue van Campenhout 10, Brussels, B 1040, Belgium.

Participants

Dr. CHEN SHUPENG
Laboratory of Resources and Environment Information System
Institute of Geography, Academy of Sciences of the P.R.
China, Building 917, Datun Rd, Beishatan Dewai, Beijing
100012, PR China.

Lord CHORLEY
President, The Royal Geographical Society
Kensington Gore, London SW7, UK.

Dr. David CLARK
National Oceanic and Atmospheric Administration
National Geophysical Data Centre, NOAA Code E/GCx1, 325
Broadway, Boulder CO, 80303, USA.

Dr. J. Terry COPPOCK
Department of Geography
University of Edinburgh, Drummond Street, Edinburgh EH8
9PX, Scotland.

Mr. Jack DANGERMOND
Environmental Systems Research Institute
380 New York Street, Redlands, CA 92373, USA.

Dr. David DANKO
Defence Mapping Agency
DMA Systems Centre, Systems Development Group, 8301
Greensboro Dr. Suite 800, McLean, Virginia 22102, USA.

Dr. Alexander V. DROZDOV
Institute of Geography, Academy of Sciences of the USSR
Staromonetny per. 29, Moscow 109017, USSR.

Dr. Earl F. EPSTEIN
National Oceanic and Atmospheric Administration
3 Pook's Hill Road #616, Bethesda, MD, 20814, USA.

Dr. Jack E. ESTES
Department of Geography
University of California, Santa Barbara, CA 93106, USA.

Dr. Michael F. GOODCHILD
Department of Geography
University of Western Ontario, London, Ontario, N6A 5C2,
Canada.

Participants

Dr. Stephen C. GUPTILL
United States Geological Survey
National Mapping Division, Office of Research, 521 National
Centre, Reston, VA 22092, USA.

Dr. Anne HENDERSON-SELLERS
Department of Geography, University of Liverpool, Roxby
Building, PO Box 147, Liverpool L69 3BX, UK.

Dr. Gary W. HILL
United States Geological Survey
Office of Energy and Marine Geology, USGS National Center,
WGS-Mail Stop 915, Reston, VA 22092, USA.

Dr. Mike J. JACKSON
Laserscan Laboratories
Cambridge Science Park, Milton Road, Cambridge CB4 4BH, UK.

Mr. Denny KALENSKY
Food and Agriculture Organisation of the United Nations
Research Technology Division, FAO, Via delle Terme di
Caracalla, 00100 Rome, Italy.

Mr. Wayne LUSCOMBE
The World Bank
Environment Department, 1818 H. Street N.W., Washington DC
20433, USA.

Dr. Duane F. MARBLE
Department of Geography
Ohio State University, Columbus, Ohio, 43210, USA.

Dr. David MARK
Department of Geography
State University of New York at Buffalo, Buffalo, New York
14260, USA.

Dr. Wayne MOONEYHAN
United Nations Environment Programme
GRID Processor Facility, 6 rue de la Gabelle, Carouge, CH
1227, Switzerland.

Dr. Helen M. MOUNSEY
Department of Geography
Birkbeck College, University of London, 7-15 Gresse Street,
London W1P 1PA, UK.

Participants

Dr. Robin PELLEW
International Union for the Conservation of Nature
Conservation Monitoring Centre, 219(c) Huntingdon Road,
Cambridge CB3 0DL, UK.

Dr. Donna J. PEUQUET
Department of Geography
Penn State University, University Park, PA 16802, USA.

Dr. David W. RHIND
Department of Geography
Birkbeck College, University of London, 7-15 Gresse Street,
London W1P 1PA, UK.

Dr. Paul G. RISSER
ICSU Scientific Committee on Problems of the Environment
Scholes Hall 108, The University of New Mexico,
Albuquerque, New Mexico 87131, USA.

Dr. Sergei B. ROSTOTSKY
IGU Commission on Global Monitoring and Forecasting
Institute of Geography, Academy of Sciences of the USSR
Staromonetny per. 29, Moscow 109017, USSR.

Dr. Alan SCHMIDT
PRIME Computer Inc.
Prime Park, Nattick, Mass, 01760, USA.

Dr. Peter SCOTT
President, International Geographical Union
Department of Geography, University of Tasmania, Hobart,
Tasmania 7001, Australia.

Dr. V. SEDOV
Intergovernmental Oceanographic Commission
Place de Fontenoy, 75700 Paris, France.

Dr. David S. SIMONETT
Department of Geography
University of California, Santa Barbara, CA 93106, USA.

Mr. Gurmakh SINGH
Pinpoint Ltd.
Mercury House, 117 Waterloo Road, London SE1 8UL, UK.

Mr. Brian J. TEW
Systems and Techniques Unit, Royal Engineers
Elmwood Avenue, Feltham, Middlesex TW13 7AF, UK.

Participants

Dr. Waldo R. TOBLER
Department of Geography
University of California, Santa Barbara, CA 93106, USA.

Dr. Roger F. TOMLINSON
Tomlinson Associates Ltd.
17 Kippewa Drive, Ottawa, Ontario, K1S 3G3, Canada.

Dr. John TOWNSHEND
NERC Unit for Thematic Information Systems
Department of Geography, University of Reading, PO Box 227,
Reading RG6 2AB, UK.

Dr. S. UNNINAYAR
United Nations Environment Programme
GRID Processor Facility, Rue de la Gabelle 6, 1227 Carouge,
Geneva, Switzerland.

Dr. Vladimir V. VISKOV
Soviet Geophysical Committee
Academy of Sciences of the USSR, ul Molodezhnaya 3, Moscow
117296, USSR.

Dr. John WOODS
Director, Oceanographic and Atmospheric Sciences
Natural Environment Research Council, Polaris House, North
Star Way, Swindon, Wilts SN2 1EU, UK.

Dr. Barry K. WYATT
Institute of Terrestrial Ecology
NERC, Bangor Research Station, Penrhos Road, Bangor,
Gwynedd LL57 2LQ, UK.

Dr. ZHANG JIN
Laboratory of Resources and Environment Information System
Institute of Geography, Academy of Sciences of the P.R.
China, Building 917, Datun Rd, Beishatan Dewai, Beijing
100012, PR China.

SPONSORS

The IGU Global Database Planning Project wishes to acknowledge with thanks the support of:

The Association of American Geographers
AutoCarto London 1986
Canadian Association of Geographers
The European Commission
Environmental Systems Research Institute
ICSU International Geosphere Biosphere Programme
National Science Foundation, USA
Natural Environment Research Council, UK
Pergamon Press, UK
The Royal Geographical Society, UK
The Royal Society
United States Geological Survey
The World Bank

OPENING REMARKS

Dr. R.F. Tomlinson

This is a meeting on global database planning and the need for it. I should make it clear from the outset that the International Geographical Union has no intent to create any global cartographic database. It is, however, vitally concerned with the design and structure of such databases because the way in which earth observations are eventually stored and integrated will effectively determine the degree to which global spatial processes can be understood. Geographers have a vital interest in this field, as the understanding of spatial processes, particularly those involving complex real-world relationships between man and the land, is fundamental to geography as a discipline. Also, the skills of geographers in spatial data handling and analysis are seen to be relevant to many aspects of this work.

The concept of global cartographic databases capable of serving many needs and contributing to the solving of complex real-world problems is considered to be a realizable prospect. It is an idea whose time has come. Quite simply, there are perceived needs for such capabilities and there is an expectation in science at large that computer hardware and software will in future provide the necessary technical capability. That may or may not be an illusion, but that is certainly a perception.

There is a wide range of perceived needs for geographical databases and spatial analysis of multi-national scope. I am referring here not to the gathering of geo-referenced data or the making of maps, but to the creation of digital databases, derived from such data, in a form amenable to subsequent analysis. I am talking about the data system needed to underpin our understanding of large parts of the globe. There are certainly problems of multi-national scope that we all can recognize: desertification in the Sahara extending over a dozen countries for which there are already databases of over a million polygons in place; acid rain that devastates the forests in North America and Europe; monitoring of fallout from nuclear disaster over many countries; tracking outbreaks of disease, not the least of which is the frightening epidemic of AIDS we hear so much about. We can think in terms of tracking insect infestations over several countries; we can talk about monitoring the reduction of the world's biomass reduction and its effect on climate - it is said that we are now losing trees at a rate equivalent to the area of Delaware each week in terms of reduction in that biomass. We see the need for data for modelling world climate, for oceanographic modelling, for marine ecological modelling over broad areas, and for multinational environmental and conservation issues that underlie databases such as the CORINE database for the whole of European Community. There are perceived needs for multinational analysis.

The military and security agencies are perhaps the largest collectors of data derived from maps. They have vested and important interests in global navigation, targeting of weapons, mission planning, deployment of forces and simulation. Much of their work ends up in the public domain. The CIA World Data Banks I and II did so and were perhaps our first digital global reference sets. The military usually put things into the public domain because there is a benefit to them in doing so. There is a payoff in other data sets which become aligned to what they have.

The International Council of Scientific Unions' (ICSU) International Geosphere-Biosphere Programme (IGBP) expresses another important perceived need for global data. The scientific unions and the countries of the world are now gathering their forces together to describe the globe. Specifically, there is to be an attempt to describe the interactive physical and chemical processes that regulate the total earth system, the unique environment that provides for life, and the changes occurring in this system and the manner in which they influence human beings and are influenced by human actions. That is what the IGBP is to address. It will result in the development of explicit models on a global scale to guide the overall program and a quantitative exploration of the future development of the planet under changing scenarios of human and natural perturbation. Clearly this is a perceived need for global data.

Similarly, the International Social Science Council (ISSC) in cooperation with the United Nations University (UNU) and the International Federation of Institutes of Advanced Science (IFIAS) is planning a parallel program on the Human Response to Global Change. These agencies must eventually

2

concern themselves with management-level strategies for human development to ameliorate the adverse human impact on the geosphere and biosphere, and hence on the living space of mankind.

In short, in multinational programs, in military and security programs, in broad scientific programs of global change and social science programs of human response to global change, there is a perceived need for geographical analysis and spatial data on a global scale.

Activity in establishing global databases is underway on several fronts, many by agencies and organizations which are represented at this meeting. Plans to develop a world digital cartographic database called MINITOPO have been announced by the Defence Mapping Agency of the U.S.A. There are similar plans originated by the IGU/ICA Joint Working Group on Environmental Atlases and Maps (since 1987 the ICA Commission on the World Digital Database for Environmental Science), which are now supported by Pergamon and Petroconsultants. There are proposals by the International Society for Soil Science (ISSS) for a World Soils and Terrain Digital Data Base (SOTER). We will hear from the United Nations Environmental Programme (UNEP) about its Global Environmental Monitoring Systems (GEMS) and the Global Resources Information Database (GRID). We will hear about the global agriculture and food databases of the UN's Food and Agriculture Organization (FAO) and the Ocean Data System and Pilot Land Data System and other global data systems from National Aeronautics and Space Administration, U.S.A. There is also a geological control map of the world (GCMW) being proposed by the International Union of Geological Science. Other related activities whose researches have impact and which are of global scope include: the IMHF-WMO-Unesco Hydrology Project (HAPEX); the COSPAR-IAMAP International Satellite Land Surface Climatology Project (ISLSCP); the Marine Continental Margins (CONMAP) digital map data base of the U.S.G.S.; related programs such as the SCOPE-INTECOL investigations of scale related to remote sensing and the CODATA project on multi-satellite thematic mapping in Tanzania. Probably there are others.

Many of these programs will involve investment of large amounts of money, resources and time, and imply long-term commitments to specific data structures. It is also likely, given the growing perception of need for global databases by a wide variety of agencies and a similar perception that advances in computer technology will allow

3

their growth and use, that a strong tendency will develop to create other global databases of geo-referenced data. It would not surprise me if we saw tens, or even hundreds of such efforts initiated over the next decade. It is possible that those we know of now, major as they seem, are just parts of a future set.

There are problems and difficulties inherent in these efforts. Problems arise from the large volumes of spatial data (initial large size and subsequent growth). The earth has $1.5 * 10^{15}$ square meters of surface area. Even the 10-meter resolution of the SPOT satellite has $1.5 * 10^{13}$ cells. That is equal to about 15 terabytes of digital data storage. If one assumes multiple coverages, then the result is $n * 1.5 * 10^{13}$. Even at one kilometer grid cells, the result is $1.5 * 10^{8}$, and such grid cells were found in projects such as the LUNR (Land Use and Natural Resource system, New York State) to be inadequate for land use planning of the type that may be required for a human response to global change.

A notable difference exists between the volume of small-scale data (which already has high numbers) and data suitable for land-use planning purposes, which have numbers between 500 and 1,000 times greater. It has been estimated that, if the Ordnance Survey's present criteria for digital mapping of the 1:50,000 series covering western Europe were used, the resulting database would contain 50 gigabytes of data for the topographical data layer alone. The prospects are not only for very large data sets, but for very many data sets; in combination, they would create databases that would be prone to failure in subsequent analytical processes. There is a real question whether data consistency can be achieved for large, highly complex, high-resolution data sets. Our knowledge that massive inefficiencies are now encountered in very large database systems makes planning for global databases imperative.

While archival storage in computers is becoming cheaper, database storage and working storage are getting cheaper at a much slower rate. It is quite possible that the data volumes expected will be unable to be accommodated rationally and economically by advancing hardware technology. Building and mounting databases are still laborious and slow processes, even for simplistic graphic data structures.

There are inconsistencies in the map series which are used as bases for data. Accuracy may be literally unknown.

There are gaps in coverages. There are maps which are created for widely different purposes from those for which they may now be used. There may be variations between the sheets of a series. There are inconsistencies in the procedures for generalization between map series.

With respect to data structures, there is a vast and continually increasing volume of data from remote sensing sources. In my opinion, there is a need to merge these data effectively with the vast mass of geographical data archives already created as a result of ground surveys and taken from detailed aerial photography. I do not think it is possible to go forward without considering that we must sensibly integrate those two vast bodies of data. I do not believe there will be a single optimum data structure for such a combination, but rather that multiple data structures are going to have to be employed.

There will be a tendency for institutions to develop global databases on their own to serve their own constituencies; sub-constituencies will suffer. Complex problem solving, requiring the use of many databases, may well be inhibited. However, given that data structures in different systems are likely, the question arises whether data from one system can be efficiently and accurately transferred to another. As a very minimum, there is a need for an examination of the structures of proposed global systems to determine the degree of comparability, the potential cross-utilization of data and the ways in which the data from different data sources can be used effectively in complex problems. Perhaps we should also disseminate widely the results of such an examination so that future designers of other global databases can be advised. Hopefully, we can undertake that sort of examination in the short term (that is, in the next six months), perhaps early enough for existing systems to take advantage of some of the results before large sums and great efforts are committed to any one particular data structure.

One basic problem underlying data structures is the incompatible definition of data elements. Typical of this situation is the lack of common world-wide sets of definitions of categories of land use and land cover (as Duane Marble mentions in his paper for this meeting), despite attempts at such classification by the International Geographical Union's World Land Use Commission under Dudley Stamp some twenty years ago.

The case will also be made at this meeting that before data structures can be effectively designed, there must be an understanding of the needs of a significant number of the users. The question that must be addressed, then, is whether this need, or this parcel of needs, will be focussed on users concerned with the physical process models of global change in the forthcoming ICSU-IGBP, or defined by a broader constituency of users responsible, let us say, for the control and management of the factors that determine that change, the managers of human development? In other words, should global databases be adopted only for low-resolution data at scale of 1:1 million or smaller, or should a globally consistent logical schema for high-resolution data, at say the 1:50,000 scale, be considered?

There are also problems arising from integration for global information systems of data from different sources at different scales and different levels of resolution. There is a whole class of problems relating to temporal and spatial scaling that must be addressed before data can usefully be used in global models. Very little work has been done on these problems at even a regional scale, much less a global scale.

As Simonett notes in his paper at this meeting, "deep-seated issues of artefacting, indeterminancy, improper extrapolation between scales, and environmental modulation of spatial error budgets are embedded in the joint use of remote sensing and geographic information systems", and, I might add, in multi-source data use of any kind. Nevertheless, the ability to integrate data with a variety of formats (raster, vector, street address, tabular) from different sources, at different levels of reliability, at different scales, by different people with different skills, using different computers in different countries, connected by communication networks, is a very real requirement in the foreseeable future, and we are faced with the problems of meeting it. Thus, to the problems of data and data volume must be added those of data interchange formats, communications protocols for high volume geo-referenced data and error analysis in the subsequent data manipulation. Michael Goodchild's paper on spatial data analysis of spherical global scale points out how little we know about error analysis of global spatial data.

Considering multiple uses of different sources of data, we immediately run into the problems of data ownership and copyright. Epstein's paper covers some of these legal issues. Examples are concerns whether national or private

6

considerations will override international and global considerations in the provision of data; the extent to which the massive amounts of geological and geophysical data generated by oil companies are in the public domain (still a matter of some judicial decision). There is judicial confusion over the basis of protecting factual compilations (in the copyright sense); in fact, there is a lack of universal adherence to international copyright conventions. There is also the matter of the effective prohibition of use that is due to limited resources - whether or not nations are prepared to support international transfers of data - to provide the people and resources that will be required to effect the transfer. We all know about budget cuts and restrictions in government spending, and how difficult it is to get people for the most important tasks. Will international data transfer be considered one of the priorities on which scarce people and resources will indeed be spent?

There is disputed representation of international boundaries (at least 200 are under dispute at the moment). Some countries may limit their participation in global data exchange if there is a perception that such action will adversely affect their boundary claims. On the other hand, it may be possible that overriding environmental and conservation issues can overcome barriers to creating large international databases for decision making purposes, such as the CORINE database, where the Member States of the European Economic Community have decided that they will indeed overcome a number of data exchange issues to achieve that objective.

I mention the word "judicial" because judicial concerns, and writing them into law, may be something that we are years away from resolving. Perhaps we should move toward guidelines and voluntary codes that might provide an interim solution which might precede judicial solutions, perhaps drawing on the OECD experience in questions in multinational exchange of personal data, where just such guidelines were produced.

Considering the perceived needs for global databases, the activities already begun, and the problems and difficulties which we can see, the International Geographical Union (IGU) recommended to its parent organization, the International Council of Scientific Unions (ICSU), of which it was a founder member, that a project be initiated to examine the problems and identify courses of action that may minimize or resolve them. It is this project on which

7

we are embarking today. It is seen as an IGU contribution to the ICSU investigations of Global Change although the results may have somewhat wider application, particularly to the management of the human response to global change.

This project consists of two meetings starting with this first one here at Tylney in the spring of 1988, where representatives of existing and planned global digital databases and researchers in the field have been brought together to gain a better understanding of the status of current efforts and the difficulties which are being encountered. At the end of this first meeting, we should have clarified some of the problems that need to be resolved and which are of interest to the participants; the results of this first meeting will be reported to the first ICSU-IGBP data meeting in Moscow in August. In preparation for the second meeting, it may be that study groups will be formed to investigate and report further on a timetable to be decided at this meeting, with the second meeting being held perhaps before a wider audience of academic, government and private sector participants.

There are four parts to this first meeting. The first is devoted to the status reports of on-going global database activities and of related research activities that will contribute to or have need for global databases. The purpose is to find out what is going on.

The second part is formed of a series of review papers on various aspects of global database design, to raise the issues inherent in such design. The purpose is to focus on the questions that have to be resolved.

The third part of the meeting will be held in plenary, and in working groups; it will endeavour to identify problem areas and opportunities for co-operation, and to plan subsequent actions.

The fourth part, the closing session, will be held in the Royal Society. At that time, we will present the results of the week's work to a wide audience drawn from government, science, academia and business.

What do we want to come out of this meeting? First, it would be useful to identify the problems that can be recognized as impediments to the good design of global databases, to describe, specifically, the nature of the problems being faced and their implications in ways that will facilitate solutions, and further to classify those

8

problems into those which are short-term, those which are medium-term and those which are long-term. Can we thereafter recommend courses of action to resolve some of these problems? There is no preconceived set of problems or answers; they will be formulated at this meeting.

Secondly, we might try to identify the opportunities for cooperation between agencies currently involved in the design of global databases. Perhaps in the short term a useful working group would be one to review existing data structures and determine possibilities of data exchange in global databases; or in the medium term, one to examine international data exchange formats or communications protocols; or, in the longer term, to tackle a more intractable problem, one to tackle international data definition and data standards. In such working groups, a decision would have to be made whether to confine the inquiry to what is required for investigations of global change or to take a broader set of natural resources management and human responses to global change. I hope that this meeting may be a starting point for cooperation between agencies along these lines. I hope that we can, under the auspices of the IGU, forge such links of expertise. Perhaps we can create structures, working groups, study projects for cooperation. There is no doubt that these are and will be needed.

Perhaps we can also establish some guidelines for building geographic databases and information systems of global scope, knowing that there will be those who will come later into the field of designing global databases. Perhaps we can distill some of the existing experience. Perhaps we can provide some examples of what we are doing. Perhaps we can spell out the areas where the difficulties exist. Perhaps we can provide methods for avoiding some of the difficulties in a set of guidelines that we can put together. The challenge for all of us at this meeting is to identify and address these most important issues.

9

LEGAL AND INSTITUTIONAL ASPECTS OF GLOBAL DATABASES

Earl F. Epstein

INTRODUCTION

The call for improved environmental and conservation policies has coincided with significant advances in information science and technology. Together, these conditions offer the opportunity to improve policy and implementation decisions based upon access to reliable, accurate, timely, and available data and information.

However, there is a lack of global data and information of a transnational scope that can be combined and used when decisions must be made. The problems are both technical and institutional.

This paper categorizes and illustrates the nature of the legal and institutional problems in global database formation. The categories are:

- National Economic, Security, and Political Policy
- Proprietary, Cost Recovery, & Revenue Generation Issues
- Confidentiality and Access
- Specific International Data and Information Regimes

National economic security, and political policy in regard to the development of both national and international resources has a significant impact on data and information exchange. That impact is seen in national posture with respect to international agreements and in national laws that restrict or encourage the flow of data and information.

Proprietary interests in data and information have both a public and private aspect. The public aspect is represented by those agencies that have a high degree of proprietary control over the form, circumstance, and cost under which data and information are transmitted. In some cases this degree of control rises to the level of effective ownership. The private aspect is represented by the

10

limits on data and information flow derived from national and international copyright laws.

Confidentiality and access are issues of increasing concern because information science and technology promote, not only the efficient collection, storage, retrieval, and dissemination of spatial data, but also their combination with and access to personal data.

Specific regimes have developed for specific data and information. The specificity may be according to the physical character of the data, such as oceanographic data, the measurement technique, such as remotely sensed data, or the program served by the data. The regimes are usually beset by the problems described above. In addition, these regimes exist as independent structures with their own data definitions, form, scale and other attributes that make it difficult to assemble information about a variety of attributes for an extensive region.

Each category is illustrated by examples, chosen to clarify the nature of the legal issues.

NATIONAL ECONOMIC, SECURITY, AND POLITICAL POLICY

Nations and individuals pursue economic, security, and political policies that reflect individual perceptions of their interests and circumstances. These individual perceptions can be inconsistent with the collective need for the formation of global databases.

National considerations are evident, for example, in the United States attitude towards the Law of the Sea Convention. The 1982 Convention on the Law of the Sea is the most recent effort to codify ocean law in an international agreement. The Convention has not entered into force for any nation, and the United States does not intend to become party to it under current circumstances. Its refusal to join the Convention, however, is due to its objection to the deep seabed portions of the Convention. It has supported the emergence of the non-deep seabed portions of the Convention as customary international law.

A less conspicuous disincentive to the flow of data and information derives from national policy. These are the specific local laws that implement elements of that policy.

An example of how local laws implement policy and discourage the flow of data and information is in the way the U.S. Department of Interior (DOI) Minerals Management Service (MMS) handles data and information submitted in connection with mineral leases. The DOI appears to rely on the general provisions of the Freedom of Information Act (FOIA) to provide the scope of protection for both commercial and financial information and for geological and geophysical data. (5 U.S C. 55b (1976)). The FOIA excludes certain categories of data from disclosure.

The FOIA provides that each agency is to make all its records available after a proper request that identifies the records and after compliance with published rules as to fees. This requirement to disclose whatever records the agency has is limited by nine specific exemptions. Applicable here is exemption 9, "geological and geophysical information and data, including maps, concerning wells."

Exemption 9 is a narrow and particularly strong statement recognizing the interest of the submitters in nondisclosure. There is little information on exemption 9; the 1966 House Report mentions it only briefly:

- This category was added after witnesses testified that geological maps based on exploration by private oil companies were not covered by 'trade secrets' provisions of present laws. Details of oil and gas findings must be filed with federal agencies by companies which want to lease government-owned land. Current regulations of the Bureau of Land Management prohibit the disclosure of these details only if the disclosure 'would be prejudicial to the interest of the government' (43 C.F.R. Part 2). Witnesses contended that disclosure of seismic reports and other exploratory findings of oil companies would give speculators an unfair advantage over the companies which spent millions of dollars in exploration (HR Report 1966).

The DOI regulations protecting geological data appear to repeat the language of certain FOIA exemptions. For example, regulations governing potash, sodium, phosphate, asphalt, and oil shale read:

- Geological and geophysical interpretations maps, and data and commercial and financial information required to be submitted under this part shall not be available for public inspection without consent of the permittee or lessee so long as the permittee or lessee

12

furnishing such data, or his successors, or assignees, continues to hold a permit or lease of the lands involved (30 C.F.R. 231.5 (1981)).

In Pennzoil Co. v. Federal Power Commission (5th Cir., 1976) appellant, arguing that the FOIA exemption automatically barred disclosure, sought appeal of the FPC's ruling that detailed gas reserves information would be available to the public. The court held that this construction of FOIA was at odds with the act's purpose and it would be an abuse of discretion for FPC to release the information without first balancing public and private interests. The agency must consider these factors: first, whether disclosure would aid the agency in fulfilling its function; second whether harm would result to the supplier of information and the public generally; third, and most important, whether there are alternatives that allow disclosure while protecting the interests of the information supplier. The court also emphasized the importance of the agency's prior policy and practices.

This example illustrates a relationship between national economic policy and specific laws that restrict the flow of data and information. Often the considerations that limit the creation of public data are most strongly expressed in these specific laws. Efforts to promote global databases must consider these specific laws, as well as the national policy.

National economic attitudes are also reflected in formal budgets for database support staff and resources. In many places these budgets are limited. For example, the International Oceanographic Data and Information Exchange (IODE) now encompasses 40 National Oceanographic Data Centers (NODC) (International Oceanographic Commission, 1986). Established in the late 1950's, this system has grown to handle a range of standard and non-standard data types. The system is regarded as sufficient now, but new pressures are arising because of:

a. increased delays between gathering of data at sea and the delivery of the data to national and world data centers;
b. increased resolution and data rate of new oceanographic instrumentation;
c. generation of remotely sensed oceanographic data sets;
d. requirement for global and basin scale integrated and consistent data sets;

13

e. requirement to have large data inventories available to users worldwide, to increase the speed of transfer of data to national and world data centres, and the need to transfer data electronically;

f. increased requirement for large climatic data sets and time series which can be updated and used with a minimum time lag;

g. greater demands by governments to see an economic return from investment in research and data banking.

In a 1986 survey of NODCs and some non-IODE data centers produced the following figures:

a. The total staff of national, and associated data centers in the world is about 500 people. Allowing for indicated levels of part-time staff, secretarial support, and for data centers performing functions such as routine chart preparation and naval support, the total dedicated to oceanographic data management at the national level is probably less than 400. This includes all scientists, managers, computer and technical staff in all nations.

b. Informal discussion shows that very few national centers allocate members of staff full-time to international transfers of data, the preparation of data for transfer to world data center, or performance of international obligations. The world centers maintain some staff for these operations, but the numbers are not available. Several heads of national centers have reported government pressures to concentrate resources on internal objectives such as port dredging, estuarine control, fishing, and maritime safety. In several national centers, the staff level has declined in the last three years.

c. A reasonable estimate of the maximum personnel available for the management of oceanographic data at the supranational level is of the order of 10% of the total, or 40 people. In the smaller data centers with less than five staff, this means less than 0.5 man-year for international commitments; in the larger data centers it is 1-2 man-years per year.

These totals represent the world-wide commitment to institutional maintenance of international oceanographic data.

National economic, security, and political policies represent a disincentive to the collective actions required to build global databases. The issue posed by these disincentives is whether they can be overcome by common environmental and resource management concerns.

When national economic, security, and political interests are served by collective action, such as in the concern about global environmental change, then national policy can encourage participation in the development of global databases. Scientists and database builders can encourage a broad view of these common concerns through education programs and through an articulation of the new tools made available by technological advances.

PROPRIETARY, COST RECOVERY, AND REVENUE GENERATION ISSUES

Proprietary, cost recovery, and revenue generation issues are about spatial data as an asset, and who derives the benefits from control of that asset.

Spatial data and information are seen by both public agencies and private individuals as an asset. However, there are several views of the nature of that asset. These include:

a.   That which should be made available by governments as a public good at public expense and placed in the public domain for general use.

b.   That which should be controlled by the public or private generated of the asset in order to optimize the recovery of costs or the generation of revenues.

c.   A combination of the above. If so, then there is an issue of the threshold that separates the two.

Where spatial data and information are treated as a public good, there is a concern about how to recover the costs of production, especially as investments in production increase.

There are a variety of national approaches. Examples of the extremes are represented by the Ordnance Survey in the United Kingdom and the United States Geological Survey (USGS), the respective national mapping organizations. The Ordnance Survey is organized as a Crown Corporation with the ability to establish the price of its products and services even, if it chooses, to set that price at what the market will bear. The USGS is limited by United States law which prohibits the exclusive control by the U.S. of government works, except by rare statutory exemption. The U.S. law (17 U.S.C.) prohibits reproduction and sale by others at a price lower than that set by the government for the original purchaser.

A mechanism for public and private control of spatial data and information, including maps, is copyright law. This mechanism is available to public agencies as well as private individuals. These laws extend to both computer software and databases. Their importance suggest an examination and summary (Karjala, 1987).

The U.S. Copyright Act protects against copying, but only of the copyrightable elements in the work; the copyrightable elements are the expression of an idea, not the idea itself. The ideas in the work are in the public domain and may be taken freely even by copying. The idea/expression distinction has come to take a variety of forms, depending upon the nature of the work in question.

For traditional literary works, like novels and plays, the scope of protection is broad. "Expression" in these works extends beyond the literal language or paraphrases of the literal language to cover elements of structure and composition. For factual, utilitarian, and technical works, however, the concept of expression is viewed much more narrowly. Copyright protection, for example, does not extend to facts, even facts discovered by original research, and the rule extends to the order of factual presentation and even theories interpreting them. It is often stated that there must be nearly verbatim copying or wholesale appropriation before infringement of a copyright in works of this type will be found.

In applying these concepts to computer software, we must first distinguish between the computer program itself and the output of the program. The program itself, as indicated, has a dual nature that necessitates particular care in reasoning by analogy. Although a program is treated formally as a literary work, because it is written in symbolic representation neither the process of its creation nor its function bears any resemblance to traditional literary works such as novels or plays. The broad concept of expression in such works should have no application to programs. Programs are seen as technology; they make computers work. At least insofar as analogy to

16

traditional copyright law is concerned, programs should be treated as factual or technical works. Absent a clearly articulated policy reason for deviating from the traditional balance drawn by copyright law between the creation of incentives and promotion of technological development, infringement should be limited to verbatim or near verbatim copying of the literal language of the program, that it is to say, the literal coding.

Even when the analogy of programs to works of fact rather than works of fiction is recognized, however, it is important to note an important difference: programs involve technological efficiencies. Moreover, they do not describe how to achieve technological efficiency; rather, they are the means for achieving it.

We must also distinguish programs from traditional "sweat of the brow" fact works, such as directories. Computer programs are not properly analogized to such works, although computer databases are. These differences must be recognized when applying judicial authority in this area.

The question is complicated by judicial confusion over the basis for protecting factual compilations. The copyright statute expressly protects compilations to the extent of the material contributed by the author, but the definition of "compilation" seems to look to the selection or arrangements of the materials or data comprising the compilation as the basis for treatment as a work of authorship. As individual facts are not protected, however, this selection and arrangement rationale for copyright protection would leave works like telephone books without copyright protection at all, because neither the selection standard (all the people in a particular geographical area) nor the arrangement (alphabetical order by last name) is original. Seeing social value in providing an incentive for the costly and time-consuming production of such factual compilations, some courts have deviated from the selection and arrangement rationale in order to supply copyright protection. The courts have found originality in the first author's effort in collecting and putting together the materials. A leading proponent of this approach argues for the notion of "authorship in the collection" as both a descriptive and a normative theory for the law of factual compilations. Such an approach is vital for coherently grounded protection of computer databases. For many databases, if the effort of collecting and placing the information into the computer is not protected, there will be nothing to protect. Some recent decisions seem to deviate from the "sweat of the brow" basis for copyrightability of factual compilations and to be returning to the selection and arrangement rationale in order to supply copyright protection.

National copyright laws and policies influence national attitudes towards international copyright law. The Berne Convention, which governs the international aspects of copyright protection in its signatory countries, has existed for over 100 years (Karjala, 1987).

The Berne Convention is not without opponents. The United States and the Soviet Union are major non-signatories.

The protection levels mandated by the Convention have increased steadily over the years. High standards of protection usually mean protection for the copyright owner, not the general public.

Copyright protection under the Berne Convention are least problematic in application to traditional literary and artistic works. Technology is another matter. Because advances necessary are taken from an existing base, similarities between new and old technology are the rule.

It is argued that advances in computer software technology cannot be distinguished from other technologies in this respect. Concern is raised that the expansive interpretations given by the courts to the protection of expression in programs may stifle rather than stimulate further advances. The effect of United States entry into the Berne Convention and the protection of information-based technology such as computer programs and databases under American copyright law has been raised as a public policy issue.

Copyright is one form of data and information control. Fees, based on access rights and the amount of data taken is another. This approach can be combined with coding or related means to prevent resale when computer based data and information are involved.

The struggle to establish a statutory exception to the U.S. non-copyright for government works and the establishment of a fee structure for Landsat products is an example of the difficulty in one nation over how to handle a particular spatial data asset.

In summary, a review of cases indicates that U.S. courts have extended broad protection to computer programs and databases under traditional copyright theories, policies, and precedents. The reliance is upon traditional notions such as substantial similarity and the idea/expression distinction, and even technical concepts such as the meaning of "literary work" or "derivative work" and what constitutes "reproduction". This tendency has been criticized on the basis that computer programs are a form of technology and adjustments to the laws are necessary to achieve an appropriate balance between incentive and the efficient diffusion of technology throughout society. While cases and statutory law support extensive protection for computer software and databases, the support is not without criticism. This criticism can influence national attitudes toward the Berne Convention developments.

The issue here is that of how to handle the proprietary status of national and private spatial databases where nations have different copyright laws and regulations. Related issues include questions of what is copyrighted - reproductions, the underlying data, or both - and whether copyright extends beyond reproductions.

CONFIDENTIALITY AND ACCESS

In almost all countries, data and information about physical features of the land and its resources are recorded on a graphical base, while information on the socio-economic aspects are compiled independently and in textual form.

The link between the two processes has, until recently, been tenuous. The disciplines and methods involved in the two processes have not been closely associated. However, it is noted that the lack of integration between the surveys of the physical aspects of an area with the surveys of the social and economic aspects is probably one of the major causes of misinterpretation of integrated surveys and of wrong decisions in land resource use and land resource development, with the subsequent risks of damage to the resources and to the environment.

The multipurpose cadastre, geographic information systems, and spatial data processing provide a basis to ensure that the risks of such damage are minimized. Even in the United States, where the concepts of a cadastre are relatively undeveloped, there has been considerably increased interest in these systems during the past decade (National Research Council, 1980 and 1983).

Interest in bringing together the spatial and socio-economic aspects of geographic data and information raises a concern about the confidentiality of personal data.

Several international conventions and agreements have been adopted dealing with the protection of personal data and transborder data flows (Mann, 1987).

First, in September, 1980, the Organization for Economic Cooperation and Development (the "OECD"), consisting of some 19 European countries together with Canada, United States, Japan, New Zealand and Australia, adopted the Guidelines on the Protection of Privacy and Transborder Flows of Personal Data (hereinafter called the "OECD Guidelines"). The OECD Guidelines were adopted by 19 member countries on September 23, 1980 and subsequently by the remaining five member countries. A further Declaration on Transborder Data Flows was adopted by the governments of the OECD Member countries on April 11, 1985. The Council of Europe Convention for the Protection of Individuals with regard to the Automatic Processing of Personal Data (the "Council of Europe Convention") came into force on October 1, 1985. The first five states to sign the Convention were Sweden (September 1982), France (May 1983), Spain (January 1984), Norway (February 1984), and West Germany (June 1985). Ratification by any state can take place only when a signatory country has adopted domestic legislation to reflect the Convention. The Council of Europe Convention will be ratified by the United Kingdom when the provisions of the United Kingdom Data Protection Act come into full force.

Unlike the Council of Europe Convention, the OECD Guidelines do not have any binding legal effect, but instead represent a voluntary code with which member states are expected to comply.

Both the Convention and the Guidelines provide for the principle of free flow of data between countries, subject to certain basic standards being adopted to provide for the protection of personal data in relation to both the public and the private sectors. The principle that member countries should facilitate transborder data flows was also set forth in the OECD Declaration adopted in April 1985. While the Council of Europe Convention applies to personal data (that is, data about identified or identifiable individuals) held in computerized form, the OECD Guidelines and Declaration deal with such data held in any form, whether printed or computerized.

In addition to the OECD and the Council of Europe, a number of other international organizations have been concerned with legal, technical and economic aspects of international data transmissions, particularly by electronic means. Some of these organizations have issued policy statements on transborder data flows while other organizations have been concerned with the circumstances in which documents transmitted by electronic means should be accepted, the means by which they may be authenticated and their use in court proceedings. Some of the international organizations which have been active in this area are the United Nations Commission on International Trade Law ("UNCITRAL"), the Hague Conference on Private International Law, the International Chamber of Commerce, the International Maritime Committee, the International Law Association, the Economic Commission for Europe, the Inland Transport Committee, the International Maritime Organization, the International Civil Aviation Organization, the International Rail Transport Committee and the Customs Cooperation Council.

The following two sections review the conventions and agreements of general application which have been adopted by the OECD and the Council of Europe.

OECD Guidelines on the Protection of Privacy and Transborder Flows of Personal Data

The preamble to the Recommendation of the Council of Europe, to which the OECD Guidelines are annexed, notes the common interest of member countries in protecting privacy and individual liberties and in reconciling fundamental but competing values such as privacy and the free flow of information. The preamble recognizes further that transborder flows of personal data contribute to economic and social development and such flows may be hindered by domestic legislation concerning privacy protection. The Recommendation calls upon member countries to take four steps to advance the free flow of information and to avoid the creation of unjustified obstacles to the development of economic and social relations among member countries, namely:

21

(i) to take into account in their domestic legislation the principles concerning the protection of privacy and individual liberties set forth in the Guidelines,

(ii) to endeavor to remove or to avoid creating, in the name of privacy protection, unjustified obstacles to transborder flows of personal data,

(iii) to cooperate in the implementation of the Guidelines, and

(iv) to agree on specific procedures of consultation and cooperation for the application of the Guidelines.

The Guidelines themselves state that they apply to personal data, whether in the public or private sector, which, because of the manner in which they are processed, or because of their nature or the context in which they are used, pose a danger to privacy and individual liberties. The term "personal data" is defined to mean any information relating to an identified or identifiable individual. Although the Guidelines apply to personal data generally, they provide that they should not be interpreted as preventing:

(a) different protective measures being taken to different categories of personal data according to their nature and the context in which they are collected, stored, processed or disseminated;

(b) the exclusion from the application of the Guidelines of personal data which do not obviously contain any risk of privacy and individual liberties or

(c) their application only to automatic processing of personal data.

The principles of National and International Application set forth in the Guidelines are intended to represent minimum standards, which are capable of being supplemented by additional measures for the protection of privacy and individual liberties. In addition, the Guidelines provide that any exceptions to such Principles, including those relating to national sovereignty, national security and public policy, should be as few as possible and made known to the public.

OECD Declaration on Transborder Data Flows

Subsequent to the adoption of the OECD Guidelines on the Protection of Privacy and Transborder Flows of Personal

Data, the OECD conducted further studies on issues relating to transborder data flow, including some of the economic issues that arise with respect to the transfer of information from one jurisdiction to another. In April 1985, the member countries of the OECD adopted a further Declaration on Transborder Data Flows that expressed the wish of such countries to promote access to information, to avoid the creation of unjustified barriers to the exchange of information, and to develop common approaches and consultative mechanisms to ensure "harmonized solutions" to issues relating to transborder data flows.

The foregoing indicates that in contrast to the OECD Guidelines, which emphasize a concern for the protection of personal privacy, the 1985 OECD Declaration refers to the economic and social benefits resulting from access to information and the common interest of Member countries in facilitating the free flow of information from one country to another. The Declaration also emphasizes the need to examine issues emerging from flows of data relating to international trade, computerized services and intra-corporate data flows. It remains to be seen whether the principles set out in the Declaration will be reflected in the removal of any barriers to the free flow of information among Member countries or to countries which are not members of the OECD.

Agreements about transnational flow of personal data represent a response to a major concern. They may serve as a model for the achievement of a regime for the transfer of spatial data.

SPECIFIC INTERNATIONAL DATA AND INFORMATION REGIMES

There are international regimes for the collection, analysis and dissemination of specific data and information. These regimes have their own hierarchical structure. They serve to define data terms, and provide an individual perspective on accuracy, scale, extent and timeliness of data and information.

The independent regimes have developed their individual practices, supported by national and international agreements. In some cases, the character of these regimes is determined as much by technology as by agreement as, for example, in the assembly of data and information by remote sensing of the environment.

Four regimes are examined as illustration of the influence of independent international data and information efforts.

The Marine Environmental Data Information Referral

The Marine Environmental Data Information Referral (MEDI) is an automated, systematic method for recording and retrieving information about marine environmental data files that exist in international centers and in national centers associated in an international network. MEDI is designed as an internationally accepted means of cataloguing such data as may be required by agencies, scientists, and administrators.

The following organizational participants have joined together to operate as a MEDI network:

IOC (International Oceanographic Commission)
FAO (Food and Agricultural Organization of the United Nations)
IAEA (International Atomic Energy Agency)
UNEP (United Nations Environmental Program)
WMO (World Meteorological Organization)
ICES (International Council for the Exploration of the Sea)
IHC (International Hydrographic Commission)
EUROCEAN (European Oceanic Association)

The IOC operated MEDI Coordination Center is located in UNESCO Headquarters in Paris. It is responsible for receiving input, answering queries, and maintaining an automated storage/retrieval system. The Coordination Center is aided by allied centers in each of the international organizations and in many national organizations.

MEDI offers:
- A catalogue and index showing details of marine data holdings of all participating centers.
- A computerized retrieval system.
- Specialized indexes for broad subject areas.
- Geographic plots of world-wide data distribution.

MEDI provides services in response to specific questions regarding the availability of data. It also provides in a unified, standard format marine environmental data with descriptions registered by international and national organizations, the data categories include:

Meteorology	Biology
Pollution	Geology/geophysics
Dynamics (currents	Radioactive pollution
tides, waves)	Fishery statistics
Physical and Chemical	Bathymetry
Oceanography	

Physical Environmental Data

Another example of the effort to establish a global database or, at least, an index to databases is represented by the World Data Center System. The World Data Center (WDC) system for international exchange of scientific data related to the physical environment of the Earth was established to ensure the permanent availability of the worldwide observations taken during the International Geophysical Year (IGY), 1957-58. Voluntary agreements for the types of data that should be exchanged were made under the auspices of the International Council of Scientific Unions (ICSU), the sponsor of the IGY program. There are three WDCs: WDC-A in the United States, WDC-B in the U.S.S.R., and WDC-C comprising a number of discipline centers in Western Europe and Japan. The WDCs were intended to supplement, not replace, the traditional scientist-to-scientist exchanges and the special data collection schemes organized in some scientific disciplines.

World Data Center A consists of the WDC-A Coordination Office within the U.S. National Academy of Sciences and eight subcenters at scientific institutions in various parts of the United States. Six of the WDC-A subcenters are operated by the Environmental Data and Information Service of the Department of Commerce's National Oceanic and Atmospheric Administration, one by the National Aeronautics and Space Administration, and one by the U.S. Naval Observatory. WDC-A is operated with national resources, but follows ICSU guidelines. The National Academy of Sciences has overall responsibility through the Geophysics Research Board and its Committee on Geophysical Data.

Most WDC-A subcenters are at the corresponding national data centers, whose large national collections are available through the WDC-A subcenters.

The data archived in the WDCs are those recommended in the ICSU Guide to International Data Exchange. Authoritative groups in international scientific organizations have compiled this guide and periodically revise it. One of the general provisions of the Guide is that WDCs will attempt to assist users in obtaining data from other archives.

The Guide consists of recommendations on data exchange for each scientific discipline. In many cases, it calls for submission of data to all WDCs for that discipline, either directly or through only one of them. In other cases, the data go to one of the WDCs, which shares its inventory with the others. The Guide also recognizes the problems associated with extremely large data programs where it is not feasible to reproduce the detailed collection for other centers; in this situation one center will service the international scientific community.

Ocean Boundaries

The delimitation of ocean boundaries between coastal states has received considerable attention in the United Nations Law of the Sea Conferences. There may have been more international adjudications on the subject than on all others combined.

The international ocean boundary regime illustrates underlying problems of data exchange. Ocean boundary data, including nautical charts, are evidence in the resolution of international boundary controversy. Inevitably, national attitudes towards these data and their submission to a common database are influenced by the evidentiary rules employed in the resolution of controversy.

Certain principles in the delimitation of ocean boundaries between states under international law relate to coastal boundary data. A nontechnical statement of modern ocean boundary law has been made as follows (Charney, 1987).

International law does not require that ocean boundaries be delimited in accordance with any particular method. Rather, it requires that they be delimited in accordance with equitable principles taking into account all of the relevant circumstances of the case in order to produce an equitable result. The equitable principles are very indeterminate and the relevant circumstances are theoretically unlimited. The indeterminacy of the legal rule was most strongly presented in the result-oriented words of the International Court of Justice in the "Case Concerning the Continental Shelf" (Tunisia/Libyan Arab Jamahiriya):

It is, however, the result which is predominant; the principles are subordinate to the goal. The equitableness of a principle must be assessed in the light of its usefulness for the purpose of arriving at an equitable result. It is not every such principle which is in itself equitable; it may acquire this quality by reference to the equitableness of the solution. The principles to be indicated by the Court have to be selected according to their appropriateness for reaching an equitable result. From this consideration it follows that the term "equitable principles" cannot be interpreted in the abstract; it refers back to the principles and rules which may be appropriate in order to achieve an equitable result.

In the more recent judgment in Case Concerning in the Continental Shelf (Libyan Arab Jamahiriya/Malta), the Court seemed to indicate that it was backing away from this extremely result-oriented approach:

Thus the justice of which equity is an emanation, is not abstract justice but justice according to the rule of law; which is to say that its application should display consistency and a degree of predictability; even though it looks with particularity to the peculiar circumstances of an instant case, it also looks beyond it to principles of more general application.

Notwithstanding the unsettled nature of the law in this area a pattern of analysis appears to have developed in the treatment of ocean boundary cases, regardless of whether they involve the delimitation of a continental shelf boundary only, or the delimitation of a single boundary for the 200-mile zone and the continental shelf. This pattern may be described, more or less, as follows: First, the tribunal describes generally the area in which the boundary dispute arises. Second, it searches the record to determine whether the parties have agreed to a specific boundary, either in a binding international agreement or in practice. If that fails, the tribunal proceeds, in the third step, to state the rule of law for ocean boundary delimitations when there is no agreed delimitation. That rule is variously described as requiring that the boundary be delimited by practical methods in accordance with equitable principles (or criteria) taking into account the relevant circumstances (or factors) in order to produce an equitable result. Fourth, the tribunal reviews all the arguments of the parties in order to determine what relevant circumstances are to be considered. By the end of this fourth step, it finds, inevitably, that all circumstances other than the geography of the shoreline are not relevant.

Having limited the relevant circumstances to geography, the tribunal proceeds to the fifth step during which it simplifies the geographic circumstances and focuses on a geometric construct of the area and the shoreline related to the boundary dispute. In the sixth step, the tribunal uses this geometric construct and various mathematical computations to generate a provisional boundary line.

Seventh and lastly, that line is checked against the many circumstances that were initially rejected and the rule of proportionality to see if the proposed line is not equitable. The proportionality test might give rise to some mathematically computed adjustments of the line. Other non-geographic facts appear to be unable to mandate an adjustment.

No one has been able to articulate exactly the values the boundary line is supposed to realize. It appears that, at bottom, decision-makers seek a line that represents a fair division of the contested area and known resources based upon analyses of maps of the area and the impact of the line.

Geographic circumstances and other relevant considerations are designed to permit decision-makers to appreciate which areas appropriately appertain to the contesting states.

The reliance on geography to resolve ocean boundary disputes places emphasis on the quality of coastal maps and data. This circumstance serves as an impetus to the establishment of international standards for coastal map-making and for international coastal data exchange. However, some coastal states may refrain from participation in such a program if there is a perception that such action will unfavorably influence their boundary claims.

Co-ordinated Information on the European Environment

In June 1985, the Council of Ministers of the European Community launched the Coordinated Information on the European Environment (CORINE) program (Wiggins et al, 1987). It's purpose is to provide information on the environment of the entire European community in a form suitable for assisting policy-making. Such data must be accurate, integrated, and readily available to the personnel for whom the system is designed. The system must be capable of dealing with large amounts of spatially-linked data from many different sources, in text, vector or raster form. The use of a geographic information system is regarded as essential. A test system has been designed for acquisition and integration of data on soils, climate, topography, and 'biotopes' (important areas for nature conservation). A data transfer format has been devised to provide for ease of transfer between various sites. Other issues being examined include the use of national and international networks and problems of integrating data when incorporating existing digital data from disparate sources into a large GIS.

This effort should be encouraged and examined to see if the goal of improved environmental and conservation policies can overcome barriers to the data assembly and that maintenance of a large international database designed for decision-makers can be achieved.

In summary, separate regimes exit because there are distinct sciences that produce the data and because there are specific problems to be solved. The result is a set of distinct perspectives on the data. The divisions are real.

The existence of distinct database regimes raises several future-oriented issues. Among these are (a) whether the new information technologies encourage or discourage the breakdown of the separate regimes, and (b) whether the global environmental and resource management issues are sufficient to overcome these problems.

CONCLUSION

Legal and institutional elements affect the development and maintenance of global databases. The variety of these aspects is revealed when attention is paid to the details of laws that support general information policies.

The classification of these policies and their supporting laws is according to national economic policy, proprietary rights, confidentiality and access, and specific data and information regimes.

The policies and laws that form these classes represent barriers against which the opportunities provided by new technology will operate.

A tension exists between individual national and individual and the common concerns of global environmental and resource management. Databases, global and otherwise, provide evidence for the resolution of controversy between people and nations. Nations and persons will not easily give to technical experts the power to create so-called neutral databases when those provide facts used to determine their interests. It remains to be seen how this tension will be resolved.

REFERENCES

Charney, Jonathan I., 1987. 'The Delimitation of Ocean Boundaries'. Ocean Development and International Law, 18, 497-532. Taylor and Francis, New York.

International Oceanographic Commission, 1986. Report presented at the Twelfth Session of the Working Committee on International Oceanographic Data Exchange, Moscow, USSR, 8-17 December 1986.

Karjala, Dennis S., 1987. 'Copyright, Computer Software, and the New Protection'. Jurimetrics, 28, 33-96. American Bar Association, Chicago, Illinois.

Karjala, Dennis S., 1988. 'United States Adherence to the Berne Convention and Copyright Protection of Information-Based Technologies'. Jurimetrics, 28, 147-152. American Bar Association, Chicago, Illinois.

Mann, J. Fraser, 1987. Computer Technology and the Law. Carswell Publishers, Toronto, Canada.

National Research Council, 1980. Need for a Multipurpose Cadastre. National Academy Press, Washington, D.C., U.S.A.

National Research Council, 1983. Procedures and Standards for a Multipurpose Cadastre. National Academy Press, Washington, D.C., U.S.A.

Wiggins, J.C., R.P.Hartley, M.J.Higgins and R.J.Whittaker, 1987. 'Computing Aspects of a Large Geographic Information System for the European Community'. International Journal of Geographic Information Systems, 1, 77-88. Taylor and Francis, London.

THE ISSUE OF ACCURACY IN GLOBAL DATABASES

Michael F. Goodchild

ABSTRACT

Very few procedures exist for estimating the uncertainty or
accuracy of products of spatial databases. Point objects
can be treated by direct extension of the theory of
measurement errors, but no suitable models exist for more
complex spatial objects. The paper reviews the available
techniques and describes work in progress. The prospects
for error evaluation and reporting will improve if objects
are tagged with relevant information, and if the data
stored in the system can be obtained earlier in the chain
of abstraction and generalization. It is argued that the
cartographic representation of data should be regarded as a
product rather than an input. The final section of the
paper reviews available techniques for global spatial
analysis, and identifies areas where further research is
needed.

INTRODUCTION

The global databases now being constructed by a number of
international agencies take data from a variety of
different sources, each with their own characteristics of
precision and accuracy. Data from remote sensors will be
subject to the errors inherent in the classification and
interpretation methods used, in the satellite platform, and
in the sensor itself, so that the relationship between the
truth as represented in the data which enters the database,
and the truth as it appears on the ground, may be complex
and obscure. Within the database the remotely sensed data
may be combined with data from maps, which is subject to
errors in digitizing, in the geodetic base on which the map
was based, in the error inherent in the figure of the earth
used as the basis for its projection, and again in the
nature of the truth which is being represented.

In this paper we review the issues surrounding error and

accuracy in global databases. Many of these occur irrespective of scale, but others are specific to the spherical geometry required at global scales. The first section of the paper discusses the state of knowledge about error modeling in spatial databases and spatial analysis, and techniques for dealing with error and estimating the accuracy of spatial database products. This is followed by a section on the more general issues arising from a discussion of error, including implications for methods of spatial data handling. The final section of the paper reviews the field of spatial analysis from a global perspective, and identifies areas where research is needed because existing methods are weak or incomplete.

ERROR MODELING IN SPATIAL DATABASES

Importance of error

The products of spatial databases may be simple responses to queries, such as the attributes of a point, the length of a line or the area of a selected polygon. More sophisticated applications are likely to result in more complex measures, such as calibrated parameters, goodness of fit statistics or simulated patterns of spatial variation. In all cases the accuracy of the results is to some extent determined by errors which will be present in the database. For example, a selected point on a soil map may not have the specified characteristics because the polygon in which it lies, and whose attributes were reported to the user, is not in fact homogeneous, although it was coded as such in the database. Similarly the area of the patch may not be a perfect estimate of the area on the ground having the coded attributes, again because of the lack of true homogeneity.

Because of the unique nature of spatial data, it is very unusual for any spatial data handling system to attempt to generate estimates of measurement error, or confidence limits, for its products. On the other hand numerous experiments have shown that actual levels of error, even for simple products such as point attributes, are far higher than one might expect given the precision with which the system operates, and in many cases unacceptable. Inaccurate products can lead to false inferences, bad decisions and even litigation (for a general discussion of error in spatial databases see Walsh, Lightfoot and Butler, 1987; for an excellent review and technical discussion see Burrough, 1986).

32

Error problems are likely to be worse in global than in local, planar databases, for several reasons. First, global databases must rely heavily on small scale data since global coverage at large scales is unlikely to be available; but small scale data is highly generalized, with much high- frequency spatial variation removed. Second, although data may be gathered at uniform spatial resolution, it is difficult to devise methods of digital representation and storage with similar uniformity. Spatial resolution varies over many common projections and over most common tesselations of the globe, leading to problems of estimating accuracy. Third, global databases are likely to combine data from numerous, incompatible sources, with problems of completeness and uniformity of coverage, and variations in definition. In fact many of the issues of data integration discussed at this conference impact directly on the question of product accuracy. For example, data from a satellite may be combined with digitized political boundaries; the two sources have entirely different types of error.

Definitions

We define the precision of a product in terms of its representation, as one half of the unit of the least significant digit. In principle one might wish that the product be reported to a precision equal to its accuracy, but in the absence of any clear knowledge of accuracy it is more likely that precision in a spatial data handling system will be determined by the software, particularly the number of digits carried in the internal arithmetic. Of course there will be occasions where for various computational reasons precision falls below accuracy (note that high precision implies a large number of significant digits, so the measure of precision will be numerically small), but it is normal to assume the reverse in most spatial data handling.

We define the accuracy of a product in terms of the magnitude of the difference between the reported value and the true value. The number of sources which can contribute to accuracy depends on how we choose to define truth. If the true value is as shown on the input document, then the errors include those introduced during the digitizing process, and during the manipulation and analysis in the system. However the input document may be an analog map, in which case the truth will be imprecise. Moreover it is unlikely that accuracy with respect to the input document will be considered acceptable, when the input document is itself an approximation to reality; accuracy with respect to ground truth is clearly more appropriate and realistic.

Unfortunately ground truth is often inaccessible or unavailable, and there are many instances of spatial data where no ground truth exists, since the object being represented in the system is itself an abstraction. Examples include soil maps, where a boundary shown on the map may be an abstraction of a transition zone between two generalized soil types.

A spatial database represents reality through objects and associated attributes. Objects may be points, lines, areas or pixels, with complex topological relationships derived from their spatial juxtaposition. Attributes may be nominal, ordinal, interval or ratio. Attributes are often assumed to be spatially invariant or homogeneous over the object; for example a soil map will associate the attributes of a polygon uniformly with every part of the polygon. Alternatively the system may infer systematic spatial variation of attributes over or between objects. For example, a topographic surface may be represented by a TIN, with height varying within each triangle in the form of a plane through the vertices, or according to a polynomial in the locational variables whose coefficients are stored as attributes of the triangle. Surfaces might also be modeled by point samples coupled with some spatial interpolation method such as Kriging, or by contours coupled with a linear interpolation algorithm.

We can partition error in the database into three types: errors in the positioning of objects, leading to distorted lines or point positions; errors in the attributes associated with objects, such as measurement errors at sample points; and errors in the modeling of spatial variation over or between objects, such as errors which result from assuming spatial homogeneity or linear interpolation. The simplest measure of accuracy for a variable would compare the database value at a randomly chosen point with the true value. While this would be an appropriate measure for query operations where the database must return the value at a selected point, it is not necessarily appropriate for more complex operations. For example, by arbitrarily offsetting the origin it is easy to see that one could estimate the areas of polygons accurately even though the database performed poorly on this measure of the accuracy of point attributes.

34

Measurement errors at points are relatively easy to describe using the Gaussian model, and the theory of errors can be used to predict their effects on derived products provided the analysis deals with each point independently. However it is much more difficult to deal with errors of positioning or modeling, because both are affected by the spatial relationships between objects.

Positioning errors

Consider a point object, such as a weather station. Errors in its position can be modeled as independent distortions of its two coordinates, although the respective standard errors may not be the same. The bivariate normal distribution is used to model distortion, and statistics based on it are used as standards in many mapping organizations. The Circular Map Accuracy Standard (CMAS) assumes a circular model with equal standard errors in the two coordinate directions and no correlation, and defines a circle within which the true point is expected to lie nine times out of ten.

Although the bivariate normal model is adequate for describing errors in individual points, it is likely that errors at neighboring points will show strong correlations, as the error in distances between nearby points is often much less than would be expected based on independent positioning errors. Similarly the errors at the vertices defining a patch are likely correlated, leading to lower than expected errors in patch area.

More difficult problems arise in defining positioning error for more complex objects such as lines or polygons. Most vector data structures represent complex objects as sequences of digitized points; it is assumed that the software will interpret the points as connected by straight line segments.

One solution to the problem of line error, and by extension polygon error, would be to model each point's accuracy using the bivariate, independent model, and to assume that the errors in the line derived entirely from errors in the points. Unfortunately this would be inadequate for several reasons. First, in digitizing a line an operator tends to choose points to be captured fairly carefully, selecting those which capture the form of the line with greatest economy. It would therefore be incorrect to regard the points as randomly sampled from the line, or to regard the errors present in each point's location as somehow typical of the errors which exist between the true line and the digitized representation of it. The latter combine the positioning errors at digitized points with modeling errors arising from differences between the behavior of the true line, and the model implied by the linear interpolation.

Secondly, the errors between the true and digitized line are not independent. If the true line is to the east of the digitized line at some location along the line, then it is very likely that its deviation immediately on either side of this location is also to the east by similar amounts. The relationship between true and digitized lines cannot therefore be modeled as a series of independent errors in point positions. To do so would lead to absurdity; the modeled line would be infinitely long, and would contain numerous loops or self-crossings.

One commonly discussed method of dealing with this problem is through the concept of an error band. The observed line is surrounded by a band of width epsilon, known as the Perkal epsilon band (Perkal 1956, 1966; Blakemore 1984; Chrisman 1982). The model has been described in both deterministic and probabilistic forms. In the former, it is proposed that the true line lies within the band with probability 1.0; in the latter, the band is compared to a standard error, or some average deviation from the true line. Blakemore (1984) has used the model to develop confidence limits on estimates of the attributes of a point.

The epsilon band model is too unspecified to be useful in modeling error in spatial databases. It is impossible to use it as a basis for simulation of distortion without some means of characterizing the position of the line within the band, and the autocorrelation of distortion. So although it might conceivably be used as the basis for predicting error in the attributes of a point, it is not sufficiently developed to allow estimates of error in line length, polygon area or more sophisticated forms of analysis.

Further clarification is necessary in dealing with line and polygon errors. In principle, we are concerned with the differences between some observed line, represented by a sequence of points with intervening straight line (or perhaps splined) segments, and a true line. The gross misfit between the two versions can be measured readily from the area contained between them, in other words the sum of the areas of the spurious or sliver polygons. To remove the effects of units of measurement we might divide

36

mismatch area by the square of the line length, although the length of the digitized line is not an unbiassed estimate of the length of the true line (Mandelbrot 1967; Maling 1968; Hakanson 1978).

To determine the mismatch for a single point is not as simple, however, since there is no obvious basis for selecting a point on the true line as representing the undistorted version of some specific point on the observed line. Most researchers in this field have made a suitable but essentially arbitrary decision, for example that the corresponding point on the true line can be found by drawing a line from the observed point which is perpendicular to the observed line. Using this rule, we can measure the linear displacement error of any selected point, or compute the average displacement along the line.

Consider a randomly chosen point on the line; this may or may not be a digitized point. Under the deterministic form of the Perkal epsilon band, this point estimates a true location which is with certainty within the epsilon band centered on the line. The probability distribution of linear differences is not specified in the model, but we might propose that it should be uniform within the error band, and zero outside. Under the probabilistic form one can calculate the probability that the true point lies within certain distances of the estimated position. Again the probability distribution is not specified. We could propose that it be normal, with mean, median and mode coincident with the estimated position, and with a standard deviation related to, and possibly equal to, epsilon. Honeycutt (1986) has accumulated evidence that the distribution of these distances is not in fact normal but bimodal, so that a finite, nonzero error on either side of the line is more likely than no error at all. Moreover the linear errors are clearly not independently distributed along the line, but strongly autocorrelated.

Studies of database error

The literature contains several discussions of the consequences of inaccurate response to queries about point attributes. In a vector database it is possible to overlay multiple polygon coverages, on the assumption that a point has the attributes of the polygon which contains it; the concatenated attributes of overlaid polygons can then be compared with ground truth. MacDougall (1975), Cook (1983), Newcomer and Szajgin (1984) and Chrisman (1987) have discussed the conceptual basis of error in map overlay and described simple experiments; in general the results show disappointingly high levels of error, even for large-scale databases.

Estimates of area imply queries about the attributes of assemblages of points, and therefore require reference to the spatial autocorrelation which is undoubtedly present in all spatial variables. Despite this there are numerous studies in the literature based on models of independence; for example Greenland and Socher (1985) used an independent norm in their study of mismatch between digital versions of the same objects (see also Rosenfield 1986; Congalton, Oderwald and Mead 1983).

Two forms of error in area estimation have been discussed based on models which incorporate appropriate spatial autocorrelation, either explicitly or implicitly. Mismatch error was defined previously as the total area between an observed and true line, or an observed and true polygon. Switzer (1975) described a model of mismatch error, which he related to the conditional probability that a point has the same (categorical) attributes as another point a given distance away. An empirical test of the model can be found in Muller (1978).

A common use of spatial databases is the estimation of the area of a coterminous patch. This might be done in a vector database by a calculation based on polygon vertices, or in a raster database by counting cells. The error of area estimation is typically much smaller than mismatch error because positive and negative errors tend to cancel eachother. An expression for the relationship between pixel size and the standard error of area estimates was obtained by Frolov and Maling (1969) using a simple statistical model, and generalized by Goodchild (1980) using fractional dimensions (see also Lloyd, 1976).

Models of database error

Although we can discuss positional, attribute and modeling errors as conceptually different sources of inaccuracy in spatial databases, it is clear that strong relationships exist between them. For example, on a soil map the boundaries represent transitions between attributes, and are therefore controlled by the same processes which determine the homogeneity of attributes within polygons, and the assignment of attributes themselves. Similarly positional, attribute and modeling errors in topographic data are controlled by the same underlying processes controlling the topography itself.

A reasonable goal of research in error modeling might be a stochastic process capable of simulating intuitively acceptable errors. If this model could be defined and parametrized, then it could be used as the basis for confidence limits on products. The model might take one of two forms. First, the process might distort an existing map from its true appearance to a simulation of its observed form. Second, the process might have no relationship to any true map, but simulate a family of versions of the same random dataset; with appropriate parameters the dataset could be made to resemble a range of real coverages. We refer to these as the "truth plus distortion" and "artificial truth" approaches, respectively. The number of required parameters is clearly greater in the second case.

Goodchild and Dubuc (1987) have described an artificial truth process which begins with random surfaces or fields. One random surface will generate an isopleth map with contour or spot height features; two or more will generate a choropleth map or polygon coverage with associated attributes. The surfaces must be continuous but need not be differentiable; the degree of spatial autocorrelation is controlled through the form of the variogram function. The surfaces are then passed through a classifier of an appropriate number of dimensions. The results have the properties of choropleth maps and it is possible to produce a range of conditions by varying the parameters of the generating process. However the number of parameters is large, and it is unlikely that any useful calibration will be possible by analysis of real datasets.

It is possible to implement a truth plus distortion process when the data source is remotely sensed imagery. Suppose the product of the interpretation and classification process is a vector of probabilities for each pixel, consisting of the probabilities that the cell is a member of each of a set of prescribed classes. Several standard classification methods are capable of yielding such vectors, including discriminant and likelihood procedures. Simple independent trials in each pixel will yield distorted versions of the same map. However the result will be only weakly spatially autocorrelated, and interpolated boundaries will tend to be unreasonably complex. Instead, the probability vector for each pixel must be modified to take account of outcomes in neighboring pixels.

Given suitable vectors of probabilities and a spatially autocorrelated realization process, it may be possible to develop appropriate techniques for attaching confidence limits to spatial database products. These will clearly lead to more useful products than those based on assignment of each pixel to a single class.

IMPLICATIONS FOR SPATIAL DATA HANDLING

All of the methods reviewed in the previous section have a common characteristic; they attempt to estimate error based entirely on the information available in the database. In this section we consider the implications of this general strategy for spatial data handling.

The accuracy of an estimate from a soil map is dependent to a large extent on the validity of the assumption of homogeneity within each of the polygons in the database. However in most cases the database contains no explicit information on homogeneity. We can assume that homogeneity is more valid in the middle of each patch than at the edges, but there have been no systematic and extensive studies of the truth of this assumption. Indirect information on the homogeneity of patches is available in the configuration of the boundary, since it is likely that more heterogeneous patches will have more complex boundaries, but again there have been no objective tests of this relationship. Moreover the processes which control the configuration of the boundary are complex, and include the predilection of cartographers for smooth curves. In summary, a polygon database likely contains very imprecise and indirect information on the accuracy of the homogeneity assumption, and more generally, it is unlikely that models of distortion can be successfully calibrated from the contents of spatial databases.

It follows that if confidence limits are to be generated for spatial database products, then additional information must be included on which to base estimates. Two general approaches seem appropriate. The more straightforward argues for tagging of objects and coverages with relevant statistics; the second, for a more radical reexamination of the contents of many databases.

Accuracy tagging

The most readily accessible indicator of accuracy of a coverage is the scale of the manuscript, in the case of

40

digitized map documents, or the pixel size in the case of remote sensing and scanning. Unfortunately there is a tendency to see spatial data handling as scale-free; despite the ease with which products can be generated at any scale from the same database, the scale of the input document is a major determinant of the accuracy of those products. For example, the accuracy of many map products is published in the form of a linear CMAS, which translates into different distances on the ground depending on the scale of the map.

However although scale may be a reasonable indicator of positional error, it is largely unrelated to homogeneity or attribute error, or to the error in line and polygon features, all of which tend to be much larger than the scale would suggest. The accuracy of each object depends on the cartographic processes which generated it, in the form of abstraction and generalization, and these are sensitive both to scale and also to the nature of the object. For example, the processes determining the accuracy of road and river features on a topographic map are quite different, despite a possibly common scale of depiction. The curvature of a river feature is a direct function of its discharge, and therefore related indirectly to its width, whereas the curvature of a road feature is related to its class and position in the hierarchy of the road network, as well as to the cultural milieu.

If scale is a determinant of accuracy then it is sufficient to tag each coverage tile in the database by the scale of its source. But the arguments just presented suggest that each object should be tagged, either by direct measures of accuracy, or by indirect indicators, such as key attributes, which might be used as predictors of accuracy once a more comprehensive theory can be developed.

Rethinking the contents of spatial databases

Much of the input to spatial databases consists of digital versions of standard cartographic products, such as soil maps. We have seen how the lack of accuracy information in such products leads to difficulties in spatial analysis, as there is no alternative but to take such data at face value, despite the obvious errors inherent in assuming homogeneity.

The cartographic view of spatial data is a highly abstracted representation, designed to display data in the most informative manner possible under the constraints of pen and paper technology. For example, the topographic map is conventionally displayed using contours, because these have been found to give informative and readily comprehended height information, and can be generated by hand using pen and paper with reasonable efficiency. Alternatives which might be more informative, such as perspective views, have not been part of the cartographic tradition because of the difficulty of generating them in a manual environment.

Spatial data handling technology is not as constrained as cartography; it is easy to generate perspective views, for example, from digital representations of terrain such as TINs or DEMs. It would make little sense to digitize the cartographic view of contours if a DEM were available, since the accuracy of heights interpolated from contours is uneven, and deteriorates rapidly as one moves away from the contours themselves. Instead much more accurate products could be generated if the DEM were input directly, allowing the cartographic view to be generated if and when desired.

In general, and from the perspective of product accuracy being taken in this paper, a spatial database should represent reality, using data which is as raw and unabstracted as possible, rather than the cartographic representation of reality, which is often highly abstracted. If the cartographic view is necessary, it can be generated from the database using appropriate rules. It is much easier to assign indices of accuracy to raw data than to abstractions and interpretations.

SPATIAL ANALYSIS ON THE GLOBE

Most of the discussion thus far has concerned general databases, independently of the specific context of the globe. We have assumed, for example, that in the case of raster databases we are dealing with a uniform tesselation and a constant pixel size. In a global database it is likely that pixels will vary in size, or that the tesselation will be nonuniform, or both (see for example Tobler and Chen 1986; Mark and Lauzon 1986).

There has been relatively little explicit consideration of the unique problems of handling global data. In some fields there exists an almost complete literature on the adaptation of standard problems in planar spatial analysis to the sphere (problems of non-sphericity will be ignored in this discussion) while in other fields there is a clear need for the development of appropriate methods. We define a method as appropriate if its results are invariant under rotation of the spherical referencing system.

One field which has received significant attention is spatial interpolation, which has obvious applications in spatial data handling, particularly in generalization from point samples to continuous surfaces. Willmott, Rowe and Philpot (1985) and Legates and Willmott (1986) have adapted distance-based methods of spatial interpolation to the sphere in methods which ensure appropriate continuity across the poles. Spline interpolation has been developed for the sphere by Wahba (1981), Freeden (1981), Lawson (1984), Renka (1984) and Dierckx (1984); Jupp and Kent (1987) have considered the special problem of fitting a smooth path to time-dependent events on the sphere. Finally spectral methods are particularly appropriate on the sphere and have been used for spatial interpolation by Balmino, Lambeck and Kaula (1973), Swarztrauber (1979) and Dierckx (1986).

Statistical hypothesis tests for spatial distributions on the sphere can be developed from spherical distributions. Mardia (1972) and Batschelet (1981) review a number of stochastic processes yielding unimodal, bimodal and linear distributions on the sphere and additional tests are given by Costanzo and Gale (1984). While these can be used as the basis for models of error in point positions on the sphere, as with planar data there are no obvious ways of dealing with more complex objects.

The problem of measuring central tendency and dispersion on the sphere was first discussed by Fisher (1953). A more recent and extensive literature deals with the problems of finding one or more locations on the sphere which minimize functions of distance, in other words spherical extensions of planar locational analysis (see for example Drezner and Wesolowsky 1978; Aly, Kay and Litwhiler 1979; Katz and Cooper 1980; Drezner 1981, 1983, 1985; Wesolowsky 1983; Drezner and Wesolowsky 1983). One of the more interesting motivations for this research concerns the optimal paths of earth observing satellites.

Many of the standard methods of planar spatial analysis have yet to be adapted to the context of the sphere. For example there is as yet no extension of the Douglas and Poiker (1973) line generalization algorithm, and only limited literature on the generation of Thiessen polygons and polygon skeletons. There is no spherical version of point pattern analysis, and no literature on spatially autocorrelated processes. It is clear that much research needs to be done in developing a complete set of spatial analytic techniques for the spherical case.

CONCLUDING REMARKS

In this paper we have considered a number of outstanding issues in spatial analysis and spatial statistics which affect the development and use of global databases. Some of these are common to the planar case; there is a similar lack of methods for attaching confidence limits to the products of spatial data handling in both cases. Others are unique, and the previous section has identified some of the areas in which there is a need for further development of analytic methods.

It would be naive to suppose that suitable models of error can be devised, particularly in the short term. There are good reasons to believe that appropriate models will be difficult to calibrate and deal with because of the large numbers of parameters involved. Effective solutions are likely to require much better understanding of the processes which create spatial variation than we currently possess. However the incentive to develop such understanding is substantially higher now than it has been, because of the development of spatial data handling technology. And irrespective of the number of parameters, there are valid uses of simulation models in studying the effects of controlled data parameters on the performance of spatial data handling systems.

Perhaps the greatest improvement in the understanding of error in spatial databases will come when the database representation is seen as the source rather than the product of the cartographic view of the data. If objects can be tagged with accuracy information; if the raw data from which the cartographic view was derived can be included in the database; and if the products of remotely sensed imagery can be tagged with vectors of class probabilities, then far more information will be available on which to base estimates of reliability.

REFERENCES

Aly, A.A., D.C. Kay and D.W. Litwhiler, Jr., 1979. "Location dominance on spherical surfaces". Operations Research 27 972-81.

Balmino, G., K. Lambeck and W.M. Kaula, 1973. "A spherical harmonic analysis of the earth's topography". Journal of Geophysical Research 78 478-81.

Batschelet, E., 1981, Circular Statistics in Biology. Academic Press, London and New York.

Blakemore, M., 1984. "Generalization and error in spatial databases". Cartographica 21 131-9.

Burrough, P.A., 1986. Principles of Geographic Information Systems for Land Resources Assessment. Monographs on Soil and Resources Survey No 12. Oxford University Press.

Chrisman, N.R., 1982. "Methods of spatial analysis based on errors on categorical maps". Unpublished Ph.D. thesis, University of Bristol.

Chrisman, N.R., 1987. "The accuracy of map overlays: a reassessment". Landscape and Urban Planning 14 427-39.

Congalton, R.G., R.G. Oderwald and R.A. Mead, 1983. "Assessing Landsat classification accuracy using discrete multivariate analysis statistical techniques". Photogrammetric Engineering and Remote Sensing 49 1671-8.

Cook, B.G., 1983. "Geographic overlay and data reliability". In Proceedings of the US/Australia Workshop on Design and Implementation of Computer-Based Geographical Information Systems ed. D. Peuquet and J. O'Callaghan. IGU, Amherst, New York, 64-9.

Costanzo, C.M. and N. Gale, 1984. "Evaluating the similarity of directional data". Professional Geographer 36 182-7.

Dierckx, P., 1984. "Algorithms for smoothing data on the sphere with tensor product splines". Computing 32 319-42.

Dierckx, P., 1986. "Spectral approximation on the sphere". SIAM Journal on Scientific and Statistical Computing 7 611-23.

Drezner, Z., 1981. "On location dominance on spherical surfaces". Operations Research 29 1218-9.

Drezner, Z., 1983. "Constrained location problems in the plane and on a sphere". IIE Transactions 15 300-4.

Drezner, Z., 1985. "A solution to the Weber location problem on the sphere". Journal of the Operational Research Society 36 333-4.

Drezner, Z. and G.O. Wesolowsky, 1978. "Facility location on a sphere". Journal of the Operational Research Society 29 997-1004.

Drezner, Z. and G.O. Wesolowsky, 1983. "Minimax and maximin facility location problems on a sphere". Naval Research Logistic Quarterly 30 305-12.

Douglas, D.H. and T.K. Peucker, 1973. "Algorithms for the reduction of the number of points required to represent a digitized line or its caricature". Canadian Cartographer 10 112-22.

Fisher, R.A., 1953. "Dispersion on a sphere". Proceedings of the Royal Society of London, Series A 217 295-305.

Freeden, W., 1981. "On spherical spline interpolation and approximation". Mathematical Methods for the Applied Sciences 3 551-75.

Frolov, Y.S. and D.H. Maling, 1969. "The accuracy of area measurements by point counting techniques". Cartographic Journal 6 21-35.

Goodchild, M.F., 1980. "A fractal approach to the accuracy of geographical measures". Mathematical Geology 12 85-98.

Goodchild, M.F. and O. Dubuc, 1987. "A model of error for choropleth maps with applications to geographic information systems". Proceedings, AutoCarto 8. ASPRS/ACSM, Falls Church, Virginia, 165-74.

Greenland, A. and R.M. Socher, 1985. "Statistical evaluation of accuracy for digital cartographic data bases". Proceedings, AutoCarto 7. ASPRS/ACSM, Falls Church, Virginia, 212-21.

Hakanson, L, 1978. "The length of closed geomorphic lines". Mathematical Geology 10 141-67.

Honeycutt, D.M., 1986. "Epsilon, generalization and probability in spatial data bases". Unpublished manuscript.

Jupp, P.E. and J.T. Kent, 1987. "Fitting smooth paths to spherical data". Applied Statistics 36 34-46.

Katz, I.N. and L. Cooper, 1980. "Optimal location on the sphere". Computers and Mathematics with Applications 6 175-96.

Lawson, C.L., 1984. "C1 surface interpolation for scattered data on a sphere". Rocky Mountain Journal of Mathematics 14 177-202.

Legates, D.R. and C.J. Willmott, 1986. "Interpolation of point values from isoline maps". American Cartographer 13 308-23.

Lloyd, P.R., 1976. "Quantization error in area measurement". Cartographic Journal 13 22-6.

MacDougall, E.B., 1975. "The accuracy of map overlays". Landscape Planning 2 23-30.

Maling, D.M., 1968. "How long is a piece of string?". Cartographic Journal 5 147-56.

Mandelbrot, B.B., 1967. "How long is the coast of Britain? Statistical self-similarity and fractional dimension". Science 156 636-8.

Mardia, K.V., 1972. Statistics of Directional Data. Academic Press, London and New York.

Mark, D.M. and J.P. Lauzon, 1986. "Approaches for quadtree-based geographic information systems at continental and global scales". Proceedings, AutoCarto 7. ASPRS/ACSM, Falls Church, Virginia, 355-64.

Muller, J.-C., 1978. "Map gridding and cartographic errors: a recurrent argument". Canadian Cartographer 14 152-67.

Newcomer, J.A. and J. Szajgin. "Accumulation of thematic map error in digital overlay analysis". American Cartographer 11 58-62.

Perkal, J., 1956. "On epsilon length". Bulletin de l'Academie Polonaise des Sciences 4 399-403.

Perkal, J., 1966. "On the length of empirical curves". Discussion Paper No. 10, Michigan Inter-University Community of Mathematical Geographers, Ann Arbor.

Renka, R.J., 1984. "Interpolation of data on the surface of a sphere". ACM Transactions on Mathematical Software 10 417-36.

Rosenfield, C.H., 1986. "Analysis of thematic map classification error matrices". Photogrammetric Engineering and Remote Sensing 52 68-6.

Swarztrauber, P.N., 1979. "On the spectral approximation of discrete scalar and vector functions on the sphere". SIAM Journal of Numerical Analysis 16 934-49.

Tobler, W.R. and Zi-tan Chen, 1986. "A quadtree for global information storage". Geographical Analysis 18 360-71.

Wahba, G., 1981. "Spline interpolation and smoothing on the sphere". SIAM Journal of Scientific and Statistical Computing 2 5-16.

Walsh, S.J., D.R. Lightfoot and D.R. Butler, 1987. "Recognition and assessment of error in geographic information systems". Photogrammetric Engineering and Remote Sensing 53 1423-30.

Wesolowsky, G.O., 1983. "Location problems on a sphere". Regional Science and Urban Economics 12 495-508.

Willmott, C.J., C.M. Rowe and W.D. Philpot, 1985. "Small-scale climate maps: a sensitivity analysis of some common assumption associated with grid-point interpolation and contouring". American Cartographer 12 5-16.

APPROACHES TO THE EFFICIENT DESIGN OF
SPATIAL DATABASES AT A GLOBAL SCALE

Duane F. Marble

ABSTRACT

There is a growing desire on the part of many organizations to assemble and utilize spatial databases (dealing, for example, with data elements such as soils, terrain, vegetation, etc.) which are defined on a planetary basis and which are to be created at scales allowing the representation of substantial levels of local detail (e.g. at scales as large as 1:250K).

The organizations engaged in creating these databases must overcome many substantial problems arising from physical and institutional factors. These include the sheer volume of any spatial data which is to be handled on a planetary basis, and the often incompatible definition of data elements (e.g. the lack of a common, world-wide set of definitions for land use/land cover categories). The developers must also respond to the fact that these global databases, in order to retain any long-term viability, need to be structured in a fashion which will remain as responsive as possible to the varied and changing needs of a large and changing multi-national user community.

In addition, each single factor, global data base must be constructed in such a fashion that its structure is compatible with its ultimate inclusion in a planetary geographic information system (PGIS) which will include a number of other global databases. To do otherwise would be unbelievably short-sighted.

The solution to these development problems is most commonly realized through efficient, structured design of the spatial database system. This paper reviews the characteristics of a successful spatial database design and briefly outlines some of the more important modern, structured approaches to the development of the information critical to successful spatial database design and to subsequent geographic information system operation.

INTRODUCTION

For hundreds of years geographers, and other scientists, have been gathering, storing, manipulating and using spatial data. The resultant databases have been stored for many thousands of years in analog form as maps at a variety of scales, and they contained invaluable data describing the nature of the world around us. The existence of these map databases permitted the undertaking by society of a wide variety of activities that would have been difficult or impossible without access to reliable spatial data. So crucial was some of this spatial data that for hundreds of years many map databases were classified as critical state secrets and were the subject of extensive espionage operations by other countries (e.g. the discussion of early Portuguese cartography by McIntyre, 1977; as well as the more general material in Harley and Woodward, 1987).

A continuing, major concern has been the development of a detailed and accurate portrayal of our planet. Many of the early maps portrayed the entire world, as it was then known, and the generation of change traffic for these map databases via exploration consumed substantial portions of the world's resources for many centuries (Harley and Woodward, 1987). Critical technological developments of the past two decades (primarily that of geographic information systems - GIS - and secondarily that of satellite remote sensing) have placed us in a position where it is now possible to contemplate the creation of accurate and detailed planetary databases, stored in digital instead of analog form, which may be utilized in a variety of ways. The scope of such operations is daunting, but there is no doubt that the technology currently exists through which these databases may be brought into being and effectively utilized.

For the purposes of the present discussion, we will define a global database as one which covers the entire planet. Thus the global database is inherently transnational in nature, but we must recognize that in many cases not all areas contained in the database will be treated equally. For example, a planetary database related to ocean surface temperatures will by its very nature contain little information on land areas and the level of data availability within any specific data layer may change significantly from place to place.

Examining Our Spatial Data Inheritance

The first thing which must be clearly understood about creation of the initial, digital global databases is that they will generally not be created de novo using newly collected spatial data. Remote sensing technology permits this to take place in a limited number of areas (e.g. sea surface temperatures), but in most of the areas of critical interest it will be necessary to rely heavily upon conversion of the contents of the vast mass of map archives which have been created as a result of ground surveys and detailed air photography carried out over the last several decades and which the global database developer has "inherited".

What state is this inheritance in? Embarrassingly poor when it is examined closely. One is immediately struck by the massive variations which exist in quality, timeliness and coverage even within the most basic data elements. In addition, substantial variation is present because of the national orientation of some of the previous efforts to create composite map databases on a global scale. In past decades, not only did each national survey generally work to its own set of standards, but these standards also displayed an understandable tendency to shift over time as data collection technology and our understanding of spatial data handling improved. For example, even today the United States is not covered by topographic quadrangles created to a common standard of map accuracy. This is not surprising, given the size of the nation and the significant amount of resources required to create a single topographic map, but problems of this sort must be explicitly recognized in any attempt to merge disparate, original map databases into a planetary whole.

The Role of Spatial Database Design

It is generally agreed that problems of this sort must be dealt with in a systematic fashion in order to prevent corruption of the resultant database. The overall activity which addresses the structure of the database, the definition of its contents, and the validity of the data which is to be placed in it, is known as database design. Utilization of standard design methodologies is relatively common in construction of today's commercial, non-spatial databases (e.g. Teorey and Fry, 1982; Teorey et al, 1986; and Date, 1986), but the general use of these approaches in spatial data handling situations - and their adaptation to the special problems of spatial data - is relatively new (Calkins and Marble, 1987).

Why must we design the global, spatial database? For much the same reason that we currently design smaller, operational, spatial databases: to avoid failure and to escape, in so far as possible, the massive inefficiencies often encountered in very large database systems. Failure of spatial data handling systems, as we have seen in the past, comes in a variety of forms. One of the most subtle of these, but also the most damaging in many ways, is the failure of the database (or the GIS within which it is embedded) to maximize its utility over as large a user group as possible. This often arises out of an initial, highly restricted perception of the potential uses of the proposed spatial database.

A classic example of this type of database failure may be seen in the operations of a commercial mapping company who created a carefully crafted digital road map of a European country but who saw no reason to include topological structuring in the road database. This very narrowly defined database was used in the automated drafting of an excellent road map of the country, but subsequent users who wanted, for example, to compute shortest paths found it unusable despite the hundreds of thousands of dollars which had been expended upon its careful construction. This gross failure could have been easily and inexpensively avoided through the use of structured spatial database design methodologies.

One major problem frequently arises when inconsistent local data dictionaries are brought together with insufficient attention being given to the resolution of their differences. This represents a really massive problem with respect to creation of global spatial databases since between some nations there are no consistent, unambiguous definitions of - for example - soil types. Significant efforts have been made over the past several years to create such soil classification schemes, but they have not been uniformly adopted and even where they have, signif-icant quantities of older materials must be translated into the new classifications.

Another major problem which must be avoided in creation of a master global database is the continued adherence to the out-moded concept of map sheets as database components. The spatial data contained in the global database may have been originally derived from digitization of map sheets, but edge matching must take place when a sheet is entered into the database so that the spatial data contained on that sheet are neatly and correctly joined to the corresponding data elements derived from adjacent sheets. This operation produces what is commonly termed a "seam less" spatial database. This database structure has been common in geographic information systems for some time (e.g. the discussion of the Canada Geographic Information System - CGIS - in Tomlinson, Calkins and Marble, 1976), but it has not yet been commonly accepted by some major production agencies (e.g. the digital products of the U.S. Geological Survey's National Mapping Division represent map sheets in which no attempt has been made to provide consistent data across sheet edges).

Why is the edge matching of individual sheets of such importance? Without it, each user of the database must develop and implement a separate methodology for solving the problem - this is clearly inefficient and easily leads to errors and inconsistencies in the resultant product. Also, it is clear that the organization creating the original, digital database will have superior access to the original sources needed to resolve the discrepancies often encountered in the process of database construction.

The use of a structured design methodology for the spatial database leads to the explicit identification of these and other problems before massive investments are made in actual database construction. It must be understood that current design methodologies are strong in the areas of initial problem identification and while certain strategies for problem resolution may suggest themselves, the ultimate solution of the problems which have been identified is up to the database developer. Problem resolution at this initial stage is often relatively inexpensive; in any case, it is far cheaper than completely rebuilding the spatial database at a later date in order to compensate for initial oversights.

Institutional Roles in Database Design

If design of the global database is so critical, who is to be responsible for carrying it out? The answer may be found in the traditional complex of institutional roles associated with the geographic information system. These include:

- Primary and secondary users of the GIS/database.
- Data collection organizations.
- The operator of the GIS/database system.
- The system sponsor.

In a normal GIS situation, the primary user, operator and sponsor are not uncommonly found within the same organization. However the construction of global databases represents a new situation and the definition of the various institutional roles is far from clear.

Typically it is the system sponsor, or the sponsor's consultants, who create the initial spatial database design. Continued maintenance and development of the design are most often associated with the database administration functions associated with the system operator. What organizations are to be associated with these roles in the creation of various global databases? This question must be successfully addressed before viable design and development of the global database can begin.

Characteristics of a Good Spatial Database Design

Thus, firm identification of the institutional components supporting the proposed global database represents the first characteristic of a successful design. The players must be identified, roles assigned and accepted, and there should be no confusion on the part of anyone as to where the responsibility lies for design, implementation and continued maintenance of the global, spatial data base.

Second, arising out of this clearly defined institutional structure, there must be a clear and detailed knowledge on the part of the database designer of the needs of all significant users of the proposed database.

Third, a consistent, logical structure must be defined for the spatial database. This structure must be comprehensive enough to support all user needs which have been identified as being of a critical nature while maintaining adequate flexibility to meet future changes in these needs.

MODERN APPROACHES TO THE DESIGN OF GLOBAL, SPATIAL DATABASES

Modern methodology in spatial database design emphasizes activities which are generally based upon top-down design with successive refinements being introduced at each step

(Teorey and Fry, 1982; Date, 1986). Associated with this top-down design process is a multi-step, design review methodology (similar to that often used in software design and development, e.g. King, 1984) which detects most system design errors and provides opportunities to correct them early in the process before database implementation has taken place. This general design methodology, which was developed for non-spatial databases, can be combined with the pioneering work done by Calkins and formalized in his GIS Structured Design Model (Calkins, 1982) to create a composite methodology which is specially adapted to the design of complex spatial databases. The methodology used for this type of database structuring consists of a series of three major steps:

Requirements Formulation and Analysis

This initial activity involves the establishment of organizational objectives and the derivation of specific database requirements (covering both database contents and processing operations which are to be performed on the data) based upon these objectives. The primary techniques used involve structured interviews with management and technical personnel as well as detailed content analysis of all existing and proposed products which rely upon spatial data. If a digital, spatial database is already in use, its content and the existing patterns of data element utilization are also carefully examined.

Conceptual Design

This second phase of the GIS/database design study concerns itself with the description and synthesis of the diverse users' information requirements into an integrated database design. The approach normally taken is based upon the development of a number of individual user views of the database (termed "local views" or "sub-schemas") and the subsequent merging of these local views into a single, coherent, global view of the database. The process by which the various local views are merged into an overall conceptual model of the database is termed "view integration".

The resulting global view (or "schema") represents an integrated conceptual model of the database which contains and supports all the defined local views. This global view forms the basis for all subsequent implementation and maintenance operations. The Database Administrator (DBA) is responsible for maintaining the global view and for authorizing and implementing any modifications which must be made to it as patterns of spatial data utilization shift within the organization (e.g. the decision to create a new analytic product may require that new spatial data elements be added to the database or that the definition of some existing elements be modified).

Implementation Design

Given that a consistent, logical representation of the database structure (the global view) has been created, this structure is then refined and detailed in this stage.   The primary objective here is to use the conceptual model of the database as input to create a specific, detailed schema or global view which is capable of being actually implemented within the context of an existing spatial database management system or geographic information system. Matching the conceptual model to the more restricted models supported in an efficient fashion by commercial, turn-key systems is an important part of this phase, as is the formal adoption of the master data dictionary which specifies in detail the nature of each data element to be included in the database.

DERIVATION OF A CONCEPTUAL MODEL FOR THE GLOBAL SPATIAL DATABASE

The procedure used to derive the conceptual model of a global, spatial database normally equates each unique product or use of the database with an individual local view.   The work to be carried out in creating the conceptual design then consists of four major steps:

1. Identification of the data content of all appropriate spatially-related products and the establishment of a local data dictionary for each one;

2. Preparation of Entity-Relationship (E-R) diagrams for the individual products;

3. Consolidation of the individual E-R diagrams into an integrated view covering all outputs, together with consolidation and rectification of the local data dictionaries into an integrated data dictionary;

4. Transformation of the resultant global view (representing all spatial products) into a final conceptual model of the database.

The Entity-Relationship approach to database definition is strongly recommended for use in the global database design process since it represents a general methodology for describing the elements of a database, the relationships between elements, and the attributes associated with either elements or relationships (Chen, 1977; Chen, 1980; Chen, 1983; Davis et al, 1983).

Entity-Relationship modeling represents a viable tool for cartographic database definition for two reasons. First, it is a flexible technique, which allows the analyst to freely modify the tool to fit the nature of the specific database design problem. The primary utility of the E-R approach is that it provides the database designer with a mechanism for ensuring consistency of definitions of the data elements, even while providing a substantial degree of flexibility. Any inconsistencies discovered during the process of preparing individual views of the products of the spatial database can easily be resolved during the view integration process. A second major reason for choosing the E-R approach to define the global, spatial database is its generality. While the E-R approach is independent of any physical implementation of the database, it does support mapping of the resultant conceptual model into any of the three major approaches to database implementation - relational, hierarchical and network data models. As was demonstrated by Calkins and Marble (1987), it is also capable of providing a mapping of a conceptual database model involving spatial data into one of the most standard GIS data models - the arc/node model.

Components of the Entity-Relationship Approach

The elements of the Entity-Relationship approach are:

1.   Entities - which are objects or things which are represented in the E-R diagram by a rectangle (an entity might be a highway link, a town, etc.);

2.   Relationships - the linkage between objects or things (entities), such as "belonging to" or "owning" or, in the spatial case, "connected to." These linkages are represented in the E-R diagram by a diamond shape;

3.   Attributes - characteristics of either entities or relationships, such as, in the present instance, the population of a town or the type of a highway. Attributes are represented by ellipses or circles in

the summary diagrams. The diagrammatic notation of the E-R approach is shown in Figure 1, which also includes an example of the description of a highway link in E-R notation.

ENTITY - RELATIONSHIP APPROACH

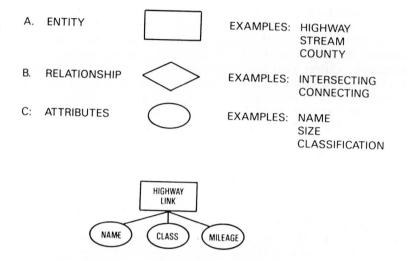

Figure 1: Basic Components of the Entity-Relationship Diagramming Technique (from Calkins and Marble, 1987)

To illustrate the use of the E-R approach in design of a large spatial database, selected portions of a large, master cartographic database design study conducted for Rand McNally & Co. are described below (this example is taken from Calkins and Marble, 1987).

The first step, data content analysis, was carried out on a large number of Rand McNally atlas products. Based upon these product examinations, lists were prepared indicating data element (spatial entity) presence by product for subsequent input into the preparation of the individual E-R diagrams.

The preparation of the individual diagrams was based on the "entities-relationships only" option of the E-R model as the attribute sets were fairly consistent across all the products examined. This permitted simplification of the local views without compromising the design process. The attributes were maintained, in this case, as a separate list for ease in the construction of the data dictionary.

Local views in this case were defined at the product level. Two such views are presented here as examples: the transportation features from the state maps contained in the Road Atlas and the transportation features from the Randway State maps. Figures 2, 3, and 4 show a sample section of a map from the Road Atlas (the original is, of course, in color), the corresponding E-R diagram for the transportation features, and a similar E-R diagram representing the transportation component of the Randway State map. Constructing the local views utilizing a similar graphic format allows for easy comparison to identify instances where conflicts may exist between local views.

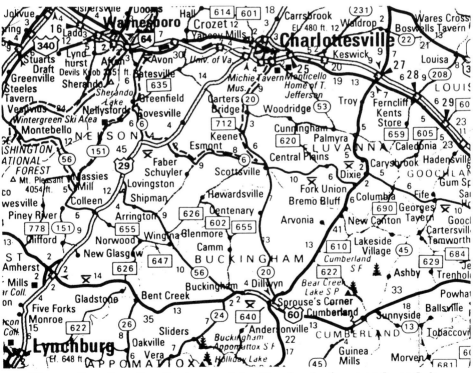

Figure 2:   Sample Cartographic Product (reproduced by permission) (from Calkins and Marble, 1987)

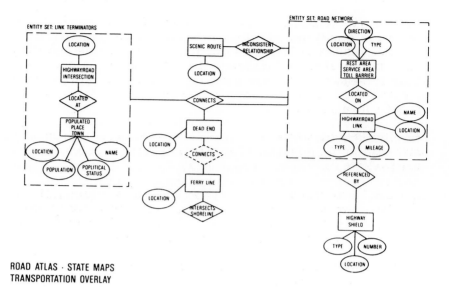

ROAD ATLAS · STATE MAPS
TRANSPORTATION OVERLAY

Figure 3: Entity-Relationship Diagram of the Transportation Elements of the Rand-McNally Road Atlas (from Calkins and Marble, 1987)

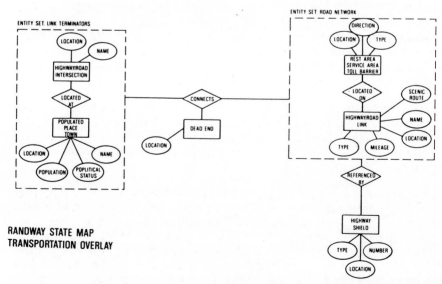

RANDWAY STATE MAP
TRANSPORTATION OVERLAY

Figure 4: Entity-Relationship Diagram of the Transportation Elements of the Randway Series Maps (from Calkins and Marble, 1987)

Consolidation of the E-R diagrams (View Integration)

The most important part of the E-R modeling process is the construction of composite views of the database. This process, known as view integration, consists of bringing together, in a series of pair-wise comparisons, local views to form higher-order views which are, in turn, merged into a global view which is capable of supporting all elements of each local view.

The individual views created in the previous step are subjected to the following processes during view integration:

1. Simple merging of the individual views to consolidate them into a single, logical and consistent higher order view (including resolution of inconsistent entries in the resultant, composite data dictionary);

2. Performing selected transformations on entities relationships and attributes, to convert the consolidated view into a desirable and correct, representation of the proposed database.

The merging process involves the resolution of any differences between individual E-R diagrams and resolution of any definition problems in the local data dictionaries. The result of merging the two transportation views described earlier is shown in Figure 5. Resolution of data dictionary inconsistencies is one of the most difficult tasks at this stage - regretfully, it will be a very common one in most global, spatial database designs.

The process of merging, resolving inconsistencies, and performing selected transformations continues until all local views have been incorporated into a single E-R representation. This then represents the final "user" view of the data base.

The final conceptual model of the master spatial database (in topological form) in the example drawn from Calkins and Marble (1987) is not substantially different from those en countered in many modern geographic information systems. What is important is that the database design illustrated here was arrived at through a structured process which guarantees that the resulting database organization would be able to generate all the cartographic products required by the organization as well as several new, non-cartographic, products. The design and construction of global, spatial databases must follow very similar paths.

By utilizing the design approach outlined in this example, the risks involved in the development of a large, expensive database can be substantially reduced (and there can be no doubt that any planetary database will be both large and expensive). Finally, the useful life of the global, spatial database should be substantially extended, again contributing to the economic viability of the automated cartographic production system.

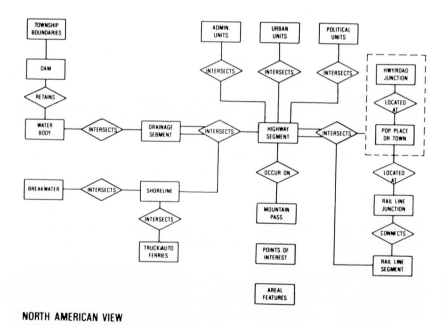

NORTH AMERICAN VIEW
(ENTITIES AND RELATIONSHIPS ONLY)

Figure 5: Global View Representing All Elements Contained in all Rand McNally Atlas Products Covering North America (from Calkins and Marble, 1987)

Summary of Database Design Steps

The general approach which should be utilized in the design of any spatial database, and global databases in particular, may be summarized as follows (it is assumed that an appropriate institutional structure is in place):

A.   Identification of important components of the potential user community.

B.   Development of user requirements and establishment of query types and frequencies.

C.   Development of detailed information on spatial data sources, data quality, and data flows associated with each proposed use of the global, spatial database.

D.   Creation of a comprehensive data dictionary covering all spatial and non-spatial attributes that are included in each user's local view of the database.

E.   Development of an overall logical model of the database which defines its structure in such a way that the local views of all users are supported. This must involve resolution of any data dictionary conflicts which have been discovered.

F.   Mapping of the overall logical schema into specific database implementation plan.

G.   Additional view integration operations leading to specification of the necessary characteristics of the software system(s) which will make use of the database.

SUMMARY

There is no question that the successful creation of any global, spatial database is a task of substantial magnitude. The resources, both monetary and professional, which must be expended are large and extreme care must be taken to insure that the end product is of maximum utility to the widest possible group of users, and that it exhibits the substantial power and flexibility which will be needed if the database is to change over the succeeding years to meet the changing needs of its users and the challenges posed by new technologies.

Careful, structured design will not insure the success of the resultant database, but it will insure that the probabilities are strongly biased in the direction of success.

REFERENCES

Brathwaite, Ken S., 1988. Analysis, Design, and Implementation of Data Dictionaries. McGraw-Hill Book Co.

Calkins, Hugh W., 1982. 'A Pragmatic Approach to Geographic Information System Design', in Proceedings, U.S./Australia Workshop on Design and Implementation of Computer-Based Geographic Information Systems ed. Peuquet and O'Callaghan. Amherst, NY: IGU Commission on Geographical Data Sensing and Processing.

Calkins, Hugh W. and Duane F. Marble, 1987. "The Transition to Automated, Production Cartography: Design of the Master Cartographic Database". The American Cartographer, 14(2).

Chen, Peter, 1976. "The Entity-Relationship Model - Towards a Unified View of Data". ACM Transactions on Database Systems, 1(1), 9-36.

Date, C.J., 1986. Relational Database: Selected Readings. Reading, Mass: Addison-Wesley Publishing Co. (See especially Chapter 19 "A Practical Approach to Database Design").

Harley, J.B. and David Woodward, 1987. The History of Cartography: Volume I, Cartography in Prehistoric, Ancient, and Medieval Europe and the Mediterranean. Chicago: The University of Chicago Press.

King, David, 1984. Current Practices in Software Development: A Guide to Successful Systems. New York: Yourdon Press.

Marble, Duane F. The Design and Implementation of Geographic Information Systems. (in preparation)

Pressman, Roger S., 1987. Software Engineering: A Practitioner's Approach. (Second Edition). New York: McGraw-Hill Book Company.

Simonett, Otto, 1988. "Using GIS in a Global Context: The Global Resource Information Database (GRID)", in Proceedings , Eighth Annual ESRI User Conference.

Teorey, Toby J. and James P. Fry, 1982. Design of Database Structures. Englewood Cliffs, NJ: Prentice-Hall.

Teorey, Toby J., Dongqing Yang, and James P. Fry, 1986. "A Logical Design Methodology for Relational Databases Using the Extended Entity-Relationship Model", Computing Surveys, 18(2), 197-222.

Tomlinson, Roger F., Hugh W. Calkins and Duane F. Marble, 1976. Computer Handling of Geographical Data. Natural Resources Research Series XIII. Paris: The UNESCO Press.

ISSUES INVOLVED IN SELECTING
APPROPRIATE DATA MODELS FOR GLOBAL DATABASES

Donna J. Peuquet

ABSTRACT

Current GIS technology has revealed severe shortcomings in meeting the performance requirements of very large, heterogeneous databases. At the root of these performance problems is a lack of sufficiently efficient and flexible data models that can be selected and tailored to a specific environment with predictable results.

The present paper examines the primary types of data models currently available in light of the functional requirements for any global, multi-purpose geographic database. In evaluating these options, it is quickly seen that no single data model can meet these requirements. Directions for future research are suggested that are necessary for the construction of database systems based on a dual model.

INTRODUCTION

For fifteen to twenty years after construction of the first geographic information system, building and maintaining a geographic database required a level of manual effort and expense that would quickly dominate the entire system as the size of the desired database grew. As a direct result, operational databases tended to be limited in size, regardless of the intended scope of the completed database. Much attention was similarly given in the research community to efficient data capture and input, and relatively little attention was given to the final form in which the data would be represented.

This situation is now dramatically different. The volume and variety of spatial data currently available in digital form is increasing at an exponential rate due to the advancement of data capture and input techniques over the past twenty years and to the availability of data from Landsat and other automated data capture devices. The recent rapid increase in data availability from a variety

66

of sources and the corresponding demand for its use has caused a major crisis in the handling of these data. Chronic problems are being experienced with exploding data volumes for on-line storage, rapidly increasing times needed to perform many fundamental tasks as well as narrowness in the range of application as the size of the area and the precision and variety of the data grow. These problems render much of the existing digital data inaccessible for large-scale manipulation and analysis. Nevertheless, national- and global-scale, high-resolution, general-purpose geographic database systems are currently being built.

Increasing attention to the way data are represented as being the primary cause of these difficulties spawned a debate as to whether raster- or vector-type data models are the 'best' approach for large multi-purpose systems (Peuquet, 1979; Chrisman, 1987). There has also been increasing activity in the development of new methods for representing geographic data in digital form. Until recently, however, the attention of the research and development communities was focused on narrow refinements of existing approaches.

Continuing inability to overcome volume, speed and integration difficulties has led to the realization that there is a lack of an organized body of representational theory regarding digital spatial information. Such knowledge is essential before global-scale database formats can be successfully designed or evaluated in any systematic or predictable fashion.

As a step in this direction, the purpose of the current paper is to give an overview of existing alternative digital representations for spatial data within an organized conceptual framework, and to examine the advantages and disadvantages of possible options for global database models in light of functional requirements. In the following discussion, current requirements for global-scale databases will first be briefly examined after the definition of some essential terms. Then, a number of general approaches for representing spatial data will be reviewed. Based on this, some observations regarding how varying representations, as well as their inherent advantages and disadvantages, are interrelated. Finally, some conclusions and recommendations for future work on deriving spatial data representations within this context will be given.

REQUIREMENTS FOR GLOBAL-SCALE GEOGRAPHIC DATABASES

Definitions

The term 'data model' is defined as the conceptual data representation scheme. The term 'data structure', however, refers specifically to the programmable implementation of a data model within the context of lists, pointers, etc.

Since no model or abstraction of reality can represent all aspects of reality, it is impossible to design a general-purpose data model that is equally useful in all situations. This is particularly true when dealing with complex phenomena. For example, some spatial data models, when implemented in a digital environment, are good for plotting, but very inefficient for analytic purposes. Other data structures may be excellent for specific analytical tasks, but may be extremely inefficient for producing graphics.

To illustrate the magnitude of the task of building a global-scale, multiple-purpose geographic database and clarify the resultant functional requirements, one example project will now be briefly examined and compared to current capabilities.

The Current Situation

Known functional geographic, multi-layer databases of modest resolution (e.g. 30 meter pixel resolution) tend to be functionally limited to something in the order of several counties of continuous areal coverage before the amount of disk space and central memory required, as well as search times, become unacceptable. Nevertheless, NASA is currently designing a database system that is intended to organize and integrate all spacecraft data for the entire earth. The objective is to make that data accessible to the earth scientist. The data volumes that will be generated by this effort is far beyond anything we have experienced so-far. The earth has nearly 1.5×10^{15} square meters of surface area. Thus, a single complete coverage of Spot data at 10 meter pixel resolution would total approximately 1.5×10^{13} pixels. If we assume that a single data value for a pixel can be stored in one byte, a total of about 1.5×10^{13} bytes, or 15 terrabytes of storage would be required. We also have to assume that multiple coverages would be desired for time series data. This means that the total number of pixels at this resolution would be n x (1.5×10^{13}), where n is the total

68

number of coverages. We also have to assume that data captured at other scales, such as Landsat, are also to be stored, with multiple coverages as well. The anticipated data volumes of these databases are such that they cannot be rationally or economically accommodated by advancing hardware technology. These data are also collected on a continuing basis at a very rapid rate.

Associated with total data volume is the issue of search efficiency. Search techniques currently used for responding to a user request for a particular class of data values tend to be exhaustive in nature. This means that as the total number of data elements increases, the time required to search a database increases as well in a direct linear relationship.

In addition to raw reflectance values from satellites, data derived from imagery and other sources would be highly desirable for a system that is truly useful for analytical purposes. These data may be conceptually areal, linear or point-type in nature, such as land use/land cover, hydrology, roads, and population. Data models are thus required that are also flexible enough to represent many different types of data. Attempts to integrate the vastly expanded variety of data into new or existing systems have proven extremely difficult, at best. The most common current solution for building heterogeneous spatial databases is to use a number of data models within the same database. This necessitates the need for a substantial conversion overhead in using such databases in varying application contexts.

We are only now achieving awareness in the GIS community that an additional issue must also be addressed in the design of a multi-purpose, global-scale database model: Spatial relationships between entities tend to be imprecise and application-specific, and the number of possible spatial interrelationships is very large. The definitions of these objects tend to be inexact and context-dependant (e.g. State College, PA may be a city to some to live there, but not to most others). This means that definitions of objects can change over time with changing applications.

In addition to these technical performance issues that represent a formidable technological challenge, there is the human relations challenge of dealing with inflated expectations. The well-publicized successes toward achieving large, heterogeneous databases in the area of 'conventional', i.e. non-spatial, Database Management Systems (DBMS), and a lack of realization of some significant limitations in the direct application of that technology in spatial data handling, is responsible for under-estimation of the magnitude of the task within the geographic realm.

Functional Requirements for Global Databases

As the size and scope of the database becomes very large, the importance of the above considerations becomes magnified into a number of functional requirements that become critical to its success. General functional data model requirements in a global-scale context can be stated as the following:

A global-scale, multi-purpose geographic database must be able to:

- handle extremely large volumes of both coordinate and descriptor data in a compact and application-efficient manner,
- handle a wide range of heterogeneous data types,
- accommodate a wide range of applications contexts,
- handle data at a number of scales,
- be dynamic, allowing frequent additions and modifications to the database, in addition to easy initial generation, and
- allow inexactness to be accommodated while also incorporating a mechanism for automatic integrity checks.

The relative importance of each factor varies with the particular type of data to be used, the application mix and the overall operational needs of the users. Inefficiencies, even major and obvious ones, can often be tolerated if the database is small or infrequently used. In these cases, it is often more cost-effective to absorb the extra time and computing costs than to bear the expense of careful initial construction or retroactive fixing of a system. For any type of large database, however, overall space and time efficiency becomes a critical factor. Even in a governmental context where internal and external use of the database often is not expected to be self-supporting, inefficiencies in a very large and frequently used system tend to multiply into a major drain of resources.

The last requirement addresses an additional issue of maintaining the integrity of the data once it has been

70

recorded. Assuming that the database is dynamic, being continuously added to, edited, and used by numbers of people, there must be some means to check automatically for logical inconsistencies at the time of data entry, and to check the existing database in case of possible corruption from hardware failure, etc.

In light of these requirements, we will now examine a number of geographic data modeling approaches.

CURRENT OPTIONS FOR REPRESENTING GEOGRAPHIC DATA

Basic Types

The numerous models that have been developed for representing Geographic data in digital form can be classified into the two basic types of vector and tessellation-type models. As shown in Figure 1, the basic logical unit of a vector data model corresponds to a line (i.e. vector) on a map. In this sense, vector-type data models are one-dimensional, consisting of strings of coordinates recorded along each individual line on the original map. The locational definition of a line entity can be viewed as a stored attribute of that line. Points can be represented in a vector data model as lines of zero length (i.e. one x-y location). The spatial interrelationships between objects or locations, however, must either be explicitly recorded, thereby increasing the volume of stored data, or computed each time they are required (e.g. areal adjacencies). There are many forms of vector models used in geographic database contexts. These were reviewed in Peuquet (1984).

Tessellation (i.e. polygonal mesh or mosaic models) represent the logical dual of the vector approach. With tessellation models, the basic data unit is a locational cell within a polygonal mesh of adjacent, non-overlapping cells. Information identifying entities is stored in individual cells as attributes of a particular locational cell. This class of data model includes any infinitely repeatable pattern of a regular polygon or polyhedron. An intrinsic property of tessellation models is that the order of the data in the digital file is determined by its location in space. Unlike vector structures, spatial interrelationships are implicit in the raster data structure itself. There are three possible regular tessellation models, as shown in Figure 2a; square, triangular and hexagonal. All three of these have been

Analog

Original Contour Map

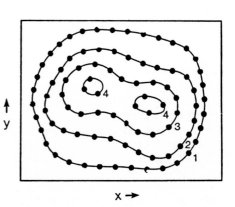

Vector

Vector Organization
(basic element = line)

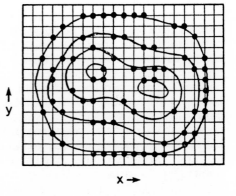

Tessellation

Grid Organization
(basic element =
grid vertex or grid cell)

Figure 1

used to some extent in a geographic database context, although the grid, or square tessellation, has been heavily predominant. Each regular tessellation model has differing functional characteristics which are based on the differing geometries of the elemental polygon (Ahuja, 1983).

In terms of overall processing and storage efficiency, no single tessellation model is better than the others. Algorithms initially devised for operation on square grids can easily be modified to work for the case of a triangular or hexagonal mesh. These, in fact, have been shown to have the same order of computational complexity (Ahuja, 1983).

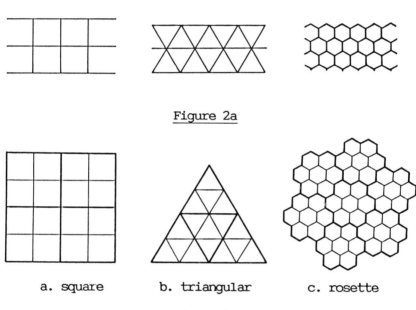

Figure 2a

a. square   b. triangular   c. rosette

Figure 2b

Global Tessellation Models

To satisfy one of the requirements for a global, multi-purpose geographic database, each of the basic tessellation models has a hierarchical form in that the elemental polygons can be arranged in a repeating pattern, as shown in Figure 2b. This allows representation of data at multiple scales. There are additional advantages of a regular, recursive tessellation of the plane relating to storage and performance efficiency. As a result, this particular type of data model has received a great deal of attention within Computer Science and GIS communities for a growing range of spatial data applications (Samet, 1984). The most studied and utilized of these models is the area quadtree, based on the recursive decomposition of a grid (c.f. Figure 3).

It is, unfortunately, topologically impossible to cover any spherical surface, such as the earth, with a non-overlapping square or rectangular grid. Although it is possible to convert stored cartesian coordinates for a portion of the database to an appropriate projection for analysis or map display, the real problem is to design an single, integrated global data model for representation of the database.

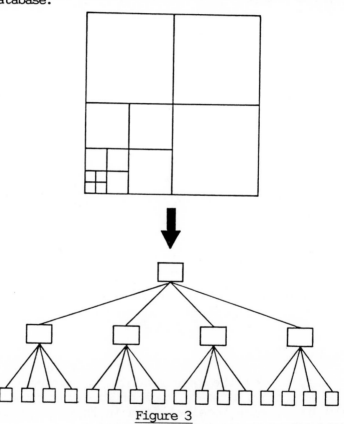

Figure 3

Nevertheless, a regular, hierarchical spherical tessellation would have many advantages as a general purpose global data model. First of all, such a model would retain all of the desirable properties of a planar tessellation including implicit spatial relationships; geographic location is

74

implied by location in the database. Multiple scales and a regular structure is also amenable to rapid search.

For a solid composed of regular polygonal faces, we are limited to five shapes, as shown in Figure 4, known as the Platonic solids. The relative merits of each of these as a global database model were discussed by Dutton (1983). He asserted that the regular icosahedron, composed of twenty regular triangular facets, is the most promising. The primary advantage it has over the other triangular solids and the cube is that the elemental faces are smallest, thus best approximating the sphere. The regular duodecahedron is not suitable as a global, hierarchical tessellation model, since pentagons cannot be recursively subdivided into smaller pentagons.

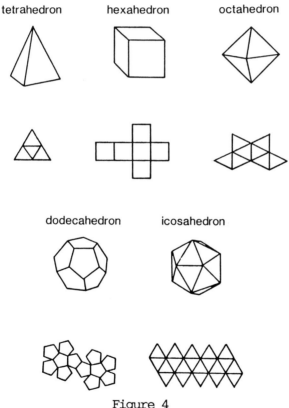

Figure 4

One might assume that the major drawback of any hierarchical tessellation model for a high-resolution global database is that the number of polygonal cells at each successive subdivision would increase geometrically, producing a data volume explosion of unmanageable size. Upon closer inspection, however, it is noticed that the size of each polygon must also decrease geometrically with successive subdivisions. The result is that small polygons are achieved after a surprisingly few subdivisions. In the case of the icosahedron, for example, each triangle has an edge length of only 17.2 miles after eleven subdivisions (i.e. level twelve of a triangular quadtree). This yields a cumulative total of 1,417,176 faces (Dutton, 1983).

The primary problem with the spherical triangular tessellation is that subdivision does not produce equal area triangles. Although the method for calculating the size of any individual triangle at any position and level within the hierarchy is well known, it is computationally complex. This would impose a significant burden in a high-resolution, multi-layer global database context. Tobler and Chen (1986) have therefore suggested a global quadtree projection based on the square tessellation, but provides adjustments to allow essentially complete coverage.

EVALUATING THE OPTIONS

As noted in the introduction of this paper, there had been a debate in the past as to whether raster- or vector-type data models were the 'best' approach for multi-purpose GIS. Nevertheless, it has become increasingly common knowledge through experience that a tessellation or vector model alone is insufficient. Specific types of representations seem to be intrinsically better than others for specific tasks.

Recognizing that vector and tessellation models are logical duals of each other, we can readily see why this is so. Some tasks are location-oriented (e.g. overlay and distance calculations), and others are object-oriented. The data to be input to each should thus be in the corresponding representational form to provide the most effective view of the problem (and the solution!).

The key, then, is to construct an integrated, dual data model such that redundant information is minimized among different storage structures while still serving a specified range of application contexts, with a minimum amount of conversion overhead. This goes far beyond the mechanics of efficient data model conversion algorithms.

A unified body of representational theory is required that we have only recently begun to build (Peuquet, 1988). Further knowledge is needed on how the different basic models, and the components of those models, relate to each other.

This includes, for example, a formalization of spatial relationships and their characteristics. Current GIS technology can currently handle only simple queries that involve a single spatial relationship at a time, such as distance or areal inclusion. More complex queries must be broken down by the user into sequences of simpler, binary forms. The reason is that how spatial relationships are defined can often be context dependant. Human interpretation is therefore needed at each step. The development of a spatial algebra for combining spatial relationships in unambiguous (and machine interpretable) expressions is therefore a particularly difficult unsolved problem. This problem is tightly bound with the representational form of the information. Such an understanding of spatial relationships is also required before the concepts of Relational Databases can be used to full advantage.

None of the existing options discussed above are able to accommodate the functional requirement of handling imprecision and context-dependant definitions. Research is currently underway, however, on how to extend existing models to meet this requirement by incorporating techniques developed within the field of Artificial Intelligence. Techniques have also been developed within the field of AI for non-exhaustive, heuristic search on large databases.

SUMMARY AND CONCLUSIONS

This paper has attempted to give an examination of the functional requirements for a data model for implementing a global geographic database and a subsequent evaluation of current options.

It has been seen that recent work on tessellation models shows great promise for meeting some specific efficiency, versatility and integration requirements, but would not be sufficient by itself as a general-purpose data model.

It has been seen that significant advances in a number of theoretical areas are needed before the functional requirements can be met. This does not mean that current efforts are doomed to failure. Rather, the limitations of current technology must be acknowledged in short-term expectations and design of the development effort. System designs must also remain flexible enough to allow for the incorporation of new concepts as they become available.

REFERENCES

Ahuja, N., 1983. 'On Approaches to Polygonal Decomposition for Hierarchical Image Decomposition'. Computer Vision, Graphics & Image Processing, 24, 200-214.

Chrisman, N., 1987. 'Fundamental Principles of Geographic Information Systems'. Proceedings, Auto-Carto 8, 32-41.

Dutton, J., 1983. 'Geodesic Modelling of Planetary Relief'. Proceedings, Auto-Carto VI, 186-201.

Peuquet, D., 1984. 'A Conceptual Framework and Comparison of Spatial Data Models'. Cartographica, 21, 66-113.

Peuquet, D., 1979. 'Raster Processing: An Alternative Approach to Automated Cartographic Data Handling'. American Cartographer, 6, 29-139.

Peuquet, D., 1988. 'Representations of Geographic Space: Toward a Conceptual Synthesis'. Annals of the Association of American Geographers, forthcoming.

Samet, H., 1984. 'The Quadtree and Related Hierarchical Data Structures'. ACM Computing Surveys, 16, 187-260.

Tobler, W. and Z. Chen, 1986. 'A Quadtree for Global Information Storage'. Geographical Analysis, 18, 360-371.

CARTOGRAPHIC DATA INPUTS TO GLOBAL DATABASES

David Rhind and Peter Clark

ABSTRACT

Cartographic data will form an important input to global
databases. This paper describes the relevant characteristics of maps as a data source; it reviews the map series
which might contribute to such global databases, especially
those of relevance to the International Geosphere -
Biosphere Project (IGBP) of the International Council of
Scientific Unions (ICSU). It also considers the possible
role of the military, who are currently much the largest
collectors of data derived from maps.

INTRODUCTION

Remote sensing and cartographic processes produce mutually
complementary data sets (SCST 1984). Cartography, based at
least in part upon ground survey or checking, provides
human-assigned data such as place names and administrative
boundaries, gives (in many countries) a product of superior
geometric properties to satellite-derived imagery,
encapsulates a more useful classification of features (e.g.
of land use) and provides a historical dimension to the
data. On the other hand, remote sensing data are largely
unaffected by variations in national data collection
practices, give near-synchronous and repeated views of
large parts of the earth, are collected in disaggregated
digital form and are now (normally) readily obtainable. It
is evident, therefore, that integration of data from these
two sources offers the most promising approach to globally
coherent, up-to-date and scientifically valid databases.

Cartographic data, however, vary greatly in their
characteristics. This paper defines these characteristics
so far as the map series liable to be of most value to IGBP
are concerned. It also examines how the more serious of
the problems could be resolved or (at least) ameliorated.
We begin with an attempt to infer user needs since these

can circumscribe the types of maps which need to be considered as data sources.

CARTOGRAPHIC DATA NEEDS FOR IGBP

At a stage where the detailed form, focus and financing of IGBP are not yet finalised, it is impossible to set out user needs with any degree of certainty. But, on the grounds of what can be handled by existing and soon-to-be available technology and on the basis of existing known plans of various agencies, the following current developments and trends have major implications for the way in which we should proceed :

- information for areas of the globe covered both by land and sea will be required.

- map-derived data from sources at less than 1/5 million scale are so highly generalised as to be merely caricatures of reality. They are of use only as 'backcloths' to generalised maps of global distributions of environmental phenomena (as, for instance, is to be the case in the IGU - sponsored project led by J.T. Coppock to create thematic maps of the natural environment and human modifications of it; this will draw upon remotely sensed data and possibly upon data held by the World Data Centres).

- equivalent data from larger than 1/50,000 scale maps will simply not be available in the foreseeable future (see below) and the coverage of digital 1/50,000 scale map data will be very patchy.

- there is a distinction between use of maps simply as a 'backcloth' or locational framework to the portrayal of other spatially varying phenomena (even if customised to the user's particular needs) and as a source of data aggregated for specified areas. Many existing cartographic data sets permit the former but not the latter. In general, a database approach which permits both is to be preferred.

- the detail and quality of the data required will vary with the individual application but, in collaborative work, these must be determined by the most demanding agreed application. Simplifications of this 'best' version can then be generated for other applications.

- because maps have long been used as data storage devices, encoding of thematic information such as geology and soils will be as necessary as basic topographic data (though this is not true in all fields e.g. global climate modelling)

THE CHARACTERISTICS OF MANUALLY PRODUCED MAPS

This section considers those characteristics of maps which, in general terms, affect the utility of data derived from them. Any one particular map source will require careful evaluation (e.g. see Bond 1973, Farrell 1987) and factors such as the particular time series provided by different editions may be relevant to individual projects. General accounts of map characteristics may be found in standard texts such as Robinson <u>et al</u> (1987) and Keates (1973); Robinson and Petchennik (1976) have addressed some of the more philosophical aspects of depiction of information in map form.

Map accuracy

'Map accuracy' is taken to cover the accuracy of all (or, usually, only selected) features shown on the map, irrespective of the source of the errors. Surprisingly little has been written on the accuracy of maps in recent years (see, for instance, Crone 1953, Thompson and Davey 1953, Haasbroek 1955, Thompson 1956 and 1960, Glusic 1961, Greenwalt and Schultz 1962 and 1963, Greenwalt 1971, Thompson 1971 and 1983 and Greenland <u>et al</u> 1985) - at least until the advent of national and international data transfer standards (e.g. see Chrisman 1986). Each national mapping agency has generally set its own map accuracy standards though some of these are not generally available. Perhaps the best known are those of the USA; table 1 reproduces how those which relate to map scales of relevance to IGBP were summarised by Thompson (1983). It should be noted that not all US maps need to conform to the standard; those conforming should bear a label to that effect.

81

Table 1: Relevant US National Map Accuracy Standards (revised in June 17th, 1947), as specified by the Bureau of the Budget (now OMB).

1. Horizontal accuracy:
   For maps on publication scales of 1/20,000 or smaller, not more than 10% of the points tested shall be in error by more than 1/50th inch. These limits of accuracy should apply in all cases to positions of well-defined points only. Well-defined points are those which are easily visible or recoverable on the ground, such as the following: monuments...., intersections of roads, railways, etc.... In general what is well defined will also be determined by what is plottable on the scale of the map within 1/100th inch..

2. Vertical accuracy:
   For contour maps on all publication scales, not more than 10% of the elevations tested should be in error by more than one-half the contour interval. In checking elevations taken from the map, the apparent vertical error may be decreased by assuming a horizontal displacement within the permissable horizontal error for a map at that scale.

3. The accuracy of any map may be tested by comparing the positions of points whose locations or elevations are shown upon it with corresponding positions as determined by surveys of a higher accuracy. Tests shall be made by the producing agency...

It is obvious that these standards have certain shortcomings, including :

- they do not match to conventional statistical descriptors of error. Thompson (1983), however, has described how USGS convert these standards into RMSE figures; these equate to 100 feet for horizontal positions on a 1/100,000 scale map and 0.3 of the contour interval (CI) in the vertical. Accepting the capability of introducing allowable horizontal error into the latter ensures that the allowable RMSE tolerance in elevation is 0.3 CI + 100t, where t is the tangent of the mean angle of slope over the sample. Parenthetically, Chrisman (pers.comm.) has pointed out that the Australian Survey Corps publishes each of its maps with a note of the standard deviation in both X, Y and Z of the errors therein!

- being based upon the concept of fixed and retrievable points, they do not measure variations in shape of features; it is, for instance, quite possible that the RMSE is acceptable overall yet the shape of the features being portrayed are grossly in error. Conversely, the error may be above the tolerance acceptable but the shape may be instantly recognisable. This probably arises frequently on all maps smaller than 1/50,000 scale because of the generalisation required to separate linear features such as roads, rivers and railways to make them distinguishable.

- they only pertain to one of the two elements of map accuracy (i.e. accuracy in 3D position). Content (or classification) accuracy has been examined in a number of papers (e.g. Rosenfield 1986) in regard to specific mapping (e.g. land use maps) but the standards do not consider such errors as the labelling of places and the spelling of names.

- some apparent errors of commission or omission would not be regarded as such by cartographers. Hence - and especially on small scale maps - it is conventional to select which features are shown not only on the grounds of pre-defined criteria but also on the grounds of context. The classic example is the inclusion of oases in deserts even though on population or size criteria these settlements would not be shown if adjacent to larger urban areas. It is also a frequent suspicion that cartographers have a preconditioned concept of how 'full' a map should appear!

- they are substantially irrelevant to thematic maps which portray such features as geology or population density. The geology map comprises information which is frequently based on inference and hence can not be validated without (at least) enormous expenditure of time or effort; population density - and many similar constructs - are computed using some defined algorithm and are normally based upon area aggregate data. Hsu and Robinson (1970) have considered the accuracy of isopleths used to portray these data.

- they do not provide a means of separating out systematic and 'random' errors (e.g. see figure 1)

Recent proposals to replace these map accuracy standards have been made by Merchant (1987). These are currently under discussion.

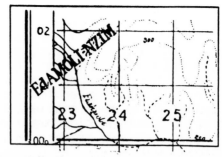

Figure 1: The 'elephant' contour on map from Gold Coast Survey (Bond, 1973)

No such accuracy standards are known to have been specified for map series which cover the whole globe. Since these are invariably derived from compilations of national map series at larger scales but with varying accuracy criteria and on different map projections, origins, etc., it seems unlikely that they everywhere match up to USGS or comparable standards. Anecdotal evidence (S.Guptill, pers. comm. 1988), however, suggests that the Defense Mapping Agency does apply the National Map Accuracy Standards (NMAS) by producing two classes of maps - Class A maps meet the standard and Class B meet a standard half as stringent as NMAS (i.e. the horizontal error threshold for maps smaller than 1/20,000 scale is taken to be 1/25th inch).

Resolution

Maps, unlike air photographs or satellite imagery, do not provide a fixed level of resolution. This arises from three factors :

- the smallest feature which it is possible to draw at any particular scale. This relates only, of course, to linear and areal features. Some of the most skilled manual cartographers (e.g. the Swiss or Japanese) include colour - filled areas smaller than 0.5mm across. Most other maps are somewhat coarser than this; the ONC charts generally exclude all areal features smaller than 0.8 mm.

- the main task for which the map is created. Charts for aircraft navigation clearly have different resolution (and content) requirements than do those of wall maps. Areal entities of a size far below any reasonable threshold for portrayal may be symbolised as points if sufficiently important (e.g. as in the case of oases or military bases other than one's own)

- the idiosyncracies of the individual cartographer. This is examined below.

Two conclusions may be drawn from all this. The first (suggested by Guptill) is that, as for accuracy, resolution is best sub-divided into that for 'position' and that for 'content'. The second conclusion relates to both categories: the concept of resolution so far as maps are concerned is best regarded as a 'fuzzy' one : on the basis of personal experience and observation (there seems to be little work on this except in the context of generalisation - see below), any one document may actually contain almost an order of magnitude variation in resolution if defined in conventional scientific fashion.

Up-dating

Many maps in the world were published at least twenty (and, in some cases, over 40 or more) years ago (Brandenberger and Ghosh 1985). Worse still, it is often difficult to obtain reliable and geographically disaggregated inform- ation on when the maps were last up-dated and from which sources. One of the great advantages of some military mapping is that regular and well-defined up-dating of at least certain features on the map is carried out. Howman (1983), for instance, described how the PACE database derived from the 1/500,000 scale TPC maps for much of Europe is up-dated every six months. These data have already been supplied to the European Commission for use in the environmental information system in the CORINE project (Wiggins et al 1987, Wyatt et al 1988).

Generalisation

'Generalisation' is the term given by cartographers to simplification of an image so as to permit it to be reproduced in legible form at a smaller scale or for accompanying the portrayal of another geographic distribution. Rhind (1973) argued for several qualitatively different types of generalisation; Brassel (1985) has provided schema for coping with different types of generalisation. The movement of features such as lines or areas to reduce overcrowding, elimination of classes or of individual features, and reduction of graphic complexity are perhaps the most common types (see figure

2). This has implications for the nature of data derived from maps, manifested in two different circumstances:

- the statistical properties of any individual variable and of the relationship between two or more variables are scale-dependent (see, for example, Gardiner's 1982 demonstration with lengths of rivers and the other properties of stream networks). In part, this has been empirically expressed by Topfer's Law (Topfer and Pillewizer 1968) and the tendency for features to increase in length towards a limit of their 'true, 1:1 scale' length is sometimes known as Steinhaus' Paradox. Clearly, then, comparison of data sets derived from maps at two widely different scales is liable to introduce

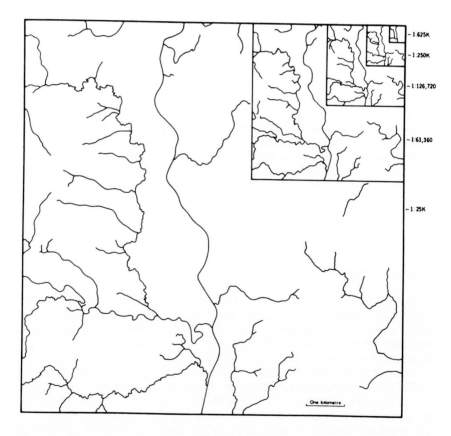

Figure 2: Maps of the same river system at different levels of generalisation (from Gardiner, 1982)

gross bias. In practice and despite numerous empirical studies and 'Topfer's Radical Law', we have incomplete knowledge about the generality of generalisation effects. Most work (e.g. McMaster 1983, Jones and Abraham 1987) has concentrated solely on trying to produce automated solutions which match manual simplification of individual lines - unrealistic in terms of what happens in real mapping. Even the more ambitious automated approaches to automated generalisation, such as those based on treating lines as having fractal properties (e.g. Buttenfield 1985) or of devising data - dependant generalisation of lines (Buttenfield 1987), remain relatively simple in terms of what seems to happen in manual cartography. Indeed, such research work is only tangentially relevant to our concern - the quality of data derived from maps - and, in this, the human element in the generalisation is responsible for inconsistencies in interpretation of the (often rather non-specific) generalisation rules: differences in generalisation may therefore be found even within sheets in the same map series (see figure 7).

- where two data sets are being overlayed but have been derived from two different base maps, geographically small but catastrophic errors usually occur - such as soils apparently being in the sea. This is an unavoidable consequence of using small scale map sources compiled by different agencies. It is ameliorated by compiling (wherever possible) all data sets on one standard base map - as in CORINE - or by moving to larger scales of maps, especially those derived from national mapping agencies (since these are created to rather higher and publicly defined standards).

Classification inconsistencies

Unless the maps used have been compiled from comprehensive and consistent raw data, it is likely that they will record data using a variety of classifications. Different selections of contour levels, of land use types, of transport links and most other features on topographic maps are commonplace in dealing with maps emanating from different sources. Even in dealing with supposedly single source maps (e.g. ONC) these have inevitably been compiled from national series and - at best - the classifications used represent a lowest common denominator. The dramatic loss of detail in using data based on two different but overlapping classifications has been demonstrated from land use by Rhind and Hudson (1980).

Internal Consistency

Perhaps the most significant characteristic of maps as data sources has already been touched upon: the internal inconsistency in their properties arising from human involvement in the compilation process. This is entirely understandable: consider the situation where two sets of maps, each on a different map projection, are to be fused together to make an international series. It is quite likely that minor errors have been made in manually compiling each map which, after algebraic transformation, ensures that no fit will occur and remedial measures have to be taken along the junction. This therefore creates a third element in the generalisation process. One particular example of this has been encountered in the European Commission CORINE project: the soil map of Europe was compiled on top of ONC series maps (see Wiggins et al 1987) but, to ensure the capability to display all the map sheets on one wall, the soil boundaries at the sheet edges were adjusted manually! This is non-evident on the final paper map but obvious when the maps are overlain on others; it had to be rectified by a second stage transformation, using 'rubber sheeting' methods and several thousand control points gleaned from the 'correct' maps which were thus used as a template.

By its very nature, it is difficult to put bounds on the magnitude of the inconsistency effects. Reasonable estimates can, however, sometimes be made through a knowledge of who compiled the map and the techniques used.

EXISTING GLOBAL MAP SERIES

Topographic maps of the land area

Pending the publication of the multi-volume review edited by former ICA Vice-President Boehme, the most up-to-date global survey of what is currently available in paper map form is by Parry and Perkins (1987). This also draws upon the results of periodic surveys by the UN (Brandenberger and Ghosh 1985). Figure 3 illustrates the global coverage of maps produced by national mapping agencies at 1/100,000 scale or larger whilst figure 4 shows the extent of coverage by continent at the four scale ranges employed by the UN. Figure 5 illustrates the findings of the last

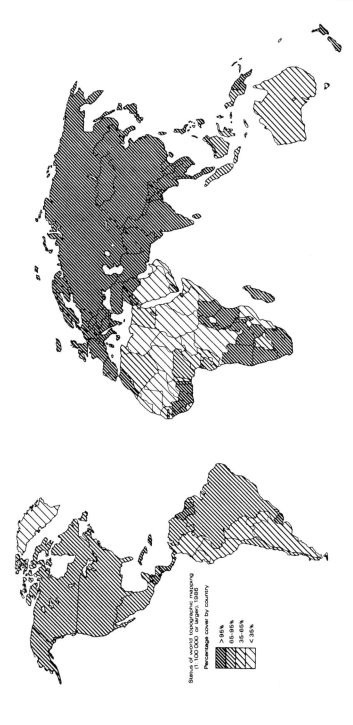

Figure 3: Global coverage of maps at 1/100000 scale or larger (Parry and Perkins, 1987)

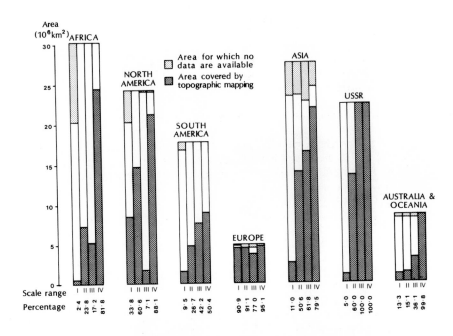

Figure 4: Extent of coverage by continent of four map scales (Brandenberger and Ghosh, 1985)

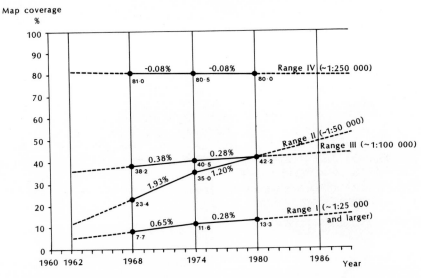

Figure 5: Change in global map coverage (Brandenberger and Ghosh, 1985)

three UN surveys so far as extensions of global coverage of national topographic mapping is concerned. The conclusions which may be derived are as follows :

(i)   truly global coverage does not exist even at 1/250,000 scale though only South America does not have 80% coverage.

(ii)   many of these maps are very out-of-date.

(iii)   the coverage is only expanding rapidly at the 1/50,000 scale range but, at present, only about two-fifths of the land area of the globe is covered at this scale.

(iv)   even if they exist, these coverages may not be available in their totality to international science. In some countries (e.g. India, Greece and the Soviet Union) substantial restrictions are placed upon the availability of medium-scale topographic mapping. The globally complete (or at least very extensive) topographic map series of interest to IGBP and which are known, in theory at least, to be available are shown in table 2.

It should be noted that the largest scale of complete coverage of the globe is currently given by maps at 1/1 million scale. In the absence of specifically designed topographic maps, the most widely used products - ONC and TPC - are actually charts designed for air navigation but show selected topographic detail.

Comparisons of these are, however, of great relevance to IGBP. Figures 6(a) and 6(b) show comparisons between maps from different series for the same area. The variations in level of generalisation are apparent (especially in the originals) but such variations are not wholly consistent: Series 1404, for instance, is much more detailed in some parts of Europe than is ONC but the reverse is true in the UK. Moreover, inter-sheet variation is evident: figure 7 shows the quite different appearance of the same lake as shown on overlapping ONC sheets.

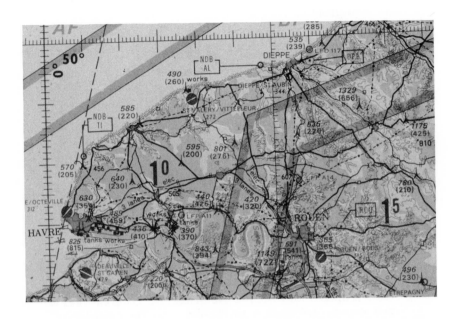

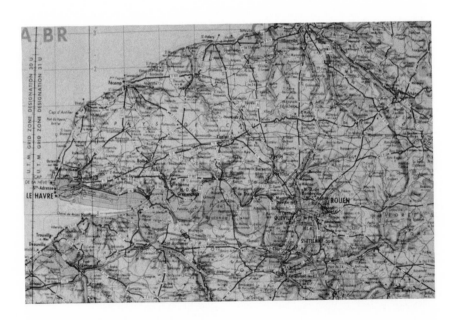

Figure 6: Comparison of ONC and Series 1404 1/1m scale
            maps in one area

92

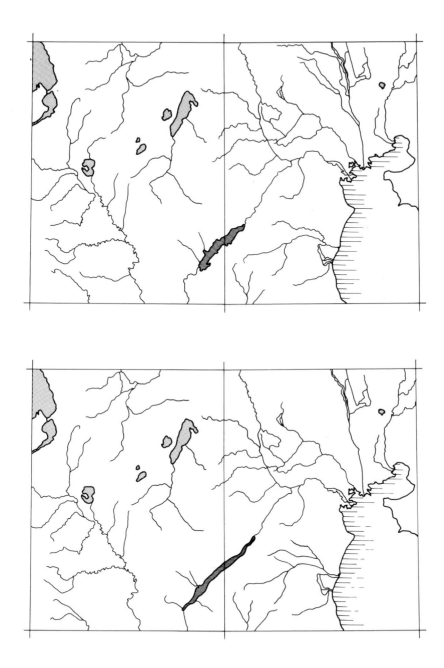

Figure 7: The same area on two different sheets in one map series

Table 2: Global, near-global or intended global map series

	Source	Scale	Sheets
1.	Series 1106 (US Defense Mapping Agency)	1/5 million	12
2.	Institute Geographique National, Paris	1/5 million	34
3.	Global Navigation and Planning Chart (GNC, produced by DMA)	1/5 million	26
4.	Karta Mira series (produced by a consortium of Eastern European mapping agencies)	1/2.5 million	234
5.	Jet Navigation Chart (JNC, produced by DMA)	1/2 million	125
6.	International Map of the World	1/1 million	2122 (750)
7.	Series 1301 (military version of IMW)	1/1 million	
8.	Operational Navigation Chart (ONC, produced by DMA, UK D.Mil. Survey and others).	1/1 million	271
9.	Series 1404 World (UK DMS and others)	1/500,000	coverage very incomplete
10.	Tactical Pilotage Charts (TPC)	1/500,000	1000 (300)
11.	Series 1501 (JOG)	1/250,000	incomplete, unavailable, except for e.g. Canada, Norway

Sources Stegena (1979), Williamson (1983), Parry and Perkins (1987), the Royal Geographical Society and the UK Ministry of Defence. Bracketed figures are the number of sheets actually published.

Globally available oceanographic map series

Though large areas of the oceans of the world (notably in the North Atlantic) are published at larger scales, the largest scale comprehensive coverage of the world's oceans is provided by the GEBCO series (Scott 1981). The General Bathymetric Chart of the Oceans is published by the International Hydrographic Organisation (IHO) at Monaco; currently in its fifth edition, this covers the world in 16 sheets at 1/10 million scale and two sheets at 1/6 million scale. More interestingly, it was compiled from plotting sheets at 1/1 million scale made available by different hydrographic offices. GEBCO is now controlled by a joint Guiding Committee of the Intergovernmental Oceanographic Commission (IOC) and the IHO. A sixth edition is planned sometime before the end of the century but the future of the series is closely linked with developments in digital bathymetry: there has been a vast increase in depth data available directly in digital form.

At the other extreme, one of the best mapped areas of the world is the Mediterranean: the International Bathymetric Chart of that sea is at 1/1 million scale, in 15 sheets and was published in 1981 from plotting sheets supplied at 1/250,000 scale.

Non-topographic global map series

In general, thematic maps of the world have been produced for wall chart purposes and are thus at significantly smaller scales than the best available topographic maps. In fact, thematic maps (such as of geology or soils) are generally available at two different scale ranges which do not overlap: global maps are available at 1/5 million or smaller scales and national series are available at anything between 1/5000 and 1/250,000 scales. The biggest problem in compiling the latter into improved versions of the former is usually the different classifications for the same phenomena used in different countries (e.g. see Dudal and Batisse (1979)).

Table 3: Non-topographic global or near global map series

	Source	Scale	Sheets
1.	Geological World Atlas (Commission for the Geological Map of the World/ UNESCO)	1/10 to 1/20 million	22
2.	Tectonic Map of the World incomplete	1/2.5 to 1/5 million	incomplete
3.	Metallogenic Map of the World (CGMW/UNESCO)	1/2.5 to 1/5 million	incomplete
4.	World Climatological Atlas	not known	almost complete
5.	Soil Map of the World (FAO)	1/5 million	18

NOTE: many other map series are published at continental scale (e.g vegetation) and larger scale versions of the map series above are often available, particularly in Europe (e.g. the soil map of Europe at 1/1 million scale, based upon ONC)

Source Parry and Perkins (1987)

EXISTING GLOBAL DIGITAL CARTOGRAPHIC DATABASES

Few complete global databases which have been derived from maps are known to exist at present. Though many outlines of countries have been digitised at small scales, perhaps the two best digital files in general use are World Data Bank 2 and Mundocart. The former was compiled from maps at between 1/1 million and 1/4 million scales and, like WDB1, was subsequently distributed at nominal price to the public sector through the National Technical Information Service or its national distributors. It consists of world coastlines and country boundaries, some transport links, etc. held as 7 million coordinate pairs in an unstructured or 'spaghetti' fashion. It has subsequently been converted into topologically structured form by the Environmental Systems Research Institute. Mundocart is a commercial product produced by digitising selected features from the ONC charts; in general, it is of significantly higher quality than (the earlier and cheaper) WDB 2.

Plans to compile more detailed and comprehensive global cartographic databases have been announced by an International Cartographic Association Commission (Bickmore 1988) and also by the Defense Mapping Agency. Both are based upon encoding the ONC charts. At the time of writing, collaboration between the two groups concerned had not been agreed.

Finally, the GEBCO oceanographic maps of the world are currently being digitised by the Institute Geographique Nationale in Paris.

THE DIGITISING BOTTLENECK

Different tasks have different data requirements: thus global climate models do not (currently, at least) have any use for anything other than cartographically coarse data (with all that is implied in shifting of position by generalisation). Nonetheless, it is clear that considerable use might be made even of data derived from maps at 1/1 million scale (Bickmore 1988). The encoding of these data is still, however, a major bottleneck. This becomes ever more true if the maps to be digitised are 1/250,000 or 1/50,000 scale: though not available everywhere, these are of much better accuracy, resolution and consistency than ONC or similar scale maps and could be used for many more scientific purposes.

Some indication of the problem, however, is given by the 20 Mb or so required to hold one Ordnance Survey 1/50,000 scale map in topologically stored form. Though this figure is particular to the data structure, to the software system used and to the area of the map, it is reasonable to infer that it suggests some 50 Gb of data would be required to cover the European Community alone. Whilst an absurdly small sample from which to generalise, this would imply a global database (excluding Antarctica) of about 1.6×10^{12} bytes of data! Though in practice all the data on the map might not be required, the 'capture' of this geometry, adding attributes to lines and points, checking the resulting data and correcting any mistakes is not trivial - even for national territories - using existing technology.

This paper can not cover recent developments in digitising technology in any detail (but see Woodsford 1986, Waters, forthcoming); it is worth summarising, however, some of the relevant developments. It seems, for instance, that

manually controlled, vector digitising using cheap (e.g.
PC) workstations is still the most common, flexible and -
in certain circumstances - the cheapest form of data
capture. Scanning systems - both raster and vector - are
being increasingly used where speed is paramount, where the
maps are of high quality and in sufficient volume or, in
some cases, where suitable specifications have been agreed
before the maps are drawn manually (e.g. as with the new
USGS 1/100,000 scale maps: see Guptill 1983, Callahan
1983). In general, complex coding at the digitising stage
is giving way to basic coding and automated restructuring
(such as generating topology 'on the fly') and, in some
cases, to object level coding and automated recognition of
the nature of the features (see de Simone 1986).

It is also worth noting that the costs of digitising -
which can be large (Bickmore (1988) estimates about 1.5
million pounds for encoding the bulk of the features from
the 271 ONC maps) - are related to four main factors.
These are labour costs, overheads (including the digitising
system), the digitising specification and the client's
quality assessment requirements. Recent studies on large
scale OS maps in the UK have shown that varying the last
two factors can reduce costs to small fractions of original
levels. This, however, has important implications for the
ease and flexibility of future use of the data. In
general, contractors will tune their procedures so as just
to pass the acceptance tests since digitising is highly
competitive and becoming a global business.

THE ROLE OF THE MILITARY

Some of the developments which have already occurred in
global databases have arisen from the role of the military
and of the security services. Thus World Data Bank 1 and
World Data Bank 2 originated in the CIA. Since the
military are actively involved in encoding topographic data
and since they have the capability to enforce the use of
data transfer standards, it is at least possible that they
will become of increasing importance to IGBP and the rest
of the scientific community - subject to the data sets
being produced to a specification relevant to our needs
and, of course, of them being made available to the
civilian community. At the time of writing, for instance,
the US Defence Mapping Agency has announced that an RFP
will be issued in April 1988 for the digitising of the ONC
maps; there are some indications that the resulting data
will be made available to the civilian sector but at an

unknown price. Other discussions are known to be taking place in the military on the possible digitising of 1/250,000 scale maps covering large areas of the world. To complicate the issue still further, at least two commercial enterprises are known to be contemplating the digitisation of the ONC maps - a possibility facilitated by the lack of copyright control over map series originating in the USA.

It is already known that NATO have agreed a common specification for data exchange formats for data derived from 1/50,000 scale maps. In the UK, components of about half these maps have been digitised and are on sale in Digital Elevation Model and contour form via Ordnance Survey. Maps of the whole of the Federal Republic of Germany have already been digitised in topologically structured form and coverage of other countries in Europe is proceeding, albeit at widely different rates. The military need for such cartographic-derived data is for navigation, targetting, mission planning, forces deployment and training on simulators. Summaries of data needs and future plans for at least the British military - presumably typical of many others - are given by Harvey (1987) and Lankaster (1987). No information has been found on plans of other military alliances (e.g. SEATO, Warsaw Pact forces) for meeting their topographical data needs but, in totality, it seems likely that these will be similar in general terms and will span much of the globe over the next 10 to 20 years.

The level of topographic detail required for global modelling (e.g. down, for some applications, to some of the features shown only on 1/50,000 or larger scale maps) is already available in paper map form for much of the world where it exists (except for certain international boundary areas and in other sensitive zones such as India's coastal strip). Given this, there may be a case for an approach by ICSU/IGBP through their national contact points or through their national mapping agencies (where these are civilian organisations) to the military: this is discussed further below.

CONCLUSIONS

The conclusions from this and associated papers in the Global Database Planning Project proceedings are clear :

- though the precise relationship between cartographically -derived data sets and those obtained from remote sensing is unclear and subject to change (e.g. depending on the success of automated map production from SPOT stereo imagery), it seems clear that both types of data will form important components of at least some - and probably many - IGBP studies.

- the existing availability of topographic (and hence other) maps to the general public is such that comprehensive and reasonably consistent global coverage is only possible at present at scales of 1/1 million or slightly larger. Thus the existing Bickmore (1988) or US DMA plans are the best which can be achieved at this time without multinational co-operative agreements.

- in the next ten years or so, however, partial but substantial data sets encoded from much larger (e.g 1/50,000) scale maps will appear. The scientific community will find these of greater value because they suffer less from the generalisation and accuracy problems described above. Their use will demand greatly improved data handling facilities over what is currently available or even, in some respects, what is planned.

- the military have an increasing need for such data sets for their own purposes. In Western Europe at least, many of the maps involved are not classified though more restrictions exist elsewhere. In principle, the international scientific community might gain great advantage from early discussions with appropriate representatives on the likely availability of such data and on its classification and data structure. At least two different models for such discussions are obvious. The first is that the scientific community through IGBP deals directly with representatives of military alliances. Possibly a more promising approach is to build a hierarchical structure through involving national mapping agencies as intermediaries between IGBP (plus its national committees) and the military. It would be naive to expect complete global success from any such liaison with (in some cases) competing organisations, especially as map scales get larger and questions of national security become more significant. Yet to ignore such a potential data source would be folly.

ACKNOWLEDGEMENTS

Warm thanks are due to the following who helped in various ways: V. Andrews, N. Chrisman, P.F. Dale, P.F. Fagan, S. Guptill and R. Waters; the authors alone, however, are responsible for all opinions expressed in this paper.

REFERENCES CITED

Bickmore D.P., 1988. 'World Digital Database for Environmental Sciences (WDDES)'. Proc. Global Database Planning Project, Tylney Hall.

Bond, B.A., 1973. 'Cartographic source material and its evaluation'. Cartographic Journal 10, 1, 54-8.

Brandenberger, A.J. and Ghosh S.K., 1985. 'The world's topographic and cadastral mapping operation'. Photogrammetric Engineering and Remote Sensing 51, 4, 437-44.

Brassel, K.E., 1985. 'Strategies and data models for computer-aided generalisation'. Intl. Yearbook of Cartography 25, 11-28.

Buttenfield B.P., 1985. 'Treatment of the cartographic line'. Cartographica 22, 2, 1-26.

Buttenfield B.P., 1987. 'Automating the identification of cartographic lines'. American Cartographer 14, 1, 7-20.

Callahan M., 1983. 'Digital cartographic data products using raster scanning techniques'. Proc AutoCarto 6, 392-9. American Congress of Surveying and Mapping, Washington.

Crone D.R., 1953. 'The accuracy of topographic maps'. Empire Survey Review, 12, 88.

de Simone M., 1986. 'Automatic structuring and feature recognition for large scale digital mapping'. Proc. AutoCarto London, ed. M. Blakemore, vol 1, 86-95.

Dudal R. and Batisse M., 1979. 'Soil map of the world'. Nature and Resources 14, 1, 2-6.

Farrell, B., 1987. 'Map evaluation' in Parry R.B. and Perkins C.R. op cit, 27-34.

Gardiner V., 1982. 'Stream networks and digital cartography'. Cartographica, 19, 38-44.

Glusic, A.M., 1961. 'The positional accuracy of maps'. AMS Technical Report 35, Army Map Service, Washington DC.

Greenland A., R.M. Socher and M. Thompson, 1985. 'Statistical evaluation of accuracy for digital cartographic databases' in Digital representation of spatial knowledge (Proc. AutoCarto 7), 212-21. ACSM, Washington DC.

Greenwalt C.R. and Schultz, 1962. Principles of error theory and cartographic applications. ACIC Reference Publications 96, St Louis.

Greenwalt C.R. and Schultz, 1962b. Map Accuracy Evaluation, Part I: Evaluation of horizontal map information. ACIC reference publications, St Louis

Greenwalt C.R. and Schultz, 1963. Map Accuracy Evaluation, Part II: Evaluation of vertical map information. ACIC reference publications, St Louis.

Greenwalt C.R., 1971. Users guide to understanding chart and geodetic accuracies. ACIC Reference Publication 28, St Louis

Guptill S., 1983. 'An intermediate scale digital cartographic database'. Proc. AutoCarto 6, 563-9. American Congress of Surveying and Mapping, Washington.

Haasbroek N.D., 1955. Investigation of the accuracy of plotting and scaling off. Netherlands Geodetic Commission.

Harley J.B., 1975. Ordnance Survey maps : a descriptive manual, Ordnance Survey, Southampton.

Harvey M.J., 1987. 'Meeting the future defence requirements for digital geographic data'. Paper presented to 1987 International Conference of Royal Institute of Navigation.

Howman C., 1983. 'The Production of Automated Charts for Europe (PACE) project'. Proc. Conf. Commonwealth Surveyors. Paper G3, Cambridge.

Hsu M-L and Robinson A.H., 1970. The fidelity of the isopleth map, University of Minnesota Press, Minneapolis.

Jones C.B. and Abraham I.M., 1987. 'Line generalisation in a global cartographic database'. Cartographica 24,3,32-45.

Keates J.S., 1973. Cartographic design and production, Longman, London

Lankaster J.S., 1987. 'Database requirements within Military Survey'. Paper presented to the 1987 International Conference of the Royal Institute of Navigation.

McMaster R.B., 1983. 'A mathematical evaluation of simplification algorithms'. Proc. AutoCarto 6 267-76, ACSM, Washington DC.

Merchant D.C., 1987. 'Spatial accuracy specifications for large scale topographic maps'. Photogrammetric Engineering and Remote Sensing 53, 7, 958-61

Parry R.B. and Perkins C.R., 1987. World mapping today. Butterworths, London

Rhind D.W., 1973. 'Generalisation and realism within automated cartographic systems'. Canadian Cartographer, 10, 1, 51-62.

Rhind D.W. and Hudson R., 1980. Land Use. Methuen, London.

Robinson A.H. and Petchenik B.B., 1976. The nature of maps: essays towards understanding maps and mapping. Univ. of Chicago Press, Chicago and London.

Robinson A.H., Sale R. and Morrison J., 1987. Elements of Cartography. Wiley.

Rosenfield C.H., 1986. 'Analysis of thematic map classification error matrices'. Photogrammetric Engineering and Remote Sensing, 52, 68-76.

Scott D.P.D., 1981. 'Mapping the Oceans' depths: the General Bathymetric Chart of the Oceans (GEBCO)'. Nature and Resources, 17, 6-9.

SCST, 1984. Remote Sensing and digital mapping. Report of the House of Lords' Select Committee on Science and Technology, 2 vols., Her Majesty's Stationary Office, London.

SSC, 1977. Cartographic generalisation. Cartographic Publication Series, 2. Swiss Society of Cartography, Zurich.

Stegena L., 1979. 'Geoscientific world mapping : facts and representations'. World Cartography, 15, 77-89.

Thompson M.M. and Davey C.H., 1953. 'Vertical accuracy of topographic maps'. Survey and Mapping, 13, 1.

Thompson M.M., 1956. 'How accurate is that map?' Survey and Mapping, 16, 2, 164-74.

Thompson M.M., 1960. 'A current view of National Map Accuracy Standards'. Survey and Mapping, 20, 4,

Thompson M.M and Rosenfeld G.H., 1971. 'On map accuracy specifications'. Survey and Mapping, 31, 1, 57-64.

Thompson M.M., 1983. Maps for America. 2nd edition, US Geological Survey, Reston, Va.

Topfer F. and Pillewizer W., 1966. 'The principles of selection'. Cartographic Journal 3, 1, 10-16.

Waters, R., forthcoming. 'New developments in digitising: interactively controlled raster to vector conversion'. Proc. EuroCarto 7, ITC Enschede

Wiggins J., Hartley R.P., Higgins M.J. and Whittaker R.J., 1987. 'Computing aspects of a large geographical information system for the European Community'. Intl. Jl. Geogr. Info. Systems 1, 77-88.

Williamson L.E., 1983. 'A survey of cartographic contributions of international governmental organisations'. Government Publications Review 10, 329-44.

Woodsford P., 1986. 'Cartographic digitising - technical trends and economic factors'. Proc. AutoCarto London, ed. M. Blakemore. Vol.2, 472-9.

Wyatt B., Briggs D. and Mounsey H.M., 1988. 'CORINE: an information system on the state of the environment in the European Community'. Proc. Global Database Planning Project meeting, Tylney Hall.

CONSIDERATIONS ON INTEGRATING REMOTE SENSING AND GEOGRAPHIC INFORMATION SYSTEMS

David S. Simonett

INTRODUCTION

Aircraft and satellite-borne sensors provide much primary data for geographic analyses. Other geographic information is also used to improve and extend the classification and analysis of digital remotely sensed data. Despite the inherent close coupling of remote sensing and geographic information systems, only recently has much attention been paid to theoretical and practical issues in integrating remotely sensed data in GIS applications. Issues which must be addressed to realize this potential, include

- data acquisition and processing of massive quantities of satellite data
- appropriate data structures for storage and analysis of longitudinal digital remotely sensed data
- image classification, and application of contextual classifiers and expert systems
- data dissemination
- limitations on remote sensing as a source of global data
- archiving and access problems
- problems in providing internally-consistent longitudinal data sets
- problems in merging disparate remote sensing data sets
- problems in merging remotely sensed data and data from other sources.

In order to provide some background in examining these issues, the following material is presented in sequence:

(1) Material on the Earth Observing System, NASA's global science initiative. NASA proposes to address data acquisition and analyses in such major programs as the International Geosphere-Biosphere Programme: A Study of Global Change (IGBP), which was initiated under the auspices of the International Council of Scientific Unions (ICSU).

(2) A data product description for HIRIS (the high resolution imaging spectrometer to be part of the Eos instrument package). This is exemplary of the various levels of data proposed for many instruments.

(3) Some preliminary indications of the scientific issues to be addressed by the Geostationary Platform(s), now under examination by a NASA committee.

(4) A summary of an earlier meeting in 1978 (Simonett et al, 1978), which addressed geographic information system impacts on space image formats.

(5) Following this background material, the nine issues listed above are briefly surveyed.

EARTH OBSERVING SYSTEM: MAJOR EARTH SCIENCE GOALS

The goal of earth system science is to obtain scientific understanding of the entire earth system on a global scale by describing how its component parts and their interactions have evolved, how they function, and how they may be expected to continue to evolve on all time scales. The challenge in reaching for this goal is to develop the capability to predict those changes that will occur in the next decade to the next century, both naturally and in response to human activity.

Hydrologic Cycle

-   Quantify the processes of precipitation, evaporation, evapotranspiration, and runoff on a global basis.

-   Determine what factors control the hydrologic cycle.

-   Quantify the interactions between the vegetation, soil, and topographic characteristics of the land surface and the components of the hydrologic cycle.

Biogeochemistry

-   Understand the biogeochemical cycling of carbon, nitrogen, phosphorus, sulfur, and trace minerals.

-   Determine the global distribution of biomass and what controls both its heterogeneous distribution in space and its change over time.

- Quantify the global distribution and transport of tropospheric gases and aerosols and determine the strengths of their sources and sinks in the ocean, land surface, coastal and inland waters, and upper atmosphere.

Climatological Processes

- Predict climate on a probabilistic basis.

- Determine the response of the atmosphere to changes in the ocean circulation and heat content, land surface, and solar input.

- Determine the role of sea and land ice cover in controlling global climate.

Atmospheric

- Understand the coupling of the chemical, radiative, and dynamic processes of the troposphere, stratosphere, and mesosphere.

- Determine the coupling between the lower and upper atmosphere.

- Extend deterministic weather forecasting towards its theoretical limit.

Oceanic

- Measure the mesoscale to large scale circulation of the ocean and acquire a better understanding of the long term variability in this circulation.

- Determine the global heat, mass, and momentum coupling between the ocean and atmosphere.

- Understand the processes controlling the dynamics of sea ice and its interaction with the underlying water.

Solid Earth

- Determine the global distribution, geometry, and composition of continental rock units.

- Understand how episodic processes such as rainfall, runoff, dust storms, and volcanism modify the surface of the earth.

- Determine the relation between the factors of climate, topography, vegetation, and the geologic substrate, and the processes of soil formation and degradation.

Science and mission requirements working group recommendations

- A program must be initiated to ensure that the present time series of earth science data are maintained and continued. Collection of new data sets should be initiated.

- A data system that provides easy, integrated, and complete access to past, present, and future data must be developed as soon as possible.

- A long-term research effort must be sustained to study and understand these time series of earth observations.

- Eos, the Earth Observing System, should be established as an information system to carry out those aspects of the above recommendations which go beyond existing and currently planned activities.

- The scientific direction of the Earth Observing System should be established and continued through an international scientific steering committee.

The Earth Observing System: Essential elements of the Concept

- Eos is the centerpiece in implementing NASA's Earth System Science Program.

- Long-term, consistent data sets are essential for a successful Earth System Science Program.

- An information system approach is an integral part of the program.

- Research and operational payloads/data systems must be developed and implemented together.

- Eos is to have international scope in system provision, use, and benefit.

- The ICSU/International Geosphere-Biosphere Program forms a major framework of the Eos approach.

- Eos will be a key part of the U.S. effort on monitoring global change.

Table 1 shows a tabulation of the satellites and instrument payloads envisaged for Eos. This is followed by Table 2 which lists the instrument acronyms applicable to Eos.

DATA PRODUCT DESCRIPTION FOR HIRIS

(as given in the HIRIS Instrument Panel Report - HIRIS, 1987).

As an example of the proposed data products which will be available from Eos instruments, the data product description for the HIRIS instrument (High Resolution Imaging Spectrometer; see HIRIS, 1987) is given below:

The following data products will be available to HIRIS investigators from the HIRIS Ground Data Processing System. The normal product will be Level 1B data. The availability of higher-level products will be determined after potential demand is identified. Possibly, the HIRIS ground data processing system will distribute coded algorithms so that users can create higher-level products on their own computer systems.

Level 0 - Basic telemetry stream and archive format, as received from HIRIS. These are normally not available as a data product.

Level 1A - HIRIS instrument data augmented with ancillary data necessary to compute geographic locations and translate data into radiometric units, i.e. radiometric and geometric calibration information, satellite ephemeris, attitude, time, and sensor information.

Level 1B - Level 1A HIRIS data in orbit-sequential format that have been converted to radiometric units, including equalization between detectors. Data are geometrically raw but are augmented with ancillary data necessary to compute geographic locations.

Level 2 - Geophysical or environmental parameters in orbit-sequential format, derived from a Level 1A or 1B image. Desired products and algorithms await specification by community. Some

Table 1: Eos Baseline Planning Scenario: ao 14 Jan. 1988

PLATFORM	NASA POLAR PLATFORM-1	ESA POLAR PLATFORM
Altitude/Equator Crossing Time and Node	824 km 1.30 p.m. Ascending	824 km 9.30-10.30 a.m. Descending
Research Instruments	MODIS - N MERIS (MODIS-T) HIRIS ITIP AMSR SCATTEROMETER-1 RADAR ALTIMETER-1 CR MAG MPD PPS-PODS	HRIS ATLID GLRS SCATTEROMETER-2 RADAR ALTIMETER-2 SAR-C ATSR CSR (ERBI-S) MAG MPD PPS-PODS AMIR
Operational Instruments	AMRIR (2) AMSU (2) ERBI-NS + ERBI-S SEM GOMR	AMRIR (2) AMSU (2) ERBI-NS SEM
Other	ARGOS 2 S & R DB WBDCS (proposed)	ARGOS 2 S & R DB

PLATFORM	NASA POLAR PLATFORM-2	JAPANESE POLAR PLATFORM
Altitude/Equator Crossing Time and Node	824 km 1.30 p.m. Ascending	800 km 10.00 a.m.-12 noon
Research Instruments	SAR PEM IR-RAD SUSIM SUB-MM MLS F/P-INT MAG MPD	OCTS AVNIR LAWS AMSR (SAR-L) SAR-X
Other	DB	

OTHER RESEARCH INSTRUMENT CONCEPTS NOT ASSIGNED TO SPECIFIC
PLATFORMS:

	LASA	CIS
	ESTAR	AIRS
	NCIS	ACR

Table 2:   Acronyms Baseline Planning Scenario, January 1988

ACR	Active Cavity Radiometer
AIRS	Atmospheric Infrared Sounder
ALT	Radar Altimeter (1-NASA, 2-ESA)
AMIR	Advanced Microwave Imaging Radar
AMRIR	Advanced Medium Resolution Imaging Radiometer
AMSR	Advanced Microwave Scanning Radiometer
AMSU	Advanced Microwave Sounding Unit
ARGOS 2	Data Collection System (French)
ATLID	Atmospheric Lidar
ATSR	Along Track Scanning Radiometer
AVNIR	Advanced Visible & Near IR Radiometer
CIS	Cryogenic Interferometer/Spectrometer
CR	Correlation Radiometer
CSR	Conically Scanning Radiometer
DB	Direct Broadcast
ERBI	Earth Radiation Budget Instrument (NS-Non-Scanner) (S-Scanner)
ESTAR	Electronically Scanned Thinned Array Radiometer
F/P INT	Fabry Perot Interferometer
GLRS	Geodynamics Laser Randing System
GOMR	Global Ozone Monitoring Radiometer
HIRIS	High Resolution Imaging Spectrometer
HRIS	High Resolution Imaging Spectrometer (ESA)
IR-RAD	IR Radiometer
ITIR	Intermediate Thermal Infrared Radiometer
LASA	Laser Atmospheric Sounder and Altimeter
LAWS	Laser Atmospheric Wind Sounder
MAG	Magnetometer
MERIS	Medium Resolution Imaging Spectrometer
MLS	Microwave LIMB Sounder
MODIS-N	Moderate Resolution Imaging Spectrometer - Nadir
MODIS-T	Moderate Resolution Imaging Spectrometer
MPD	Magnetospheric Particle Detector
NCIS	Nadir Cryogenic Interferometer Spectrometer
OCTS	Ocean Color & Temperature Scanner
PEM	Particle Environment Monitor
PPS-PODS	Precise Position System - Precise Orbit Determination System
S&R	Search and Rescue
SAR	Synthetic Aperture Radar (C, L, & X-Bands)
SCATT	Scatterometer (1-NASA, 2-ESA)
SEM	Space Environment Monitor
SUB-MM	Submillimeter Spectrometer
SUSIM	Solar UV Spectral Irradiance Monitor
WBDCS	Wide Band Data Collection System

(Level 2 HIRIS data cont'd.)
processing could be computationally intensive, for example, it could require atmospheric correction. Possible products are identification of specific minerals, surface reflectance corrected for atmospheric scattering and absorption, leaf area index, coastal ocean phytoplankton, terrestrial aerosols, snow cover, and bioluminescence.

Level 3A - Level 2 or Level 1B data mapped to a geographic database, using satellite ephemeris information only. Because resampling is involved, this is not reversible to Level 1B or Level 2.

Level 3B - Level 2 or Level 1B data mapped to geographic database, using satellite ephemeris information and ground control points. Processing would take considerably longer than for Level 3A data. Because resampling is involved, this is not reversible to Level 1B or Level 2.

Level 4 - Model output or results from analyses of lower-level data, not measured by HIRIS but derived from HIRIS data and ancillary data measured at ground surface, multiple HIRIS images, or data from other satellite instruments. Possible examples are surface radiation balance integrated over some time period, and near-surface atmospheric water vapor. The distinction between Levels 2 and 4 is that Level 2 (and 3) products are derived from a single multispectral image, without the necessity for additional data.

Since it is anticipated that some investigators will have time-critical requirements for field experiments that necessitate quick data turnaround, preliminary-look data products for two spectral bands ($0.65\,\mu$m and $1.6\,\mu$m) will be provided in response to a specific request.

SCIENTIFIC ISSUES POTENTIALLY TO BE ADDRESSED BY
GEOSTATIONARY PLATFORM(S)

The scientific issues to be addressed by Geostationary Platforms are related to those of Eos, but are designed to take advantage of the frequent observations possible for low- and mid-latitudes (roughly $0°$-$35°$ north and south latitude) possible from geostationary orbit - from every 5 minutes for small areas to half-hourly to hourly for full-disk observations.

The committee examining scientific issues to be addressed and potential instruments is in the midst of its deliberations, hence no definitive statement can as yet be made. The committee is divided into three panels, examining respectively (1) physical climate, (2) the hydrologic cycle, and (3) biogeochemical cycles, essentially a parallel treatment to Eos, but seeking experiments and data for which geostationary platforms are optimal.

In many instances, the Geostationary Platform spatial resolutions will be poorer than those of Eos, but will be more frequent. While overall data volumes will certainly be less than Eos, they are likely to be of the same order of magnitude as Eos, and may well involve as many as ten (10) final instruments, including a high resolution imaging spectrometer.

Thus, overall data volumes from the Eos and Geostationary Platforms combined could well be nearly double that of Eos alone - a very large data volume indeed.

SUMMARY OF KEY CONCLUSIONS OF AN EARLIER MEETING ON GEOGRAPHIC INFORMATION SYSTEM IMPACTS ON SPACE IMAGE FORMATS (Simonett et al, 1978)

As Geographic Information Systems increase in number, size, and complexity, the format compatibility of satellite remote sensing data becomes increasingly more important. Because of the vast and continually increasing quantity of data available from remote sensing systems, the utility of these data is increasingly dependent on the degree to which their formats facilitate - or hinder - their incorporation into Geographic Information Systems. To merge satellite data into a geographic information system requires that they both have a compatible geographic referencing system. The cost of converting satellite data to a compatible format may be too large for many users. Greater acceptance of satellite data by the user community will be facilitated if the data are in a form which most readily corresponds to existing geographic data structures.

At the 1978 meeting, although most users agreed that a common format was desirable, the actual structure of that format was the subject of debate. However, the following general points represented a consensus of the user

community at the workshop (Simonett et al, 1978), and are
included here because they continue to be of relevance:

- A procedure for windowing and reformatting satellite
  data so that it could directly overlay such standard
  data bases as USGS map quadrangles would increase the
  utility of remote sensing data in geographic information systems. If this procedure is initiated, it will
  result in the attraction of new users, in reduced
  handling and processing time for all users, and in
  overall cost savings.
- New geographic data bases designed to provide the
  public with information and serve the needs of federal
  and state agencies should be structured to offer
  maximum flexibility for conversion by external users.
  Both polygon and gridded approaches to a data base
  structure must continue to be evaluated. Both types
  may need to be supported by providers of image
  products.

The conference also made recommendations on general formats
for future digital image products as follows:

- There should be two distinct families of digital
  imagery available to users as standard products:

  - Uncorrected video data, either in completely
    unaltered, "raw" form, or radiometrically
    calibrated but not destriped, but with substantial
    header and annotation information.
  - Fully processed data, which has been
    radiometrically corrected, including destriping,
    and geometrically rectified to a UTM, or other
    appropriate projection, and also that
  - Processed data should be available in certain other
    projections and formats as "special order"
    products, for which a somewhat longer order
    turnaround would be acceptable.

Other recommendations on annotation were as follows:

- The best and most complete annotation should be made
  available to users of either raw or reformatted
  satellite data. All forms of annotation currently
  provided should continue to be provided as well as the
  following information:

  - Type of projection, if applicable.
  - Sampling interval in meters on the ground.

- Up-to-date algorithms and coefficients for converting digital radiance numbers to actual space upwelling radiances.
- Several ground control points identified in image and standard georeference coordinates.
- More accurate geodetic grid ticks and nadir/format center coordinates (preferably designated in latitude and longitude).
- More accurate spacecraft positional (altitude and attitude) information.
- More spatially specific cloud coverage estimates.

Recommendations on image rectification were as follows:

- The rectified imagery should meet the following specifications:

  - The map projection employed should be conformal and the pixels should be aligned in an easting direction, amenable to Cartesian referencing. Universal Transverse Mercator was the projection preferred by users attending the conference. (Other projections may now be preferred, such as that suggested by Tobler and Chen (1986) employing quadtrees and authalic coordinates).
  - Rectified imagery should be indexed to existing USGS 7-1/2 minute quadrangle topographic maps, whereon sample locations should be fixed.
  - Resampling should be done only once and should either preserve the nominal spatial resolution of the sensor, or, if confirmed by further study, transform to one of a series of standard resolutions, e.g. binary (16, 32, 64, 128, . . . meters), or a sequence preferred by some users of 10, 25, 50, 100, 250, . . . meters (10/25 series). (An alternative system is the Tobler and Chen (1986) quadtree approach).
  - Projections other than the recommended UTM standard should be available upon request, but the transformations should be done from the raw data to avoid resampling data more than once.

- In terms of assessing the effect of image rectification on image data accuracy the following was recommended:

  - Further investigations should be undertaken to determine the effects of various resampling algorithms, including double resampling, on

115

radiometric and spatial fidelity, and classifier performance.

- The rectification algorithms used should be provided with the data to the user community, and algorithms for forward and inverse transforms between a variety of standard projections should be available for distribution to users.

Spatial resolution of the standard products

- "Raw" digital data should preserve the nominal spatial resolution of the imaging sensor.
- The "corrected" digital data should be resampled at an interval selected from the binary series (i.e. 2^n meters) or the "10/25" series. For Landsat-D, a suggested resampling interval would be 25 or 32 meters.
- Data compression techniques which irreversibly degrade spatial resolution should not be employed.
- Precise evaluations of the effects on spatial resolution of any resampling algorithms employed should be made available, either by broader dissemination of existing studies or by the initiation of new ones.

Radiometric resolution

- NASA should continue to improve their calibration procedures, and make all algorithms and constants available to the users through EDC (EROC Data Center).
- Data in which striping is present must be available to the users in uncorrected form.
- Pathwise calibration on an entire strip should be employed, to minimize scene-to-scene and along-track within-scene variations.
- Future video data should be represented as 8-bit unsigned binary integers in the range 0-255.
- Further investigation (and/or broader dissemination of existing data) is needed regarding the effects of resampling on radiometric fidelity, and on the feasibility of applying atmospheric corrections at the system level.

ISSUES IN INTEGRATING REMOTE SENSING AND OTHER DATA IN GEOGRAPHIC INFORMATION SYSTEMS

As early as 1976, Everett and Simonett summarized anticipated satellite impacts on science as follows:

- Stimulating the development of new hypotheses and theories in the natural and social sciences.
- Providing opportunities for partitioning other aggregated natural and social data (e.g. census data).
- Improving multistage sample designs in research and applications development, the selection of sites for more detailed scientific study, the calibration of other components of an integrated resource management system, and the evaluation of the interaction of static and dynamic components of the environment.
- Providing a basis for extrapolation, interpolation and refinement of scattered scientific observations, and for the making of unique observations feasible only with an ERS (Earth Resources Satellite) system.
- Stimulating the development of new science models which may be raised with ERS data to higher efficiencies than are now feasible.
- Opening, through storage of a unique, internally consistent longitudinal data set, unparalleled opportunities for developing quantitative hindcasting and forecasting models.

These anticipated impacts on science have still only partially been realized, and will not be fully realized unless the following issues are addressed both by the remote sensing and the GIS communities.

Data Acquisition and Processing of Massive Quantities of Satellite Data

A wide array of Eos and Geostationary Platform satellite sensors will supply information on atmospheric physics and chemistry for climate and pollution studies; ocean data on currents, surface temperatures and biological productivity; and terrestrial geology and soils, topography, hydrology, ecology, land use and land cover. Repeat global coverage is now and will continue to be of the order of hours or days, at spatial resolutions ranging from meters to kilometers. Data volume is immense and will grow larger; for example, global coverage with 80m Landsat MSS amounts to 320 gigabytes of 4-channel data. Data volume from the Earth Observing System is expected to be many times as large as shown in Table 3 and Figure 1. Anticipated abilities to handle these data volumes, in mainframes, distributed systems and in archiving are shown in Tables 4 and 5, and Figures 2, 3 and 4. That from Geostationary Platforms will be of an equivalent order of magnitude. Opportunities for integrating such data into GIS, and of exploiting rich capabilities in data pre-processing and

Table 3: Data expected from a number of missions in the land, ocean, and atmospheric sciences

Mission	Status	Year	Data Expected
GEOS, G,H	Ongoing	Ongoing	1.5×10^{13} bits/yr
NOAA F-J	Ongoing	Ongoing	10^{13} bits/yr
ERBE	Approved	1984	10^{12} bits/yr
LANDSAT D,D'	Ongoing	Ongoing	10^{14} bits/yr
TOPEX/POSEIDON	Planned	1988	10^{12} bits/yr
Geopotential Research Mission	Planned	1991	10^{12} bits/yr
SIT B,C,D	B=Funded C,D=Planned	1984, TBD	6×10^{14} bits
Shuttle Imaging Spectrometer	Planned	1989	10^{13} bits
Earth Observing System	Planned	1990s	10^{12} bits/day

NOTE: Current volume of Landsat data is approximately 10^{14} bits, while 2×10^{13} bits of other data exist. Current volume at NSSDC is approximately 7×10^{12} bits.
(After NAS, 1986, p 15.)

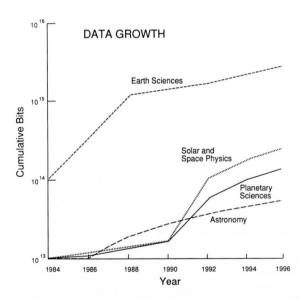

Figure 1: Projected growth rates for space science data, based on data from tables. Earth orbital missions assumed to last for 5 years, except for operational satellites and the space telescope, which are projected as continuing data producers. (After NAS, 1986, p.6)

Table 4:   Projected advances in computational capabilities
           assuming constant cost

Processor type	Typical Current Cost $1000	Performance, millions of operations per second		
		1983	1986	1995

Work stat-	25-50	1	6	50 (integer)
ion (68000)		0.05	1	15 (floating pt.)
Multiuser	100-300	1	4	15 (integer)
(VAX)		0.8[a]	3.6	12 (floating pt.)
Scientific	500-5000	100	300	10,000 (integer)
processor		50	150	5,000 (float. pt.)
		2 Mbps	10 Mbps	100 Mbps (I/O rate)

----
[a]If equipped with optional floating-point hardware.
Assumptions:
1. For other than floating-point arithmetic, four work
   station instructions are used to perform the equivalent
   of one scientific processor instruction.
2. For other than floating-point arithmetic, two VAX-type
   instructions are used to perform the equivalent of one
   scientific processor instruction.
3. The validity of these ratios depends greatly on the type
   of computation being performed. (After NAS, 1986, p.52).

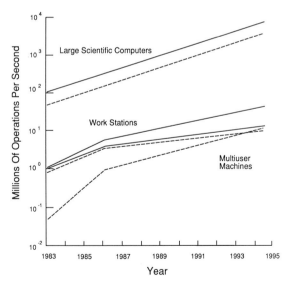

Figure 2:   Projected growth of processing capabilities at
constant cost.   Upper bounds are for integer and lower
bounds for floating point operations. (After NAS,1986,p.53)

119

Table 5: Projected advances in data storage, assuming constant cost and access time

Function	Cost/ Systems, $1000	Access Time, ms	Typical Fetch Size, bytes	Total Size (bytes)		
				1983	1986	1995
Working storage	5	100	5K	2M	20M	200M
Data base	20	30	10K	500M	2000M	8000M
Archive	500	30,000	100M	10^{12}	10^{13}	10^{16}

(After NAS, 1986, p. 58).

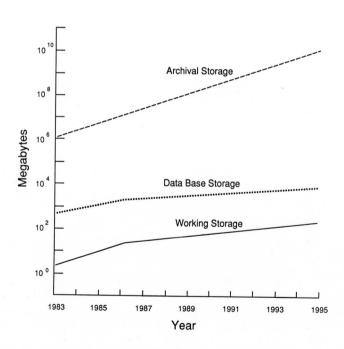

Figure 3: Projected growth of storage capacity at constant cost (after NAS, 1986, p.59)

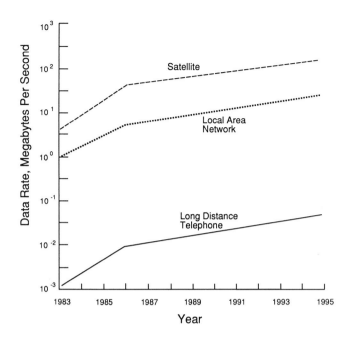

Figure 4: Projected growth in communications at constant cost (after NAS, 1986, p.63)

(Data acquisition and processing cont'd).
analysis are as yet poorly developed. They need to include the incorporation of existing information to allow for selective acquisition (e.g. areas of change, areas with specified attributes), for selective resolution (e.g. depending on the intrinsic grain of different environments), and for scene sampling, among many such possibilities. This conference will need to examine this area closely.

Advanced Data Structures for Storage and Integration of Remotely Sensed Data

There is probably no single optimal structure for efficient storage of raster-based sensor data. Depending on the nature of information to be extracted from the sensor signal (e.g. topography, biomass, fires, hydrology), and on the nature of the environment under investigation, the original raster data may be better stored in vector form , as a spatial hierarchy (e.g. quadtree or hextree), or uncompressed. Appropriate structures for efficient data browsing are also an open question. Efficient storage and data searching will demand development of geographic information systems with fully integrated processing of vector and raster data.

The availability of repeat imagery now allows for environmental monitoring and updating of a GIS. In practice, updating can be difficult and time-consuming due to problems of registration and scene-specific properties such as illumination and atmosphere, which limit the utility of automated approaches. There have been some efforts to incorporate expert reasoning for a more sophisticated approach to automated change detection, but such developments are at a very early stage.

Scene Classification, Contextual Classifiers and Expert Systems

GIS capabilities have been used to incorporate ancillary information on environmental variables such as topography or soils, in order to improve mapping accuracy over that achieved based solely on spectral information. A GIS can also aid in sampling to calibrate sensor data or to assess map accuracy through regional stratification or interpolation. Much additional information can be extracted from digital imagery by taking advantage of contextual information supplied with a GIS. Quadtree-based sampling of both low-frequency and high-frequency joint spatial/categorical ements might be employed.

A further extension for scene classification is the application of expert or knowledge-based classifiers. This approach may be less scene-specific than more conventional statistical pattern recognition, offering the hope for truly general classification algorithms. To date, knowledge-based classifiers have been applied mainly to spectral information, but there is great potential for using additional layers of information in a GIS-based approach.

Data Dissemination

Only a small fraction of remotely sensed data are actually used for mapping and monitoring, in part because of the technical challenge and cost of image processing and classification, and the difficulty of merging the product with other geographic data. This problem will tax the international science community, as well as NASA, in attempting to deliver on the Eos promise. If inadequately addressed, the potential is there for overpromising and underdelivering - certainly of data in a directly usable format and without massive amounts of reprocessing. Fuller utilization of remotely sensed data will require improved institutional arrangements for processing and formatting imagery, so that it is compatible with GIS systems. In particular, suppliers of image data need to account for user needs in terms of GIS hardware and software design, and the integration of image data with other diverse data sources.

Limitations on Remote Sensing as a Source of Global Data

An important area for the attention of this conference and subsequent workshops is that of limitations on remote sensing as a source of global data. What data needs to be obtained on the ground to calibrate remote sensing data - where, when, and with what accuracy? What ancillary data is necessary to drive remote sensing-based models? Can spatial modeling be employed with ecosystem models in such a way that remote sensing can be coupled with the modeling of change in ecosystems? Questions such as these are only now being examined by the remote sensing community.

Archiving and Access Problems

NASA has been very concerned over both archiving and access problems, and has been strongly urged by the science community to improve both archiving practice and access times and products. This conference will need to review details of NASA proposals for the Land and Ocean Data Systems. At the time of writing, the Ocean Data System is the more advanced of the two, and much work remains to be done on Land Data Systems. Global geographic information system impacts on such data systems should be examined in subsequent workshops.

Problems in Providing Internally Consistent Longitudinal Data Sets

Everett and Simonett (1976) note that many sources of data, including censuses, are plagued by inconsistencies, and the relative consistency of remote sensing data is emphasized as one of its stronger attributes. They also note that "consistency [in remote sensing data] is inversely related to the degree of environmental complexity in space and time and the size of the area being examined, and is directly related to system resolution. . . . These relations also suggest that a high order of consistency for a very large area of, say, continental dimensions may be obtained only if a small number of very general categories are specified". This issue is also appropriate for workshop attention.

Problems in Merging Disparate Very Large Remote Sensing Data Sets

The design for Earth System Science will require scientists to handle not merely very large data sets, but also very many data sets, from imaging and non-imaging sensors. Very few are presently equipped to handle such data. It will require not only tight temporal and geographic referencing for a given time, but also combined temporal/spatial referencing over extended periods of time, depending on the types of models to be employed. NASA and other space agencies are well aware of this problem, which dwarfs that of present NOAA data sets, and which will push the system capabilities into failure-prone areas.

Problems in Merging Remotely Sensed Data with Data from Other Sources

Among the issues which need to be examined in merging remotely sensed data with data from other sources are: (1) the quality of the various data sets, and the effects of data quality on error propagation in modeling; (2) establishment of physically-based or index relations between remote sensing data and other data, to enable data substitution to be employed; (3) the degree to which missing data in any data set can be tolerated. These examples are given to indicate how very little work has been done on employing integrated remote sensing/geographic information systems on a regional, let alone a global, scale. Deep-seated issues of artefacting, indeterminancy, improper extrapolation between scales, and environmental modulation of spatial error budgets are embedded in the joint use of remote sensing and geographic information systems, as noted by Everett and Simonett (1976) and Simonett et al. (1983).

BIBLIOGRAPHY

Anselin, L., 1987. 'Model Validation in Spatial Econometrics: A Review and Evaluation of Alternative Approaches'. International Regional Sciences Review, (forthcoming).

Balour, A., T.L. Anderson, L.K. Dekeyser, and H.K.T. Wong, 1982. 'The Role of Time in Information Processing: A Survey'. ACM-SIGMOD Record 12, 3.

Blakemore, M., 1983. 'Generalization and Error in Spatial Data Bases'. Proceedings AUTOCARTO 6, 1, 312-322.

Burrough, P.A., 1981. 'Fractal Dimensions of Landscapes and Other Environmental Data'. Nature, 294, 241-242

Burrough, P.A., 1983. 'Multiscale Sources of Spatial Variation in Soil: The Application of Fractal Concepts to Nested Levels of Soil Variation'. Journal of Soil Science, 34, 577-597.

Burrough, P.A., 1986. Principles of Geographical Information Systems for Land Resources Assessment. Oxford, Clarendon Press.

Chorley, R., 1987. Report of the Select Committee on GIS, London, HMSO.

Chrisman, N.R., 1979. 'Concepts of Space as a Guide to Cartographic Data Structures' in First International Advanced Study Symposium on Toplogical Data Structures for Geographic Information Systems, vol. 7, ed. G. Dutton. Cambridge, MA: Harvard University.

Clarke, K.C., 1986. 'Advances in Geographic Information Systems'. Computers, Environment, and Urban Systems, 10:3/4, 175-184.

EOS, 1986a. Earth Observing System, Science and Mission Requirements. Working Group Report, /Volume I, 1-51, and Volume I, Appendix, A1-A55, National Aeronautics and Space Administration.

EOS, 1986b. From Pattern to Process: The Strategy of the Earth Observing System, Eos Science Steering Committee Report, Volume II, 1-140, National Aeronautics and Space Administration.

Everett, J. and D.S. Simonett, 1976. 'Principles, Concepts and Philosophical Problems in Remote Sensing' in Remote Sensing of Environment, eds. J.L. Lintz and D.S. Simonett, 85-127, Advanced Book Series, Addison-Wesley Publishing Co., Reading, MA.

Frank, W.R., 1984. 'Cartographic Errors Symptomatic of Underlying Algebra Problems'. International Symposium of Spatial Data Handling, Zurich.

Frank, A., 1984. 'Requirements for Database Systems Suitable to Manage Large Spatial Databases'. International Symposium on Spatial Data Handling, Zurich.

GIS '87 - San Francisco, Second Annual International Conference, Exhibits, and Workshops on Geographic Information Systems, 1987, Washington, DC: ACSM/ASPRS.

Griffith, D.A., 1988. 'Estimating Spatial Autoregressive Model Parameters with Commercial Statistical Packages'. Geographical Analysis, 20.

Goodchild, M.F. and B.R. Rizzo, 1986. 'Performance Evaluation and Workload Estimation for Geographic Information Systems'. Proceedings, Second International Symposium on Spatial Data Handling, Seattle, 497-509.

Goodchild, M.F. and O. Dubuc, 1987. 'A Model of Error for Choropleth Maps, with Applications to Geographic Information Systems'. Proceedings, AutoCarto 8, Falls Church, VA: ASPRS/ACSM, 165-74.

Goodchild, M.F., 1987. 'Application of a GIS Benchmarking and Workload Estimation Model'. Papers and Proceedings of Applied Geography Conferences, 10, 1-6.

HIRIS, 1987. HIRIS, Instrument Panel Report on the High Resolution Imaging Spectrometer. Earth Observing System, Volume IIc, 1-74. National Aeronautics and Space Administration.

International Geographic Information Systems (IGIS) Symposium: The Research Agenda, 1987. Washington, DC: AAG (in press).

Lodwick, G and M. Feuchtwanger, 1987. 'Land Related Information Systems'. University of Calgary Surveying Engineering Report no. 10010, Calgary: The University of Calgary.

Luang, Y., 1987. 'On the Imprecision of Boundaries'. Geographical Analysis, 19, 125-151.

MODIS, 1986. MODIS, Instrument Panel Report on the Moderate Resolution Imaging Spectrometer. Earth

Observing System, Volume IIb, 1-59. National Aeronautics and Space Administration.

NAS, 1986. Issues and Recommendations Associated with Distributed Computation and Data Management Systems for Space Sciences. National Academy of Sciences, Committee on Data Management and Computation, 1 - 111.

Oliver, M., 1987. 'Geostatistics and its Application to Soil Science'. Soil Use and Management, 3(1), 8-19.

Openshaw, S., 1987, Guest Editorial: 'An Automated Geographical Analysis System'. Environment and Planning A, 19, 431-6

Openshaw, S. and H. Mounsey, 1987. 'Geographic Information Systems and the BBC's Domesday Interactive Videodisc'. International Journal of Geographic Information Systems, 1(2), 173-179.

Openshaw, S., 1988. 'Building an Automated Modeling System to Explore a Universe of Spatial Interaction Models'. Geographical Analysis, 20.

Ripley, B.D., 1981. Spatial Statistics. Wiley: New York.

Robinson, V., 1984. Modeling Inexactness in Spatial Information Systems. Proceedings of the Pittsburgh Conference on Modeling and Simulation, Pittsburgh, PA.

Rosenzweig, C. and R. Dickinson, eds., 1986. Climate - Vegetation Interactions. Proceedings of a Workshop, NASA/Goddard Space Flight Center, Greenbelt, Maryland, 1 - 156.

Samet, H., 1984. 'The Quadtree and Related Hierarchical Data Structures'. Computing Surveys, 16(2), 187.

SAR, 1986. SAR, Instrument Panel Report on the Synthetic Aperture Radar. Earth Observing System, Volume IIf, 1-233. National Aeronautics and Space Administration.

Simonett, D.S., T.R. Smith, W. Tobler, D.G. Marks, J.E. Frew and J.C. Dozier, eds., 1978. Geobase Information System Impacts on Space Image Formats. Santa Barbara Remote Sensing Unit, SBRSU Technical Report 3.

Simonett, D.S., R.G. Reeves, J.E. Estes, S.E. Bertke and C.T. Sailer, 1983. 'The Development and Principles of

Remote Sensing' in Manual of Remote Sensing, Second edition, Volume I, 1-35. American Society of Photogrammetry.

Smith, G.R. and D.M. Honeycutt, 1987. Geographic Data Uncertainty, Decision Making, and the Value of Information. Redlands, CA: ESRI.

Snodgrass, R. and I. Ahn, 1985. 'A Taxonomy of Time in Databases'. ACM-SIGMOD Record 14, 4.

Strahler, A., C. Woodcock, and J. Smith, 1986. 'On the Nature of Models in Remote Sensing'. Remote Sensing of Environment, 21, 121-139.

Thomas, R. and R. Hugget, 1980. Modeling in Geography: A Mathematical Approach. Totowa, NJ: Barnes & Noble Books.

Tobler, W.R. and Z.T. Chen, 1986. 'A Quadtree for Global Information Storage'. Geographical Analysis, 18, 4, 360-371.

Tomlinson Associates, 1987. Review of North American Experience of Current and Potential Uses of Geographic Information Systems, in Chorley, R. ed., op cit.

Walsh, S.J., D.R. Lightfoot and D.R. Butler, 1987. 'Recognition and Assessment of Error in Geographic Information Systems'. Photogrammetric Engineering and Remote Sensing, 53, 1423-30.

Warnecke, L., 1987. 'Geographic Information Coordination in the States: Past Efforts, Lessons Learned, and Future Opportunities. Paper given at the National Governors' Association Conference, Washington, DC.

Woodcock, C. and A. Strahler, 1987. 'The Factor Scale in Remote Sensing'. Remote Sensing of Environment, 21, 311-332.

RESOLUTION, RESAMPLING, AND ALL THAT

Waldo Tobler

One of the methods used for the capture of geographical information is to pass maps through a raster scanner. In this mode one samples the data at equal increments in the x and y coordinate directions. Because the geographical maps are based on a map projection these equal map increments are not equal on the earth. The figure shows two schemes of this sort wherein equally spaced coordinates on a map are seen to be unequally spaced on a sphere. Every different map projection gives rise to a different scheme like this. For many data processing or storage operations one would like the data to be indexed at equal increments of latitude and longitude. The conversion of observations from the map grid to the uniform lat/lon grid (or the converse) is known as resampling. This is somewhat of a misnomer because one is not really collecting more information in a new sample. One is interpolating from values known at certain locations to provide guesses of values at locations at which one would like to know the values. There are many ways to do this, and many other situations in which resampling is performed.

Some other instances which require data resampling are very much like the coordinate conversion involving a map projection. For example, if the data are collected on a square grid, but because of the problem to be analyzed it makes more sense to treat the values in a polar coordinate system, then some resampling may be required. The varieties of examples such as this moving from a rectangular grid to polar coordinates, or the inverse, are of course very numerous. We mention elliptical coordinates as one additional example, and also refer to the literature on the removing of warping, skew, or distortion from remotely sensed images, cognitive images, or antique maps. The use of different geodetic datums for different parts of the world generally requires similar adjustments, as does the mosaicing of data from adjacent but different grids - adjacent UTM zones may be taken as an example. And missing, or obviously incorrect values, frequently need to be replaced in a data series. The resampling can be

applied to raster data or to vector data, and may increase
or decrease the volume of data.

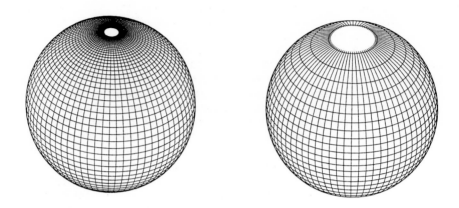

Figure 1:   Mercator Coordinates on a Sphere (Left)
            Cylindrical Equal Area Coordinates (Right)

Resampling is also often used when it is desired to compare
two or more spatial datasets, or to bring several such to a
common denominator. If one considers only square grids
then they can still differ in origin, in scale, and by a
rotation. If one further allows non-uniform rectangular
grids, or variable spatial resolution grids, or polar
grids, etc., and still wants a commonly denominated data
representation, it is clear that multiple resamplings may
be required. Polar coordinate systems - and the latitude /
longitude system falls into this category - have equal
angular resolution but unequal areal resolution.
Resampling for rotational alignment similarly must account
for unequal areal resolution. Sometimes such unequal
variation is easily taken into account. For example, to
obtain a normalized density of data on a sphere when using
the lat/lon grid one needs only to divide by the cosine of
the latitude.

The methods of resampling most frequently cited include
nearest neighbor interpolation, bilinear interpolation,
Lagrangian interpolation, cubic convolution (as an
approximation to the sinc function), and bivariate
splining.

The foregoing paragraphs are couched in terms of grids. The resampling problem for grids is much simpler than the general interpolation problem, mainly because the domain of influence of each observation is usually assumed to include only a small subset of adjacent grid cells. But for global databases information will come from irregularly arranged point samples, or from areal integrations, as well as from alternate grids and map projections, and it will be necessary to blend these into the common structure. Thus more general resampling problems must be recognized, e.g. interpolation from an irregular geographical arrangement of observations to a regular one, or from variably sized, shaped, and oriented resels to a regular lattice of cells, etc. There is an extremely large literature on these types of problems; this is referenced in the literature cited.

Resampling makes the most sense when the conversion is between systems which are about the same size. But suppose two grids differ by an order of magnitude. To be specific, suppose one set of data is sampled at points ten meters apart in two orthogonal directions and the other at a grid spacing of 100 meters. In principle the conversion could go either way, converting the 10 m data to 100 m intervals, or converting the 100 m data to 10 m intervals. But it is obvious that that in the one case we can just drop 9/10 of the observations whereas in the other case we must interpolate. And interpolation requires the invocation of some hypotheses about nature. Thus the two conversions are not symmetric in their im pact. If we measure the resolution of the two sets of data, one is at 10 m, the other at 100 m. If both are converted to a 100 m grid then the resolution of the common base is clearly 100 m. But if both are converted to a 10 m grid then the resolution of the common base should be counted as 100 m, even though the apparent grid spacing is 10 m. The implicit principle here is that the resolution of a database should be labeled to be that of the coarsest element(s) in the database. Furthermore, as a principle, resampling or interpolation cannot improve the resolution of a database. Here it is perhaps appropriate to distinguish resampling from enhancement, which, by introducing theory or information external to the database, may lead to improved resolution.

The spatial resolution of a geographical map is fairly easy to assess. This is because there is a relation between map scale and geographic resolution. This is readily obtained by observing that the smallest physical mark which the cartographer can make is about one half millimeter in size. Then the accompanying table shows a simple rule:

131

Resolution, Resampling and All That

Scale	Resolution	Detection
1/10,000	5 m	10 m
1/50,000	25 m	50 m
1/100,000	50 m	100 m
1/250,000	125 m	250 m
1/500,000	250 m	500 m
1/1,000,000	500 m	1,000 m

Or, in Anglo-Saxon Units:

1/24,000	39 feet	79 feet
1/63,360	104 feet	208 feet

The rule is: divide the denominator of the map scale by 1,000 to get the detectable size in meters. The resolution is one half of this amount. Of course the cartographer fudges. He makes things which are too small to detect much larger on the map because of their importance. But this cannot be done for everything so that most features less than resolution size get left off the map. This is why the spatial resolution is so critical.

Different countries use different map scales, (and projections and datums and data categories, etc), and a common resolution for a spatial dataset inevitably requires resampling, unless one can tolerate a global database with different resolutions in different parts of the world. This is the de facto situation with respect to different map series, and not entirely unreasonable since the data needs vary from one part of the world to another. In an electronic storage environment one needs to retain an index map of the resolution by geographic location, just as one attempts to indicate by a reliability diagram the accuracy estimate of a map. One also observes that countries with multiple map coverages tend to provide these at scales which lie at approximately equal intervals on a logarithmic line. Should electronic databases also be provided at comparable resolution intervals, or can procedures be developed which require that the data only be stored once, at a very fine resolution, with algorithms which provide the resolution (presumably reduced) appropriate for the problem to be solved? Or should one proceed as in the historical discovery and exploration of the earth, first with a crude reconnaisance and then slowly filling in the detail with more careful observations at a later time?

A dictionary definition of resolution is "the capability of making distinguishable the individual parts of an object".

Under "resolving power" the same dictionary gives the
following: "the ability of an optical system to form
distinguishable images of objects separated by small
angular distances; the ability of a photographic film or
plate to reproduce the fine detail of an optical image".
From these prototypes one can infer that one needs to know
the spatial resolution of a geographical data storage
system before one can determine the level of geographic
detail which can be observed. A system which carries too
much geographic detail is wasteful, and one which contains
too little geographic detail is useless. Thus the choice
of the appropriate level of spatial resolution is critical
to the success of a geographical data storage system. The
spatial resolution governs the ability of the system to
reproduce the fine detail of the geographic environment.
If one knows the spatial resolution of a geographical data
storage system this information can be used to compare it
to other systems.

The spatial resolution of an optical system is often
measured in lines per millimeter, or line-pairs per
millimeter (slightly different measures are used for
optical systems and for television systems). The optical
target, a series of alternating black and white lines in
the form of a wedge (or of varying line spacing and width),
makes the determination of the resolution of such a system
fairly easy to explain. Here the reference is to a linear
measure (millimeters), not to an areal measure (square
millimeters), and no account is taken of differences in
resolution in different directions nor in spatially
different parts of the lens or film. Since it is
inevitable that such differences should exist the
resolution of such a system really refers to an average
resolution.

The resolution of photographic film is very high, in the
order of 100 lines /millimeter. It is this fact which
allows one to enlarge pictures twenty or more times. But
eventually one reaches the "point of empty magnification",
beyond which nothing new appears in an enlargement; in fact
things seem to get worse after this point, and the picture
becomes more difficult to read. All resolution-limited
systems share this property. In optics the wavelength of
light is the ultimate limit. Electron microscopes are used
to see things smaller than light waves. Natural phenomena,
however, are generally not like this. The closer one looks
the more the apparent detail, a property recently made
popular through the study of Mandelbrot's fractals. It
would appear that real geographic data have an infinite

amount of detail, and assumptions regarding band width limitations are only artificial aids to analysis.

Spatial resolution in the earth sciences has long been recognized as being closely related to the sampling interval. Thus the meteorologist knows that a geographically dense net of observing stations is required to track the fine details of a thunderstorm. These storms are generally from one to five kilometers across. From sampling theory it is known that the detection of a feature is only possible if the sampling rate is twice as fine as the size of the feature to be detected. A one kilometer storm can only be observed if the sampling interval is one half kilometer - otherwise the storm could slip between the observing stations. Since observations are never perfect, the better rule of thumb is to use a sampling interval one fifth the size of the feature to be detected. This has an important implication for geographical data collection and storage; it implies that one must know the spatial size of the features in which one is interested before one starts to collect data. And one cannot expect a collection of geographic data to be suitable for all kinds of problems. Furthermore, one must recognize the existence of "invisible" phenomena and must also recognize the aliasing effects which result from the spatial size of the sampling interval.

Another method of convincing oneself of the relation between detectibility and resolution is to examine a scene using photographs which have been digitized at varying levels of resolution. The subject matter of the photograph becomes recognizable only after sufficient detail becomes available to distinguish individual features, the "parts of the object" in the dictionary definition.

Suppose one has elevations (or precipitation, etc.) sampled at irregular spatial intervals ("random" data points). Then the average influence domain of each sample point might be calculated by dividing the total area (in square units) containing the observations by the number of observations. The square root of this value is an estimate of the average resolution (in linear units), or the effective average length per observation. If, as is common practice, an interpolation is now made to a regular lattice ("gridding") for ease in subsequent processing then the average resolution provides a guide for the choice of the lattice size. One cannot add resolution to the data by picking a small lattice size, when this resolution is not available in the original observations.

134

The definition given here for spatial resolution enables one to make the calculation for point, line, polygon or raster Geographic Information Systems, and for categorical, scalar, vector, or tensor data. Comparisons between geographic information systems are most easily made when they have similar resolutions and resolution-variances.

Representing topography by a triangulated irregular network based on sample points, or rainfall stations by the dual of Thiessen polygons, has the advantage that it retains the exact resolution of the original observations. This is generally more efficient than a uniform lattice or grid, which over-resolves the data in some parts and under-resolves in others. Figure 2, depicting the counties of the contiguous United States, represents a similar situation wherein the data collection scheme is of variable

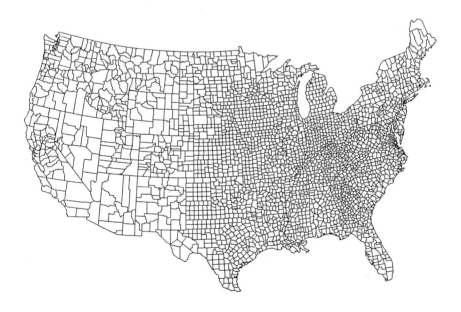

Figure 2: Map of US Resels

resolution. Notice that even with county data one could never detect anything within a city, since cities are generally less in diameter than the 86 kilometer mean resolution of this sampling scheme. For metropolitan regions and other more intensely occupied areas the data are reported using finer resolution intervals.

Also noticeable on the county map is that the resolution varies from east to west, being much finer in the east than in the west. If the resolution on a piece of film varied by this much one would send it back to the manufacturer as being defective. In the United States the spatial trend in resolution can mostly be explained by physical conditions convolved with the settlement history; the current sizes and shapes can be expected to change as conditions change. Varying the spatial resolution is an effective method of fitting the data capture scheme to "where the action is" in the data, and most administrative units do this. An important point to notice is that the average spatial resolution in polygon systems is just that - an average. The departure from this average must be considered too. Data collected on a regular square grid (uniform pixels) has a nice uniform spatial resolution, with a variance of zero, but there will some parts of the domain of interest for which this grid will be too fine, and others for which it will be too coarse. The use of orthogonal grids with varying cell sizes is as yet not common in geographical data storage systems but such grids are used in numerical simulations and in the modelling of phenomena via partial differential equations.

The temporal resolution is equally important and variable. Intertemporal resampling occurs frequently in the earth sciences; it is somewhat akin to the 'in betweening' of the animator. But the most common situation is probably that in which one has data from region A at one resolution and data from the adjacent region B taken at a different time at a different resolution and accuracy. Some estimate of the temporal derivatives is needed, as well as the spatial derivatives, in order to make these datasets comparable over both regions. Obviously theory and process models are required. Scientific models are of course data based so that we have a classic situation in which the answer to a problem is also a part of the question. Eo ipso building a data base also contributes to scientific knowledge, in an iterative fashion. Thus we leave our descendants sufficient topics for study.

BIBLIOGRAPHY

Bernstein, R., ed., 1978. Digital Image Processing for Remote Sensing, IEEE Press, New York.

Bracewell, R., 1965. The Fourier Transform and its Applications, 2nd ed., McGraw- Hill, New York

Burr, E., 1955. 'Sharpening of Observational Data in Two Dimensions'. Australian Journal of Physics, 8, 30-53.

Holloway, J., 1958. 'Smoothing and Filtering of Time Series and Space Fields'. Advances in Geophysics, 4, 351-389.

Petersen, D. & D. Middleton, 1962. 'Sampling and Reconstruction of Wavenumber Limited Functions in N-Dimensional Euclidean Spaces'. Information and Control, 5, 279-323.

Thompson, J., Z. Warsi & C. Mastin, 1985. Numerical Grid Generation. North-Holland, Amsterdam.

Tobler, W., 1969. 'Geographical Filters and their Inverses'. Geographical Analysis, 1, 3, 234-253.

Tobler, W., 1979. 'Cellular Geography' in Philosophy in Geography, eds. S. Gale & G. Olsson, Reidel, Dortrecht, pp 379-386.

Tobler, W. & S. Kennedy, 1985. 'Smooth Multidimensional Interpolation'. Geographical Analysis, 17, 3, 251-257.

Tobler, W. & Z. Chen, 1986. 'A Quadtree for Global Information Storage'. Geographical Analysis, 18, 4, 360-371.

THE WORLD DATA CENTER SYSTEM, INTERNATIONAL DATA EXCHANGE AND GLOBAL CHANGE

J. H. Allen

SUMMARY

The World Data Center (WDC) system is a dynamic network of 27 currently active data centers linking data contributors to data users. It has operated for some 30 years under ICSU guidance. The WDCs were created in 1957 as archival centers for geophysical and solar data collected during the International Geophysical Year (IGY). They were continued in 1960 as a non-governmental mechanism for international data exchange in their respective disciplines. Overall guidance is provided by the ICSU Panel on WDCs, taking into account advice from international scientific bodies associated with ICSU. Principles of WDC operations and responsibilities are published in the recently updated GUIDE to the WORLD DATA CENTER SYSTEM: PART 1, THE WORLD DATA CENTERS which also includes historical information, a description of each WDC discipline center, and a summary of new international programs, e.g. Global Change, for which WDC services will be needed.

INTRODUCTION

In 1978 the 17th General Assembly of ICSU recommended "prior to approving the initiation of new projects in the fields of geophysics and solar-terrestrial physics, the Executive Board should ensure that the planning for these projects includes clear provision for data collection, archiving and distribution and that such plans have been developed in consultation with the ICSU Panel on World Data Centres". The International Geosphere-Biosphere Program (IGBP), "Global Change", is one of the newly emerging ICSU global scientific programs. To facilitate cooperation with IGBP, the Panel created a liaison sub-committee. Two joint meetings have been organized in the Moscow region in August 1988 to advance data management planning and explore new discipline areas for which WDC services might aid GLOBAL CHANGE. As program data management plans are developed,

138

these will be published in subsequent volumes of the "Guide" series.

At present, WDC-A is located in the United States (9 centers); WDC-B is in the Soviet Union (2 centers); WDC-C1 is distributed in Europe (8 centers) and WDC-C2 is in Japan (8 centers). The WDCs engage in routine and special exchanges of data and information on film, on magnetic tape and floppy disks, in published or manuscript form, as data maps, and by computer mail. Lately the WDC-A centers in Boulder, sponsored by the National Geophysical Data Center, have begun experimental use of optical discs and other mass storage media for efficient data exchange, improved user access and archival data compression.

Among the challenges ahead are: how best to use the WDC system that now exists; how to create similar services for new disciplines that have not had past exchanges so organized; how to apply new technology to providing data collection, retention and dissemination services in practical ways but at a cost within reach of most scientists; and how to integrate international and national data management efforts to accomplish the goals of GLOBAL CHANGE.

HISTORY OF THE WORLD DATA CENTER SYSTEM

The World Data Centers (WDCs) were established in 1957 as part of the International Geophysical Year (IGY: 1957/58). They were to provide a mechanism for collection, duplication, long-term retention, and dissemination of geophysical and solar data collected worldwide by experimental and monitoring programs during the IGY. The WDCs were non-governmental, based on voluntary scientist-to-center submission of data that were collected and processed according to standards developed by the appropriate international scientific bodies in each discipline. In 1958 the groups operating WDCs were asked to continue providing their services for the International Geophysical Cooperation-1959, the one year extension of IGY. In 1960, the ICSU Comite International de Geophysique (CIG) invited scientists to continue sending to WDCs the data obtained in 1960 and in future years. In parallel, they asked those operating WDCs to continue their function for post-IGY data. With some changes, WDCs have served the global scientific community continuously over some thirty years.

In the mid-1950s ICSU's Comite Special de l'Annee Geophysique Internationale (CSAGI) invited Academies of Sciences of countries planning to take part in IGY to establish WDCs for one or more disciplines. They were to be operated at the expense of the organizations in the sponsoring countries according to principles laid down by CSAGI and published in the IGY GUIDE. There were many offers for WDC sponsorship and it was decided to recognize three WDCs in each discipline which would hold duplicate sets of data for the IGY period (July 1957 - December 1958). The duplication concept was intended to avoid catastrophic loss of unique data held at only one center and to make both data submission and data retrieval more convenient.

The Academies of the USA and USSR both offered to establish complete ("complex") WDCs for all IGY disciplines. These were named WDC-A and WDC-B, respectively. Academies of other countries offered to establish WDCs for some individual disciplines; these were identified as WDC-C with C1 centers in Europe and C2 in Australia and Japan. In some disciplines such as Geomagnetism and Ionospheric Physics, four centers were formed. In Oceanography and Meteorology there were only two centers (WDC-A and WDC-B). Some of the WDC-C centers were identical to "Permanent Services" coordinated by the Federation of Astronomical and Geophysical Services (FAGS) of ICSU. In their cases, the WDC services were mainly specific data analysis and processing rather than the comprehensive archiving of IGY data.

During the IGY the WDC operations were guided by an IGY Coordinator in Brussels. The flow of data from recording sites to WDCs, their copying among the centers, and the provision of requested data to scientists were thus centrally monitored. In this largely pre-computer era and without the extensive electronic communications networks available today by ground and satellite links, data initially flowed slowly into the WDCs. By late 1959, after IGY had ended, it was clear that the WDC system was successful in meeting its goals for the special experimental data collected. It was also evident that such services were needed for data obtain from continuing routine monitoring worldwide. On this basis the CIG recommended continuation of the WDC system for an indefinite period.

Data collection and exchanges were described in great detail in the GUIDE for many IGY disciplines. For example, Auroral All-Sky Camera films from a global grid of sites were duplicated and exchanged among WDCs as were riometer strip chart records of ionospheric absorption and 35mm film copies of daily magnetograms. While comprehensive duplicate data collections were important for the full IGY period, they were not practical in all cases for indefinite continued operations. The GUIDE was revised to reflect new circumstances and republished in 1963, 1973 and in 1979. Each took account of changing scientific needs and economic practicalities. Some of the original types of non-digital data exchange still continue; for example, there is a comprehensive exchange among WDCs of analog magnetograms copied on 35mm microfilm, of photographs of the solar disc in various wavelengths, and of film ionograms from a worldwide network of recording sites. There is now also a vigorous exchange of digital data in each of these fields on magnetic tape, floppy disks, and recently a CD-ROM. The various GUIDEs through 1979 did not take account of the emergent digital technology now so important to global scientific programs.

Since 1968 the WDC system has been guided by the ICSU Panel on WDCs, made up of representatives of the ICSU organizations concerned and of the WDCs themselves. The Panel oversees revisions to the GUIDE and extensions to new international scientific programs. It sponsors meetings on data exchange at General Assemblies of ICSU bodies and participates with Working Groups and program Steering Committees to develop data management plans that take account of the existence and abilities of the WDC system. The Panel monitors changes in the WDC system as centers are phased out, merged to take advantage of shared resources, and as new centers are added by countries wishing to take a more active part in international data exchange. For example, a Panel delegation has just completed a formal visit to China under sponsorship of the Academia Sinica to provide initial guidance that may lead to creation of a WDC-C3 or perhaps WDC-D in that country.

Three resolutions adopted by ICSU within the last ten years have spoken to the role of the WDC system, its need for continuing modernization, and its importance in the progress of international science. In 1978 the 17th General Assembly of the International Council of Scientific Unions meeting in Athens adopted the following resolution:

- World Data Centres: Recommends that prior to approving the initiation of new projects in the fields of geophysics and solar-terrestrial physics, the Executive Board should ensure that the planning for these projects includes clear provision for data collection, archiving and distribution and that such plans have been developed in consultation with the ICSU Panel on World Data Centres."

In 1980 in Amsterdam at the 18th General Assembly, ICSU resolved:

- World Data Centres: Noting that international geophysical programs are increasingly generating data sets which are largely, if not entirely, digital and machine readable, and therefore that it is of the greatest importance that the World Data Centres acquire the necessary equipment, procedures and personnel for the efficient processing, archiving and retrieval of data in large quantities in machine readable form,

   Recognizing that the costs of maintaining the WDCs are borne entirely by those countries in which they are located, but that the Centres are required to meet the changing needs of the international scientific community as determined by the relevant Unions, Associations, Commissions and Committees of ICSU,

   Records its deep appreciation of the enormous service provided by the World Data Centres, to the world scientific community, and invites the responsible National Agencies to consider ways and means of meeting the need for continued modernization of WDC data handling facilities.

In a 1982 resolution, ICSU noted the 25th anniversary of the IGY and the WDC system. They further noted the valuable data collected over 25 years of international and national expeditions to remote parts of the globe and in space and the important discoveries based on these data. They commended those involved for their efforts, the sponsoring countries for their financial support of programs and WDCs, and encouraged scientists within the ICSU family to avail themselves of WDC services and to be in contact with the ICSU Panel on WDCs.

In late 1987 the Panel published a new GUIDE to the WORLD DATA CENTER SYSTEM: Part 1, THE WORLD DATA CENTERS, the result of several years of work by a Task Force composed of Panel members and Discipline representatives. Much of this paper is a result of personal association with preparing the new GUIDE and is freely abstracted from it. That volume is the first of a series to be published by the

Panel. It has "a new title, a new purpose and a new format". The new title GUIDE to the WORLD DATA CENTER SYSTEM reflects the increasing use by WDCs of modern techniques for handling large data sets common to today's science. The new purpose "is to relate the World Data Centers to the major international programs of the next decade". The new format reflects a separation of what previously had been combined. Part 1 is a user-oriented source of general information on the WDC system, other systems for international and regional data exchange, and the new developing programs by ICSU bodies which are likely to impact the WDC system. Discipline volumes will continue the series (Ionosphere is Part 2 and Geomagnetism is Part 3) and there are plans to include volumes giving major program data management plans, e.g. for the World Climate Research Program, for IGBP-Global Change, and for the International Lithosphere program.

THE WORLD DATA CENTER SYSTEM CIRCA 1988

There are now 27 active WDCs comprising the A, B and C centers. These are described in detail in the new GUIDE. Many are co-located with national data centers in their sponsoring countries and share staff who must remember to distinguish when they are acting in a national role and when in a WDC role. Original WDC principles from the IGY era are still the basis for day-to-day operations but some are no longer so important. For example the provision for duplicating all data sets to assure accessibility is not needed in all fields although it may be continued for some for established scientific reasons. Communication between WDCs is now fast and effective, catalogs are available on-line or are exchanged regularly between centers. Risk of catastrophic data loss at a single center is acceptable when balanced against the cost of copying large digital data sets.

It is still thought worthwhile to have multiple WDCs for disciplines to provide foci within major global regions for collecting, archiving and reproducing some data types. To the extent these preserve duplicate databases and provide overlapping expertise, they continue to guard against significant catastrophic loss. Such WDCs are convenient for both data suppliers and users as communications hubs and for working visits. However, WDCs cannot hold all data for all disciplines or even within one discipline. Hence it is important that each WDC know about other inter-national centers and regional centers holding global data.

For these specialized centers, the WDCs provide a useful "referral" service.

During the IGY there were many speciality WDCs while today the trend is toward collecting related types of data at a few larger, comprehensive centers. This provides economy of resources, including staff, and makes available specialized equipment that is too expensive to duplicate at many sites. However, the advent of high capacity, fast personal computers and access to extensive communications networks may reverse some aspects of the trend toward centralization. For example, Solar-Terrestrial researchers in the U.S. recently proposed creating project data centers in university and institution groups selected to head large data-intensive research programs. These would commit to process and make available by computer network the data obtained in their program. Such centers might provide services first to co-participants and then to the broader scientific community, depending upon the adequacy of funding. Even in the projected distributed network mode of operation, WDCs would be principal nodes because of the data they receive and make available. Probably interest in providing continuing data services from mainly research institutions will diminish; then the WDCs offer a system with potential capacity to absorb project data center holdings of lasting value.

Digital data have not replaced all others. There are important roles for analog records on film (35mm microfilm and microfiche), for high-resolution imagery, and for published tables and graphs of data. Transmission of large amounts of digital data by telephone link or by satellite can be prohibitively expensive so we expect a continuing role for the WDC type of central facility with extensive data reception, processing, reproduction and storage capabilities for digital and other types of data.

A continuing WDC operating principle from the first days is that data are completely accessible to all scientists in all countries without exception. The concept of a "classified" or "restricted distribution" data base is foreign to WDC principles. If data are held by a WDC, they are available to anyone requesting them although sometimes charges for the cost of copying and handling are applied to requesters who are not sources of data and thereby entitled to equivalent exchanges at no charge.

WDCs are expected to fulfill data exchange requirements set out in the GUIDE, PART 1 general principles and in the discipline and program sections either as published in 1979 or in new editions when they become available. They respond to directions from the ICSU Panel and to resolutions and recommendations from appropriate international organizations. WDC-to-WDC data exchanges are made without charge as part of the continuing routine exchange process. Special requests that would cause unusual impact on staff or budget resources may bear a charge. Also, there may be special charges for data obtained from national or regional data centers and these are typically passed on by the WDC. Requests from individual scientists are handled similarly. In the case of requests for data not kept at a WDC, they are expected to assist in obtaining the data or forwarding the request to another center or institution that may be able to respond directly.

WDCs are to maintain data collections with proper facilities for their safe long-term retention and for efficient retrieval and accurate reproduction. International standards of data accuracy, clarity and durability are to be employed at WDCs and they are expected to maintain a continuing effort to explore the use of modern technology to improve techniques of data storage, communications and user access. The centers are to be open to visiting scientists from all countries and regular reports on operations and catalogs or inventories of holdings are provided that describe available data at WDCs. Where multiple WDCs have data of the same type, they are expected to prepare joint catalogs and make these available to potential users. They must endeavor to coordinate their activities, standardize data formats and cooperate in international data-gathering projects through advance planning and participation in international scientific meetings. While the data sources are ultimately responsible for the quality of data provided to WDCs, each center is expected to cooperate in reasonable efforts to assure data reliability, accuracy and quality.

Some WDCs have unique scientific and technical expertise that qualify them to provide unusual services. For example, the Auroral Electrojet (AE) magnetic activity index was for years derived at WDC-A for STP and now is produced by WDC-C2 for Geomagnetism. WDC-C2 also derives the Dst, Disturbance Storm Time, equivalent equatorial index of globally symmetrical magnetic storm effects. The WDC-C for Sunspot Index is located in Brussels, Belgium and continues producing the international sunspot number as the continuation of a series begun many years before in Zurich.

145

The World Data Center System

The following table lists all current WDCs and their coordination office or other contact for general information. Titles reflect the types of data serviced by each WDC, and the sponsoring institution is given in square brackets.

WORLD DATA CENTER - A

Coordination Office, US National Academy of Sciences, Dr. P.J. Hart.

- GLACIOLOGY (SNOW and ICE), Boulder, Colorado, USA [University of Colorado, supported by NOAA/NGDC]

- MARINE GEOLOGY and GEOPHYSICS, Boulder, Colorado, USA[NOAA, National Geophysical Data Center (NGDC)]

- METEOROLOGY, Asheville, North Carolina, USA [NOAA, National Climatic Data Center]

- OCEANOGRAPHY, Washington, DC, USA [NOAA, National Oceanographic Data Center]

- ROCKETS and SATELLITES, Greenbelt, Maryland, USA [NASA, National Space Science Data Center]

- ROTATION of the EARTH, Washington, DC, USA [U.S. Naval Observatory]

- SEISMOLOGY, Golden, Colorado, USA [U.S. Geological Survey]

- SOLAR-TERRESTRIAL PHYSICS, Boulder, Colorado, USA [NOAA, National Geophysical Data Center]

- SOLID EARTH GEOPHYSICS, Boulder, Colorado, USA [NOAA, National Geophysical Data Center]

WORLD DATA CENTER - B

Operated under the auspices of the Academy of Sciences of the USSR, Soviet Geophysical Committee, Prof. V.V. Beloussov.

- WORLD DATA CENTER - B1, Obninsk, USSR [USSR State Committee for Hydrometeorology and Control of the Environment]

146

Data held for disciplines: Meteorology, Oceanography, Marine Geology and Geophysics, Glaciology, Rockets and Satellites, Rotation of the Earth, Tsunamis, Mean Sea Level and Ocean Tides.

- WORLD DATA CENTER - B2, Moscow, USSR
  [Soviet Geophysical Committee, Academy of Sciences USSR]

  Data held for disciplines: Solar-Terrestrial Physics and Solid Earth Geophysics.

WORLD DATA CENTER - C1

Represented on the ICSU Panel on World Data Centres by Dr. H. Rishbeth, U.K.

- EARTH TIDES, Brussels, Belgium
  [Royal Observatory of Belgium]

- GEOMAGNETISM, Copenhagen, Denmark
  [Danish Meteorological Institute]

- GEOMAGNETISM, Edinburgh, UK
  [British Geological Survey]

- GLACIOLOGY, Cambridge, UK
  [Scott Polar Research Institute]

- RECENT CRUSTAL MOVEMENTS, Prague, Czechoslovakia
  [International Centre for Recent Crustal Movements]

- SOLAR ACTIVITY, Meudon, France
  [Observatoire de Paris]

- SOLAR-TERRESTRIAL PHYSICS, Chilton, UK
  [Science and Engineering Research Council of UK]

- SUNSPOT INDEX, Brussels, Belgium
  [Royal Observatory of Belgium]

WORLD DATA CENTER - C2

Represented on the ICSU Panel by Dr. M. Sugiura.

- AIRGLOW, Tokyo, Japan
  [Tokyo Astronomical Observatory, Ministry of Education]

- AURORA, Kaga, Japan
  [National Institute of Polar Research, Ministry of Education]

- COSMIC RAYS, Tokyo, Japan
  [Institute of Physical and Chemical Research]

- GEOMAGNETISM, Kyoto, Japan
  [Kyoto University, Ministry of Education]

- IONOSPHERE, Tokyo, Japan
  [Ministry of Posts and Telecommunications]

- NUCLEAR RADIATION, Tokyo, Japan
  [Japan Meteorological Agency, Ministry of Transportation]

- SOLAR RADIO EMISSIONS, Toyokawa, Japan
  [Nagoya University, Ministry of Education]

- SOLAR-TERRESTRIAL ACTIVITY, Tokyo, Japan
  [Institute of Space and Astronautical Research, Ministry of Education]

INTERNATIONAL DATA EXCHANGE OUTSIDE THE WDC SYSTEM

Many organizations provide international data services for databases of global or large regional extent but are not part of the WDC system. Reference was made above to the permanent services for astronomy, geodesy, geophysics and related sciences provided by centers of FAGS. These include:

- Bureau Gravimetrique International
- Centre de Donnees Stellaires
- International Centre for Earth Tides
- International Earth Rotation Service
- International Service of Geomagnetic Indices
- International URSIgram and World Days Service
- Permanent Service for Mean Sea Level
- Quarterly Bulletin on Solar Activity
- World Glacier Monitoring Service.

The World Meteorological Organization (WMO) is an inter-governmental body to facilitate planning between nations for the organization of meteorological programs. They have guided establishment of a comprehensive data collection, exchange, and archiving system between the national weather services worldwide.

Other groups exist to coordinate or centralize data collection for global and regional seismic data, e.g. International Seismological Center and regional seismic centers for the Mediterranean area, for Southeast Asia, and for South America. Seismic sea wave data are collected at the International Tsunami Information Center. The Intergovernmental Oceanographic Commission oversees international collection and exchange of data related to the "wet" oceans and cooperates closely with corresponding WDCs. There is a World Ozone Data Center in Canada and various other specialized centers in many countries that provide data collection, processing, analysis and archiving services.

In many countries there are national data centers, often part of a government agency or formed as part of a special project, that hold global data. As mentioned above, some are co-located with and sponsor WDC centers. Others cooperate in international data exchange in order to forward their programs. Access to data in these centers may sometimes be restricted to participants in the program or their use may be subject to other "rules of the road" developed by participants in forming the data collection.

ROLES OF WDCs IN MAJOR INTERNATIONAL PROGRAMS

World Data Centers cannot serve as passive repositories of data obtained from contributors having little other contact with the system. In order to play their main role as collection centers for monitoring data as well as data taken in special experimental campaigns, as sources of data copies, standard indices, derived summary compilations, and internationally adopted global and spatial models, the WDCs must also take part in planning and conducting international scientific programs and in analyzing the results from these programs.

During the International Magnetospheric Study (IMS: 1976-79), the WDCs developed new services in information and analysis that were unique to IMS and of such importance that they serve as models for similar services for future programs. The IMS Satellite Situation Center provided timely lists of satellite conjunctions when constellations of working satellites were well placed to perform coordinated observations, alerted scientists worldwide to plans for new satellite instrumentation, and produced

149

valuable orbit foot-track maps used to coordinate joint programs of ground-based and space observations. The IMS Central Information Exchange (IMSCIE) Office was internationally staffed and provided a clearinghouse for information about ground-based, rocket, balloon, airborne, shipboard, and satellite observing campaigns. A monthly IMS Newsletter was airmailed worldwide to some 3,000 scientists with articles about recent observations, proposed special analysis topics, results from studies that should be taken into account in planning further operations, and with a calendar of scheduled launches and expeditions for the next six months. This information resulted in many instances of voluntary cooperation between experimenters who were able to increase the impact of their programs by coordination with others. Finally, the Coordinated Data Analysis Workshop (CDAW) was developed to provide a means for researchers to combine their data in a central computer system with that from dozens of other projects and to meet in a group to study some special topic by intensive analysis of the combined on-line data using a family of custom data retrieval, analysis and reproduction programs.

DATA CENTER APPLICATIONS OF NEW TECHNOLOGY

WDCs and their affiliated national data centers are working together to apply new technological tools to solving data and information exchange, archiving and analysis problems. Data sharing networks such as SPAN and the SELDADS-II provide rapid access to large amounts of digital data. WDCs communicate via telex, facsimile and electronic mail computer links connecting Australia, Canada, Denmark, England, Japan, the USA, and the USSR in daily exchanges of data and information.

Some centers are testing both Compact Disc-Read Only Memory (CD-ROM) and Write Once, Read Many (WORM) optical discs. In mid-1987 the National Geophysical Data Center (NGDC), which operates WDC-A for STP, produced CD-ROM "NGDC-01", Geomagnetic and Other Solar-Terrestrial Data of NOAA and NASA. This CD contains 530 MBytes of digital data including two catalogs and 15 different data bases. It is provided to users with accession software to retrieve, copy and display the contents using relatively inexpensive personal computer equipment. For the first time in the history of the related but separate data bases collected on this CD, it is practical to combine them in a variety of new ways. Before the CD, many magnetic tapes would have had to be mounted and sequentially searched to obtain the data and there was no way to efficiently scan them. Now, with direct random-access and a data transfer rate of 3 Mbytes/min, one can quickly review changes in global magnetic activity (since 1868), compare them with sunspot number counts (since 1700) and solar flares (since 1955), and examine conditions in interplanetary space (since 1963); this represents a new and inexpensive data compaction and exchange medium.

Several agencies are cooperating to place spatial data onto CD-ROM and display false-color images of the ocean bottom and bathymetric contours for large regions. At NGDC the accession software is already far advanced for this purpose and we look forward to soon having the new CDs.

A WORM disc unit now is used at WDC-A for STP to store geomagnetic and ionospheric data from archival tapes on a more stable optical medium. Files of one-minute resolution Canadian magnetic observatory data are being transferred in 15 Mbyte blocks onto 400 Mbyte capacity two-sided WORM discs. Files of 35 Mbyte digital ionosonde data are also being moved onto WORM discs.

A procurement action is in progress to obtain one of the new helical scan VHS cassette digital magnetic tape units to explore how inexpensive high-capacity tapes can be combined with optical discs to provide a mixed strategy for servicing digital data. These technological innovations are either available now or soon will be available at WDCs and other centers to meet the need of new data-intensive international scientific programs.

Among the current and planned ICSU programs that are likely to involve WDCs, perhaps the largest and most ambitious is the "International Geosphere-Biosphere Programme" (IGBP), often referred to as "GLOBAL CHANGE". The Panel on World Data Centers has established a sub-committee for liaison with the Special Committee on IGBP. Members are involved with the IGBP Working Group on Data Management to plan two international meetings in August 1988 near Moscow. The first is a Study Conference on IGBP and the second is a Workshop on Geophysical Informatics.

The main goal of the Study Conference is to make significant progress toward identifying data management problems of IGBP disciplines and to begin establishing a plan to meet the different needs. This will be particularly challenging because of the diversity of disciplines involved, many without a history of organized, systematic international data exchange.

The main goal of the Workshop will be to identify how the WDC system can meet specific IGBP needs through application of available technology and where new systems of data and information exchange must be provided. Emphasis will be on the mechanics of handling large data bases to achieve program requirements within resource limitations.

CLOSING COMMENT

Certainly, the results of the IGU Global Database Planning Project meeting at Tylney will be of interest for both meetings next August. We anticipate that questions raised here and answers provided will be important input to our meetings. Of particular concern will be the progress toward having available a reasonably priced, comprehensive digital reference data base (probably on CD-ROM) to represent the global distribution of land and sea with adequate resolution for useful placement of other data collections. While there are many unanswered questions about what is needed and how the need will be met, there is great interest in the process of obtaining answers and the Panel on WDCs regards this meeting as an essential step in resolving the status of many data-related projects.

METHODOLOGY FOR MULTISATELLITE THEMATIC MAPPING: A CODATA PROGRAM ON REMOTE SENSING IN EARTH SCIENCE

Claude Bardinet

ABSTRACT

The methodology developed in the CODATA MSTM Program (1983-1986) based on the discriminatory capabilities of combined thermal and reflective data offers new possibilities in the application of remote sensing to Earth Science and environmental mapping.

The geoscientific interpretation of combined multisensory data involves all the existing geographical, geophysical and geological information and ground truth work.

Under favorable conditions of data and ground control, this approach enables re-interpretation of the known geology and geomorphology and its extension into less well-known and unmapped areas. The application of this approach to Tanzania has confirmed the advantage of combining data from METEOSAT, NOAA, TIROS-N, Landsat MSS and TM.

The methodology developed since 1986 in the context of Northern China will confirm the advantage of using combined TM/Spot data, TM/NOAA data and SPOT stereoradiometric data to map the physical environment, soil utilization and land use.

Since 1981, the CODATA MSTM Task Group has been associated with different tests concerning atlases of the albedo resulting from the application of statistical methods to satellite data. In general, the HELIOSAT station was used for computer aided mapping of the physical geographical units in North Africa.

The potential development of this research has been evaluated in the COSPAR Global Change Program.

INTRODUCTION

The CODATA Task Group on Multisatellite Thematic Mapping was established in 1982 at the CODATA General Assembly in Warsaw in order to develop a methodology for multisatellite thematic mapping. In 1983, the Task Group chose two areas of Western Tanzania as test areas. METEOSAT and NOAA were used in Western Tanzania, and METEOSAT and Landsat were used in the Iringa area. CODATA considered that since they incorporate geological, geographical and climatic data for multidisciplinary applications, the resulting maps would be useful tools, especially for regional geological mapping, mineral exploration, geomorphological mapping and land use planning.

THE CODATA MULTISATELLITE PROGRAM

The project focussed on geomorphological mapping of the test areas, ground truth work and the development of multisatellite evaluation techniques, as well as training African counterparts in the field and in the laboratory.

The following figures 1-6 give an idea of the contribution of remotely sensed data processing to Geographical Information Systems (GIS).

Multisatellite data analysis must take into account the reflectance and emission from any geographical units in the observed landscapes, including the effects of seasonal and diurnal cycles and climatic factors. Earth materials can be identified by spectral signatures in the wavelength region from 0.3 to 15.0 micrometers. The combined use of data from different satellites enables the selection of different spectral bands registered at different times for a given type of landscape. The selection of these bands should take into account the influence of many factors, e.g. the properties of the atmosphere and the landscape's physical environment, but the fundamental question is the existence and accessibility of the data. This is an important aspect of the advanced use of geographical databases. Once the question of multisatellite data acquisition has been resolved, it is necessary to carry out:

a) computerized data processing;
b) ground truth work;
c) multivariate data integration; and
d) multisatellite thematic mapping using computer graphics.

NORTH

Figure 1: GIS and geomorphological edge detection in SIR-A
radar data.

Edge detection (Sobel) of geomorphological units (Pre-
Cambrian sandstones) of the NW area of Bandiagara Plateau
(Bima, 3.45W/14.55N, Mali) using SIR-A data (pixel 40*40m,
Nov. 13, 1981, orbit 27/28). (Bardinet, Bernard et al,
1983).

155

NORTH ↑

Figure 2: GIS and contrast enhancement (MSS7 data) of
geomorphological units.

Contrast enhancement of texture and structure of the Pre-
Cambrian sandstone of the Bandiagara Plateau (Bima area,
see Fig. 1), (pixel 79*56m, MSS7-E-2434-09492, Mar. 31,
1976). (Bardinet, Benard et al, 1983).

NORTH ↑

VISUALISATION D'IMAGE MULTI   CANAL : 02 =SPOT 1.LISS3.CONSERVANT LINEAMENT SOMBRE.
BANDIAGARA-ATP-BARDINET-SPOT.30/10/81.SIMULATION.

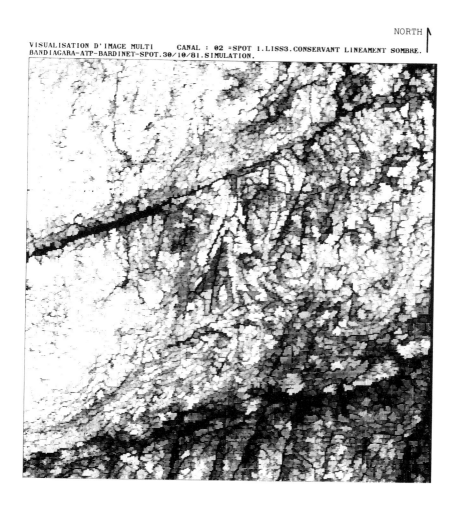

Figure 3: GIS and data smoothing (SPOT XS) of
           geomorphological units.

Data smoothing (local structure analysis) of structural
morphotype in the Pre-Cambrian sandstones of the Bandiagara
Plateau (Saoura-Si, 3.85W/15.00N), using SPOT XS1
simulation (Oct. 30, 1981, pixel 20*20m). (Bardinet and
Yu, 1987).

NORTH

VISUALISATION D'IMAGE MULTI   CANAL : 04 =RETRECISSEMENT AVEC SEUIL=80.
BANDIAGARA-ATP-BARDINET-SPOT.30/10/81.SIMULATION.

Figure 4: GIS and linear feature detection in SPOT XS.

Detection of linear features and hydrographic net in Pre-Cambrian sandstones of the Bandiagara Plateau (Saoura-Si area, see Fig. 3) (pixel 20*20m). (Bardinet and Yu, 1987).

158

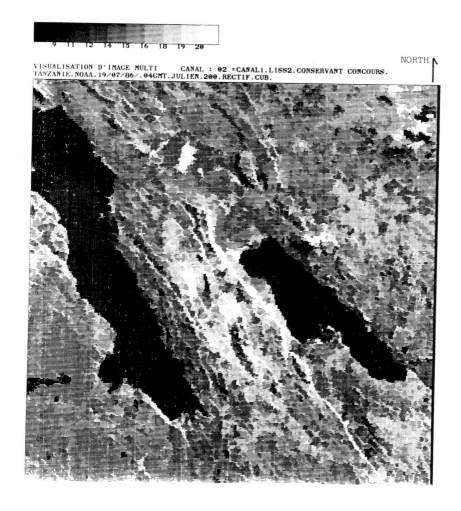

VISUALISATION D'IMAGE MULTI   CANAL : 02 =CANAL1.LISS2.CONSERVANT CONCOURS.
TANZANIE.NOAA.19/07/86/.04GMT.JULIEN.200.RECTIF.CUB.

NORTH

Figure 5: GIS and data smoothing (NOAA AVHRR) of geomorphological units.

Data smoothing of structural morphotype in the NW region (Ubendian) of Tanzania (7.00S/31.00E) in the vicinity of Tanganyika and Rukwa lakes (pixel 1*1km, NOAA AVHRR1, July 19, 1979). (Bardinet and Yu, 1986).

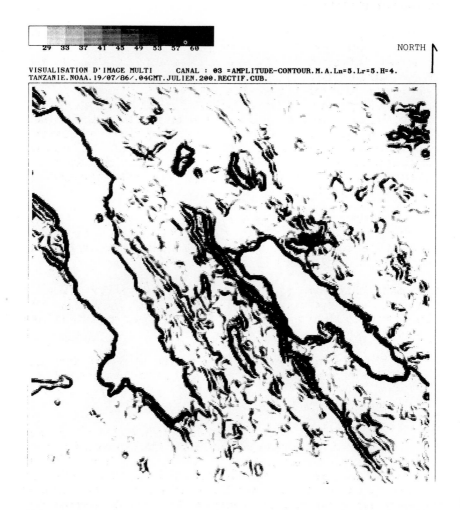

VISUALISATION D' IMAGE MULTI   CANAL : 03 =AMPLITUDE-CONTOUR.M.A.Ln=5.Lr=5.H=4.
TANZANIE.NOAA.19/07/86/.04GMT.JULIEN.200.RECTIF.CUB.

NORTH

Figure 6: GIS and linear feature detection in NOAA AVHRR.

Linear feature and edge detection of the physical units of the landscape, SW region of Tanzania (see Fig. 5) (pixel 1*1km, NOAA AVHRR1). (Bardinet and Yu, 1986).

One of the objectives of remote sensing in the Earth Sciences is to map spatial distribution of the resources on the Earth's surface. Another objective is to detect geomorphological characteristics, faults, trends and lineaments. In both cases, the level of discrimination depends on the spectral and spatial resolution, on the spectral bands, on the season and the scale of the satellite recordings.

In multispectral analysis, if we combine the albedo (visible and near infrared light) and the emissivity (thermal infrared radiation) we are able to classify the vegetation effect which depends on the angle of solar elevation and on water losses by transpiration. The reflectance properties of soils depend on soil moisture, basic soil factors, soil texture and structure. Discrimination between soil reflectance and vegetation reflectance is possible through the combined use of multispectral bands at different times during the daily and seasonal cycles. Soil, lithology and vegetation effects can be classified.

In the CODATA project we concentrated on lineament and feature detection, and on multisatellite data classification (lithology, soils and vegetation effect) (Bardinet, Gabert, Monget and Yu, 1986 and 1988).

Multisatellite data classification is based on the scale of the data, the topographic and cartographic database, and the ground truth investigation. The CODATA project tackled the following:

1)   Availability of multisatellite data. The goal of the CODATA project was to show what could be done if all the satellite information were made available to a research project.

2)   Ground control during satellite recording and ground-controlled geographic databases. This brings together specialists in the collection and handling of information within the framework of multinational cooperation. The CODATA Task Group took into account the existing thematic map of the region (Bardinet, Gabert, Monget, Yu, 1988).

3)   Information dissemination. Environmental mapping using satellite data provides a supervised interpretation of land systems in the form of atlases. The Task Group used modern methods of automatic

161

mapping by laser restitution in conjunction with the quadrichromy offset process. This is important because the overabundance of satellite information can only be justified if the results obtained from processing it become available for discussion in the scientific community rapidly and are later used by specialists in land use and earth resource inventorying.

4) Generalization and dissemination of research methods. At the very beginning, the CODATA team described its programs in a Unesco/IUGS COGEODATA training course organized in Arusha, Tanzania.

Classification, particularly for the identification of lineaments, faults, and geological boundaries, was based on the interactive use of the following: multisatellite images and classifications prepared at the Centre de Teledetection et d'Analyse des Milieux Naturels (CTAMN), Sophia Antipolis, France; geological map series 1/125,000 of Tanzania (German Geological Mission 1963-66, Bundesanstalt fur Bodenforschung, Hannover, F.R.G.); International Tectonic Map of Africa, 1/1 5000 (Unesco, 1968); Geophysical and Mineral Potential Atlas of Tanzania, Map Sheet 6 (Geosurvey Int., 1984).

The first phase of this project was conducted by the CODATA Task Group MSTM in cooperation with ESAMRDC (Dodoma, Tanzania); the Earth Sciences division of Unesco (Paris, France); the ESA-ESOC METEOSAT database (Darmstadt, F.R.G.); and the Rosenfield School of Marine and Atmospheric Sciences, Miami University, TIROS-N/NOAA database from NOAA-Nesdis. The data were processed at the CTAMN (France), in cooperation with the BGR (Hannover, F.R.G.)

The ground control was carried out by the CODATA Task Group MSTM in cooperation with the Ministry of Mineral Resources (Wizaa Na Madini, Dodoma, Tanzania) and the ESAMRDC (Dodoma, Tanzania). The first phase consisted of the following activities: preprocessed forline detection in satellite digital imagery; application of the GEOMULTI system, and multisatellite data processing, i.e. the calculations involved in order to convert different scaled images into a single scale for mapping in four-color offset by laser processing.

The second phase of the project in East Africa was carried out in the Kibaran Belt under the auspices of the GARS-IUGS-Unesco Program. The GARS Research Team (MRAC Tervuren, University of Nice, University of Paris 6, CTAMN, BRGM and PEPS) has proposed more detailed remote sensing studies at larger scales using Landsat Thematic Mapper (TM) and SPOT data. The results (1987) will contribute to an improved interpretation of the geology of the Kibaran Belt in terms of structure, lithology and mineralization.

A manual entitled "A New Method for the Application of Multisatellite Data in Geoscience Research Using METEOSAT, NOAA, TIROS-N, Landsat" is in press and will be published jointly by Unesco and MRAC Tervuren. By sharing its research with the member organizations of ICSU, the CODATA Task Group is seeking to develop multidisciplinary cooperation since it is fully aware of the need for collaboration between specialists in the different branches of the Earth Sciences and planetary environment scientists. For example, the Task Group participated in the meeting of the COSPAR Ad-hoc Group on Remote Sensing for Global Change (1987) at IAASA Luxembourg, 25-27 September 1985, and in the Workshop on "Remote Sensing of Interest to Developing Countries" (26th COSPAR Meeting, Toulouse, France, 1986).

The originality of the work carried out by CODATA should be underlined, since, at present, the results of numerical thematic mapping at different scales carried out in other programs on multisatellite data in the Earth Sciences and in the environment are not available for discussion.

In order to enlarge the field of comparison and refine the methodology, the present phase of the CODATA Program concerns research in a dry milieu in North China.

The CODATA Program on "Multisatellite Thematic Mapping in China" was approved at the 15th General Assembly in Ottawa, Canada. The first phase of the program (1986-87) consisted mainly of

1)   an inventory of the Chinese mapping projects using satellites in the Northern provinces of China and

2)   a test of Landsat MSS and TM, and SPOT XS applied to the Hebei and Shaanxi Provinces.

From 1988-89, the program will consist essentially of the following:

1) Analysis of the recent Chinese remote sensing projects using multisatellite imagery, especially TM/SPOT and NOAA. This concerns applications of remote sensing to land use and land resources mapping (such as forest fire surveying), detection of geological structures in relation to mining programs and geographical information systems using MSS, TM and SPOT.

2) Joint research by the Multisatellite Working Group of CODATA China (MTMWGC) involving the integration of high resolution imagery including TM and SPOT. The results will be printed in a series of maps at a scale of 1/50 000. The research areas selected include:

   - Tangshan City in Hebei Province and Nanbit County,
   - the Loess Plateau of Shaanxi Province in the area of Ya'an, and
   - Northern Xinjian Province.

   In Hebei and Shaanzi the research will concern mainly natural resources classification (TM and SPOT) and mapping (geomorphology and land resources) whereas in Xinjiang, it will consist mainly of comparative geological studies based on NOAA and MSS imagery.

The final stages will be to print multisatellite thematic maps of Hebei, Shaanxi and Xinjiang, and to publish a CODATA Bulletin. The multisatellite thematic maps will provide land use classification (TM SPOT in Hebei), terrain model and geomorphological analysis (SPOT in Shaanxi) and a comparative geological study of the Northern Xinjiang and its boundary areas (NOAA and MSS).

MULTISATELLITE DATABASES: APPLICATION FOR ATLASES

Statistical methods (GEOMULTI) for the geographical analysis of solar radiation from METEOSAT, NOAA/TIROS-N, Landsat MSS/TM and SPOT have been developed since 1981 using edge detection and supervised classification.

Multisatellite data analysis (Bardinet, Monget et al, 1981) was applied to Bandiagara Mali (West Africa) at a scale of 1/500,000 using combined METEOSAT and Landsat data (CTAMN and SODETEG under a contract with ESOC). An analysis was also carried out in East Africa (Tanzania) using NOAA-TIROS-N (1/2,500,000) and METEOSAT/ Landsat combined data at 1/500,000 (Bardinet, Gabert, Monget et al, 1986).

This multisatellite thematic mapping methodology has been developed primarily through the following applications:

1) 1981, multisatellite data analysis of Bandiagara-Mali (West Africa) at 1/500,000, database combined METEOSAT-VISSR and Landsat MSS (under a CTAMN-SODETEG ESA-ESOC contract) (Bardinet, Monget et al, 1988).

2) 1982-87, development of HELIOSAT station (Cano, 1983, Cano et al, 1986) (under CTAMN AFME contract); application (in Algeria) for an atlas of statistical albedo after computation of cloud cover index (Bardinet et al, 1985) and in West Africa (Michaud-Regas, 1986) (Diabat et al, 1988).

3) 1983-86, multisatellite data analysis of East Africa (Tanzania) using combined TIROS N-AVHRR (scale 1/2,500,000) and METEOSAT/Landsat (scale 1/500,000) data in the CODATA/ICSU Program (MSTM) (Bardinet, Gabert, Monget et al, 1986 and 1988);

4) 1986-88, multisatellite data analysis in IUGS/Unesco /GARS Program on East Africa (Tanzania and Burundi), using Landsat-TM and SPOT-XS and STEREO (MRAC 1987);

5) 1987-89, multisatellite thematic mapping of China, using Landsat-TM, SPOT-XS and STEREO and NOAA-AVHRR, in cooperation with the Academia Sinica (IRSA and RSGC) and CODATA-ICSU.

Comparing different methods and systems for analysis, this methodology has been applied and further developed in:

-   the CODATA-China Program (Bardinet, Chen et al, 1988)
-   the IUGS/Unesco/GARS Program on East Africa (Tanzania, Burundi), using TIROS-N, METEOSAT, Landsat TM and SPOT data (Lavreau and Bardinet, in press).

On a regional scale, these research projects may be considered relevant to the themes covered by the COSPAR Global Change Program.

Database and geographical analysis: a COSPAR program

Geological and geomorphological processes have to be studied using geographical databases.

The main innovation of the COSPAR Global Change Program (Rasool et al, 1987) where geological processes are

165

concerned lies in the elucidation of the geological record of the evolution of our global ecosystems. Particular emphasis is placed on the last two million years and especially the last 10,000 years.

Satellite measurements can indicate:

- Features and mineralization on the Earth's surface;
- Mineralization indicating the evolution of the land system and geocycle;
- The ancient and present hydrographic net;
- An inventory of the world's current soil resources, including their physical and chemical properties and the relative balance or imbalance between soil formation and erosion;
- A quantitative assessment of the materials which run off the continents and are deposited in the world's estuaries, deltas and ocean basins;
- Measurements of the amounts and distribution of the materials released into the atmosphere by volcanic eruptions, and monitoring emission of SO2 and possibly other gases.

The related parameters which need to be acquired globally are:

- Soil type and time-related changes;
- Volcanic eruptions and distribution of aerosols around the globe;
- Sediments in coastal zone waters;
- Multispectral evaluation of dynamic and permanent features.

Multisatellite thematic mapping: a geostationary database

Statistical methods for the determination of global solar radiation from METEOSAT data on Europe and North Africa were developed at the CTAMN in 1982 (Cano, 1982). Work was continued using a METEOSAT database on West Africa (1983, 1984 and 1985) (Michaud-Regas 1986).

The main results were:

1) the weekly planetary albedo for a clear sky in West Africa;
2) a cloud cover index (percentage per pixel) produced by comparing the METEOSAT data with the planetary albedo map. The aim is to produce atlases of the hourly global irradiation over Western Central Africa. This

software is implemented on a mini and microcomputer during data recording using a SDUS/WEFAX station.

This research was financially supported by the Commission of the European Communities (Project F, Solar Energy R&D) and the Franaise pour la Maitrise de l'Energie (AFME). (Cano et al, 1986) (Diabat et al, 1988).

A METEOSAT database acquisition on the HELIOSAT system

The HELIOSAT station in Carto-PC (CTAMN 1983) is an autonomous automatic working station.

The system has been designed for:

- Acquisition of satellite images of WEFAX type;
- Display of images in digital false color;
- Image processing for the computation of global radiation maps and for cloud index maps.

The database has been built using a WEFAX type receiver connected to a Personal Computer in order to produce maps of ground albedo with a 5x5 km pixel resolution. Cloud detection is performed in time series by comparing the cloud induced sensor response to the signal which would occur if the pixels were cloud free. The method uses iterative and adaptive filtering (Cano, 1982). This makes it possible to record:

- Computation of a map of the instantaneous hourly global radiation three times a day;
- the total daily radiation each day;
- the averages of hourly and daily global radiation are computed, displayed and saved on CCT every month.

Architecture of Carto-PC (CTAMN 1986)

Carto-PC is an image processing system that can be implemented on an IBM-PC XT, AT or other compatible computer (256 Kb RAM, 20 megabyte hard disk). The architecture is as follows:

- SATELLITE ANTENNA Alcatel;
- H.F. RECEIVER, Secondary Data User Station SDUS;
- HELIOSAT station;
- DECODING-DIGITIZING CARD Matrix PIP, Chorus PC Eye, AT&T Targa;
- DIGITISER TABLE Altek or Summagraphics;

- GRAPHIC CARD EGA or one compatible with TECMAR Graphics Master, Sigma Color 400, Number Nine, AT&T Targa, Matrix PIP, PGA or compatible;
- COLOR PRINTER, Canon, IBM, Quadjet or Tectronix;
- LASER JET, HP;
- SCANNER Canon or compatible;
- DATABASE SYSTEM, dBase III+;
- MAGNETIC TAPE READER, Qualstar.

The HELIOSAT system allows users to:

- Display any of the images stored on the disk;
- Choose a satellite's acquisition slots (day and time);
- Extract statistics for any geographical location present; in any images (Global radiation, Albedo, Cloud index);
- Combine satellite data with Geographical database.

CONCLUSION

Computer aided cartographic synthesis

Land use planning is more efficient if environmental decisions can be made with reference to a precise location on a map in a given cartographic projection.

Computer aided cartographic synthesis is a tool for the interactive evaluation of a large number of synthesis strategies. On this basis, geographers, geomorphologists and geologists can analyse multivariate information using powerful numerical image processing methods.

These methods include:

- satellite data acquisition and computation;
- the extraction of data from existing cartography;
- texture mapping, enhancing the visual richness of images;
- the capture of graphic input from print and non-print sources into machine-readable form, and the graphic presentation of databases;
- combining multi-source data for synthesis analysis and computer-aided mapping.

BIBLIOGRAPHY

Bardinet, C., 1987. Teledetection, Environnement et Urbanisation: de l'Image Globale aux Objets Geographiques, Applications a l'Impact de l'Urbanisation sur les Paysages en Afrique et en Chine, Two volumes, 586 pp., 5 cartes infographiques, Vol. Annexes. These d'Etat des Lettres et Sciences Humaines, Univ. Paris VIII.

Bardinet, C., Monget, J.M. and Patoureaux, Y., 1982. 'Combined Use of Daily Thermal Cycle of METEOSAT Imagery and Multispectral Landsat Data: Application to the Bandiagara Plateau (Malik)'. Proc. EARSel-ESA Symp. ESA-SP-175, 95-101.

Bardinet, C., Benard, M., Cano, D. and Monget, J.M., 1985. 'Teledetection par METEOSAT des Paysages d'Algerie et de Tunisie: Contours et classification des Unites Physiques dans l'Albedo Moyen de Mai 1979'. 1 carte couleur H.T. Mediterranee, 54(1-2), 95-106, Marseille.

Bardinet, C., Gabert, G., Monget, J.M. and Yu, Z.' 1986. Methodology for Multisatellite Thematic Mapping, CODATA Bulletin 62, 1-85, 1986, ed. Phyllis S. Glaeser, Pergamon Press.

Bardinet, C., Klerkx, J., Lavreau, J., Le Page, A., Roggeri, I., Trefoix, Ph., Weber, Ch. and Yu, Z., 1987. 'First Results of the IUGS-Unesco Programme on Geological Applications of Remote Sensing (GARS) in Eastern Africa'. Adv. Space Res. 7(3), 19-23. Pergamon Press.

Bardinet, C., Lavreau, J., Le Page, A., Roggeri, I., Rudant, J.P., Tamain, G. and Trefoix, Ph., 1987. 'Lithology Discrimination in Tropical Conditions Using TM Data Supplemented with a Radiometric Ground Survey in Western Tanzania' in Current Research in African Earth Science, ed. Matheis and Schandelmeier, pp. 333-336, Balkema, Rotterdam.

Bardinet, C., Chen, Y.Y., Gabert, G., Wan, Z.M. and Yan, S.R., 1988. Chinese Mapping Projects Using Satellites. To appear in the Proceedings of the 11th International CODATA Conference, 26-29 September 1988, Karlsruhe, F.R.G.

Bardinet, C., Gabert, G., Monget, J.M. and Yu, Z., 1988. 'Application of Multisatellite Data to Thematic Mapping'. Geol. Jb. B 67(3), 3 folded maps inserted, Hannover.

Bickmore, D.P. (Ed.), 1987. World Digital Database for Environmental Science, 90 p., Oxford.

Cano, D., 1982. Etude de l'Ennuagement par Analyse de Sequences d'Images de Satellite: Application a l'Evaluation du Rayonnement Solaire Global au Sol. These Docteur-Ingenieur, Ecole Nat. Sup. Telecom., Paris.

Cano, D., Monget, J.M., Albuisson, M., Guillard, H., Regas, N. and Wald, L., 1986 'A method for the determination of the global radiation from meteorological satellite data'. Solar Energy 37(1), 31-39, Pergamon Journals Ltd.

Carter, W.D., A. Arking, M.P. McCormick and E. Raschke, 1987. 'Remote Sensing: Earth's Surface and Atmosphere. COSPAR Workshop X, Twenty-Sixth Plenary Meeting, Toulouse 1986'. Adv. Space Res. 7(3), 1-252. Pergamon Press.

Diabat, L., Demarcq, H., Michaud-Regas, N. and Wald, L. 1988. 'Estimating Incident Solar Radiation at the Surface from Images of the Earth Transmitted by Geostationary Satellites: the HELIOSAT Project'. Int. J. Solar Energy, 5, 261-278.

Glaeser, P.S. (Ed.), 1986. Computer Handling and Dissemination of Data, Selected Papers. CODATA Bulletin 64, 1-60, 1986, Pergamon Press.

Glaeser, P.S. (Ed.), 1987. Computer Handling and Dissemination of Data. Proc. of the 10th International CODATA Conference, Ottawa 1986. North Holland.

Gruter, W., Guillard, H., Moser, W., Monget, J., Palz, W., Raschke, E., Reinhardt, R.E., Schwarzmann, P. and Wald, L., 1986. 'Solar Radiation Energy Data from Satellite Images' in Solar Energy R & D in the European Community, Series F, Solar Radiation Data (4), 100 p., Reidel Pub. Co.

Lavreau, J., and C. Bardinet, in press. Remote Sensing Applied to Geology, A Multidisciplinary Approach: the Unesco/IUGS Geological Application of Remote Sensing Program in Tanzania. GARS Report, MRAC-Tervuren.

MAB-16, 1985. Cartographie Integre de l'Environnement: un Outil pour la Recherche et pour l'Amenagement. Notes techniques MAB-Unesco, ed. A. Journaux. 1-55, 10 cartes couleur H.T., Paris.

Michaud-Regas, N., 1986. Mise en Oeuvre et Validation d'une Methode Operationnelle et Automatique pour l'Evaluation d'Atlas Solaires en Europe a l'Aide de Mesure Satellites METEOSAT. These Sc. Univ. Paris VII.

Monget, J.M., Moser, W., Plazy, J.L. and Reinhard, E., 1983. 'Climatologie Solaire et Teledetection: un Programme Europ en de Recherche Cooperative'. Ann. des Mines 1983, 86-91.

Rasool, S.I. (Ed.), 1987. 'Potential of Remote Sensing for the Study of Global Change: COSPAR Report to ICSU'. Adv. Space Res. 7(1), 1-97. Pergamon Press.

Verstappen, H.Th., Bardinet, C. and Matuda, I., 1984. Cartographie et Teledetection. Proceedings, Theme 29, 25th IGU Congress, Paris, 142-144.

A GLOBAL SOILS AND TERRAIN DIGITAL DATABASE

Marion F. Baumgardner

INTRODUCTION

It is difficult if not impossible to place a beginning date on the concept of a soil map of the world. However, it has been documented that, at an International Symposium on Tropical Soils held in Madison, Wisconsin, USA in 1960, recommendations were made that led to the establishment in the Food and Agriculture Organization (FAO) Rome of the World Soil Resources Office and, eventually to the Soil Map of the World. At the Madison Symposium, which was sponsored by the International Society for Soil Science (ISSS), a resolution was adopted which asked for the compilation of all existing soil survey material. FAO, through the World Soil Resources Office, assumed the responsibility not only of compiling the information, but also, of preparing an integrated world soil map.

The Soil Map of the World project was an enormous undertaking by FAO from a technical point of view alone. There were problems related to different schools of thought, scale to be adopted, nomenclature to be used, and the classification system to apply. A landmark of 1968 was the international agreement on the legend for the Soil Map of the World, obtained at the 9th Congress of the ISSS in Adelaide, Australia.

The World Soil Map by the 1970s proved to be a tool for development, to combat desertification, to establish complementarity between areas with different production potentials, to assess potential population supporting capacities, and to develop a framework for land evaluation.

The FAO/Unesco Soil Map of the World, published at a scale of 1:5M, was the first internationally accepted inventory of world soil resources. It was completed in 1980 and published in ten volumes with nineteen map sheets and in four languages. Recently, a working group of FAO, Unesco and the International Soil Reference and Information Centre (ISRIC) completed and published a revision of the legend

172

for this 1:5M soil map. With the cooperation of the United Nations Environment Programme (UNEP), this map has been digitized using the ARC/INFO system. It is a component of UNEP's GRID (Global Resources Information Database) in Geneva and of FAO's Geographic Information System (GIS), linking forty internal databases.

During the 1970s two new Working Groups under ISSS Commission V were established to explore the applications of new technologies to the management of soils resources. The Working Group on Soil Information Systems was charged with the responsibility of examining new data acquisition and analysis systems, including computer technology, and of reporting on how this technology can be used effectively as a tool for the soil scientist in the storage, retrieval and analysis of soils data and in the dissemination of soils information.

The Working Group on Pedology and Remote Sensing was charged with the responsibility of examining the specifications and images of new aerospace sensors and to report on and advise how this new technology can be applied in the inventory and monitoring of soil resources.

As a logical evolution of activities in the ISSS along with that of data acquisition, handling, and analysis technologies, an ISSS provisional Working Group was established in 1985 to consider the feasibility and desirability of developing a world soils and terrain digital database at a map scale of 1:1M. A background paper in support of this concept was written by W.G.Sombroek (1985) and distributed in 1985 to more than 60 soils and terrain scientists around the world for their consideration and comments. This background paper served to focus the discussions of the 40 participants in an International Workshop on the Structure of a Digital International Soil Resources Map Annex Database (Baumgardner and Oldeman, 1986). As an outcome of this Workshop held in Wageningen, the Netherlands, in January 1986, a proposal to form a working group on a Global Soils and Terrain Digital Database, the SOTER (SOils and TERrain) Working Group, was written (ISSS, 1986).

At the 13th International Soils Congress in Hamburg, West Germany in August 1986, the SOTER proposal was endorsed and the provisional Working Group was given formal status and charged with implementing the SOTER Project. During the months which followed the Congress, contacts were made with many potential national and international funding agencies to solicit support for the Project.

173

Because of their intense interest in global databases for environmental sciences, officials of UNEP expressed an interest in SOTER, especially if the Project could make a significant contribution to the assessment of degradation of global soils and terrain resources.

Fifteen soil scientists representing the SOTER Working Group were invited by UNEP to an Expert Group Meeting on the Feasibility and Methodology of Global Soil Degradation Assessment. This meeting was held at UNEP Headquarters in Nairobi in May 1987. As a result of this meeting a UNEP Project Document entitled "Global Assessment of Soil Degradation" was prepared, and in September 1987 a contract was awarded by UNEP for Phase 1 of the SOTER Project (UNEP, 1987). There are two primary tasks under this contract. The first is to produce a general soil degradation map of the world at a scale of 1:15M. The second is to develop a soils and terrain digital database at a scale of 1:1M for an area of 250,000 sq km which includes portions of Argentina, Brazil, and Uruguay. The remainder of this paper will discuss the objectives and approach to the development of a global soils and terrain digital database at a scale of 1:1M.

OBJECTIVES

The long range objective of the SOTER Project is to utilize emerging information technology to produce a world soils and terrain digital database containing digitized map unit boundaries and their attribute database, and supported by a file of chosen point data. In the implementation of the Project an attempt will be made to include in the database some minimum density of ground observation data. The database will have the following characteristics:

- general average scale, or accuracy, of 1:1M;
- compatible with global databases of other environmental resources and features;
- amenable to updating and purging of obsolete and/or irrelevant data;
- accessible to a broad array of international, regional, and national decision-makers and policy-makers;
- transferable to and usable by developing countries for national database development at larger scale (greater detail).

This is an exceedingly ambitious project, one which will require sustained, innovative effort over a period of many years.

Specific short range objectives are required in the initial phases of the Project to provide a logical and orderly sequence of activities to produce an operational world soils and terrain digital database. Emphasis will be on research, development and testing of methodologies in the field and in the laboratory and demonstration of the uses of the database. Specific short term objectives include:

- development of an implementation plan;
- adoption of a universal legend for a World Soils and Terrain Digital Database at 1:1M;
- development of guidelines for the correlation of soils and terrain mapping units;
- definition of soils and terrain parameters and specifications to be included in the database;
- development of a detailed set of specifications and logic which define the minimum set of capabilities / functions required for the database;
- selection of three specific areas of 250,000 sq km each in developing countries for initial database construction;
- acquisition and correlation of all relevant maps and data about the selected areas essential for the database;
- input of data, including digitized maps, into the database;
- test and demonstration of the reliability, accuracy and utility of the database;
- conduct of an assessment of current geographic information systems and development of recommendations on the optimal system for the SOTER Project; and
- documentation of results, conclusions and recommendations from the initial phase of the SOTER Project.

APPROACH

1. Implementation Plan.

Upon receiving financial support for SOTER Phase 1, an implementation plan was developed which defined specific tasks and assigned responsibilities and a schedule to bring Phase 1 to completion on 31 December 1989. A Project manager for this phase was assigned and the Project officially began in September 1987.

2. Universal Legend.

An international committee of soil scientists was appointed in January 1986 to develop a universal legend for soils and terrain data to be entered into the SOTER database. A draft version was distributed in March 1988 entitled "SOTER Procedures Manual for Small Scale Map and Database Compilation" (Shields and Coote, 1988). This Manual describes and contains procedures for compiling and coding the following kinds of data for entry into the SOTER database:

- Polygon file
- Terrain component file
- Soil layer file

The Manual also presents coding forms on which to enter all the attribute file data which have been translated into the universal legend from whatever soil classification system that is being used.

3. Correlation Guidelines.

The Procedures Manual in a sense serves as the primary guideline for the correlation of soils which have been mapped under different classification systems. Further refinement of correlation procedures must be developed during the actual testing of the procedures and legend during field and compilation operations.

4. Definition of Soils and Terrain Parameters for Entry into the Database.

Careful attention has been given to the amount and kinds of data to be included in the SOTER database. The tendency is to include more data than can be used or is necessary for a map scale of 1:1M. The legend committee has given tentative definitions in the Procedures Manual. The adequacy of these definitions are being tested during Phase 1.

5. Definition of Detailed Set of Specifications and Logic to Define Minimum Capabilities/Functions of Database.

In general, the SOTER Proposal specifies that the SOTER database should be accessible to a broad base of users for a broad array of uses. During Phase 1 the potential users and uses of the Database must be more clearly defined so that the minimum capabilities and functions of the Database can be specified.

6. Selection of Pilot Areas of 250,000 sq km each in Developing Countries.

During the International Workshop in Wageningen in January 1986, approximately twenty potential areas of 250,000 sq km each were suggested as potential pilot or demonstration areas for SOTER. The rationale for an area of 250,000 sq km is that it coincides with the coverage of a single sheet of the 1:1M Operational Navigation Chart (ONC) map series. The ONC maps are being digitized and will be used in the SOTER Project as a base map for overlay of soils and terrain maps. The suggested pilot areas were prioritized in terms of availability of data and interest of potential funding agencies. These priority areas included regions in South America, East Africa, West Africa, and Southeast Asia.

In consultation with UNEP, the area selected for Phase 1 is an area in excess of 250,000 sq km which includes a portion of Argentina, Uruguay, and Brazil. In March 1988 a SOTER Workshop was held in Montevideo, Uruguay, for soil scientists of the three participating countries and selected members of the SOTER Working Group. The purpose of the Workshop was to present and discuss the concepts of SOTER, to report on the availability of data for the SOTER Database, and to present and discuss thoroughly the Procedures Manual and universal legend for coding data.

During April and May 1988 soil scientists of Argentina, Brazil, and Uruguay are using the Procedures Manual in a relatively small area for translating soils and terrain data from their systems to the SOTER legend and for coding the data for input into the SOTER Database.

In June 1988 an external SOTER soils correlator will join participating soils scientists of the three countries for correlation studies. They will travel together to each of the small study areas in each country and discuss any problems they have encountered with the use of the Procedures Manual. The purpose of this exercise is to refine and improve the Manual and correlation procedures. Each country has appointed a country correlator to work closely with the external correlator in order to arbitrate correlation differences.

7. Acquisition and Correlation of Relevant Maps and Data.

The Soil Survey organizations of Argentina, Brazil and Uruguay estimate that more than 90% of the map and attribute data for the Pilot Area exist. Very little new soils and terrain data will have to be acquired. These organizations have agreed to work within the SOTER Project objective of completing the acquisition and coding of all relevant data for the Pilot Area by the end of 1988.

8. Entry of Data into the SOTER Database.

At this stage of the Project a final decision has not yet been made about this task. Several possibilities are being considered. It has been agreed that once the Database has been established, one of the places it will reside is UNEP/GRID. The objective is to complete this task and test the Database by the end of 1989.

9. Test and Demonstration of Reliability, Accuracy and Utility of the SOTER Database.

During 1989 after entry of data into the Database, attention will be given to the testing of the Database.

10. Assessment of Current Geographic Information Systems.

As yet no decision has been made on the system to be used for the SOTER Database. The major concern is that whatever system is finally selected, it be compatible with GRID and other global environmental databases. Many different commercial hardware/software systems are available today, and no doubt others will emerge in the future. It is essential that the system selected for SOTER be flexible and economically feasible.

11. Documentation of Results, Conclusions and Recommendations.

Phase 1 of SOTER is scheduled for completion on 31 December 1989. The results, conclusions, and recommendations of this phase of the Project will be documented and provide valuable guidelines and experience for the next phases of SOTER.

EXPECTED RESULTS

In general, the idea behind the SOTER Project is to improve the capability to deliver accurate, timely, useful information about soils and terrain resources to decision-makers. It is expected that a World Soils and Terrain Digital

Database will provide this improved capability of information delivery. There are other, perhaps more specific, results which are expected from the Project.

1. Orderly arrangement of resource information.

All endeavors involved in the development, management, and conservation of environmental resources require information about those resources which is normally available from a variety of sources, at different levels of detail, including format and scale. An important outcome of the operational database is to bring into being an orderly arrangement of descriptive and quantitative data about soils and terrain, easily accessible to the user community and compatible with other environmental databases.

2. Improvement in standardization and compatibility of reporting soils and terrain data/information.

Inherent in the conceptualization of the Database is the requirement for a "universal" legend and a standard system for both input and output. Another requirement of SOTER is that the Soils and Terrain Database be compatible and have overlay (registration) capabilities with world databases of other environmental resources.

3. Improvement in accessibility of soils and terrain and related resource information.

An important component of the Project is that of technology transfer, especially in the provision of training in the access to and utilization of the Database for easy extraction of a broad array of interpretive maps and information essential to resource managers and policy makers. Different methods will be explored for improving communications between the Database and the user community.

4. Dynamic resource information system with updating and purging capabilities.

One of the significant benefits of the Database, not possible with previous information systems, will be the instantaneous capability to add new data whenever such data become available and to delete incorrect, obsolete and irrelevant data.

5. Information service for national resource planning in developing countries.

Another of the expected results from an operational database is the valuable resource information service which can be made available to a variety of agencies and organizations involved in national and regional resource planning in developing countries.

6. System model for technology transfer.

As the world is being caught up in the "information revolution" there is increasing need to find innovative and useful methods for transferring this technology. The SOTER Database Project can provide an excellent vehicle for training a cadre of specialists, especially in developing countries, for using the Database, providing new data, and developing new uses of the Database. The operational World Database can also serve as a model for the design and construction of in-country databases with sufficient detail and scale (accuracy) for local and provincial use.

REFERENCES

Baumgardner, M.F. and L.R. Oldeman (eds.), 1986. Proceedings of an International Workshop on the Structure of a Digital International Soil Resources Map Annex Database. International Soil Reference and Information Centre, Wageningen, The Netherlands.

ISSS, 1986. Project proposal. World soils and terrain digital database at a scale 1:1M. Intl. Soc. Soil Sci., Wageningen, The Netherlands.

Shields, J.A. and D.R. Cook, 1988. SOTER procedures manual for small scale map and database compilation. International Soil Reference and Information Center, Wageningen, The Netherlands.

Sombroek, W.G., 1985. Toward a global soil resources inventory at scale 1:1 million. Working Paper and Preprint Series 84/4. International Soil Reference and Information Centre, Wageningen, The Netherlands.

UNEP, 1987. Global assessment of soil degradation. United Nations Environment Programme Project Document. Nairobi, Kenya.

WORLD DIGITAL DATABASE FOR ENVIRONMENTAL SCIENCES (WDDES)

David P. Bickmore

BACKGROUND

No serious digital base map of the world showing topographic relief exists today. A joint working group of the International Geographical Union (IGU) and the International Cartographic Association (ICA) was set up in 1984 under the author to explore the feasibility of developing a standard global dataset in modern topologically structured form - and by 1990.

The group has held four workshops (International Council of Scientific Unions, Paris, January 1985; World Data Centre, Boulder, November 1985; World Meteorological Office, Geneva, July 1986; Trinity College, Oxford, April 1987). These have brought together a distinguished range of geographers, cartographers and environmental scientists actively concerned with practicalities of computer mapping and Geographical Information Systems and from commercial, academic, government and international agencies in some 10 countries. A total of over 50 individuals has been involved. The Geneva and Oxford workshops have been under the chairmanship of Prof. Eric Brown (Chairman, British National Committee for Geography); three of them have been attended by Dr. F.W.G. Baker (Executive Secretary for ICSU).

A firm concensus has emerged that the scale should be 1/1m (c. 1 km resolution) where this is possible; smaller scales seem inadequate in resolution - larger scales sometimes raise national security complications. Note also that the following elements of the physical geography of the world will be portrayed: coastlines, drainage networks, land relief (contours at c. 300m intervals, spot heights) and bathymetry (contours at 1000m intervals, depth values). In addition, we shall represent statistical (e.g. provincial) boundaries, built-up areas, and place names of the above. The estimated size of such a database is about 5 gigabytes.

Our objective is to produce tapes, compact disks, etc. rather than printed maps; and the purpose is to enable correlation analysis and modelling of new and existing datasets for the environmental sciences. Users will thus have their own control of: selected area; projection; scale; features of interest to them, and of the graphics by which they are represented. In addition, users will also be able to measure or manipulate many spatial elements such as: area; distance; connectivity (e.g. river networks); and - via terrain modelling - slope and aspect.

This is seen as a timely international development, e.g. by ICSU's Committee on Data for Science and Technology (CODATA), whose workshop on Environmental Data (May 1986) emphasised the urgency of 'harmonising' location data globally to avoid a plethora of different base maps. The project also has relevance as a practical background device ('stage scenery') in programmes such as ICSU's International Geosphere Biosphere Programme (IGBP), the International Soil and Terrain Map and Database (SOTER) of the International Society of Soil Science (ISSS), and the Global Resources Information Database (GRID) under development by UNEP (who funded the Geneva workshop).

Funding for these preliminaries was provided by ICA, IGU, ICSU and more specifically by ICSU's Scientific Committee on the Geosphere Biosphere. A detailed report was accepted by ICA (October 1987) and work continues under an ICA Commission. (Copies of the report may be obtained from Pergamon Press, Oxford).

The IGU/ICA Group are in no doubt that the main motivation for the project is a scientific one, both in planetary or global sense and as a locational device for a range of environmental sciences. That said, the Group is very much aware of initial project costs of at least £3M and is very sympathetic to recouping these by selling the data as widely as possible and in a variety of forms and ways. ICSU resolutely supports the Group's intention to regard the project as a publishing venture with the bulk of the funding coming form commercial sources and with map-editing, quality assurance and database developments being underwritten by a scientific board.

A UK Government report entitled Handling Geographic Information (May 1987) under the Chairmanship of Lord Chorley points to a general trend which unquestionably favours providing locational data in digital (GIS) form and for many administrative as well as scientific uses. At the same time the quite new market for such data in digital form is still very difficult to predict and professional market research data is sparse on quantities of deliverables that should be provided, and at what prices.

SOURCES

A database is no better than the sources from which it is derived. Early discussion by the Working Group explored sources for the project. In effect there were some five possibilities.

a) Brand new compilations specially commissioned afresh for digitising for this project. In the main, it was evident both that this approach would be beyond our resources (time and funds) and that the necessity for undertaking them for most of the land surfaces was of questional value (see, however, under Antartica below).

b) Remote sensed data initially appeared as a new and attractive source for our purpose. However, the cost of simply acquiring such data, let alone interpreting it, seemed to increase our total budget by * 4. Moreover, Landsat data omit relief and patently do not show boundaries or names. This is not to write off the usefulness of remote sensed data as revision material in particular regions and after interpretation into e.g. 1/250k mapping. And radar altimetry may within a decade or so provide the means of making a successor to WDDES in some respects.

c) Individual national maps already in digital form (e.g. Canada, 1/2.5M and India, 1/4M) have some theoretical attractions. However, the assembly of such data into a consistent global database poses great practical problems, e.g. detailed inconsistencies between national datasets produce major 'edge match' problems. Furthermore, about 90% of the countries of the world do not have such data in digital form, and most of those who do have such data so not include contours. An exception to this is Australia (see below).

d) Existing digital world databases. Several of these are available though none seemed appropriate. One, World Data Base II (WDBII) was prepared a decade ago by the American CIA and provides digital cover at 1/3M scale; however, it omits relief and its data structure ('spaghetti') makes it inappropriate for analytical tasks. An up-dated version, WDBIII, with administrative sub-divisions but without relief or any GIS structure is currently said to be in hand for official US agencies only. Our Working Group responded negatively to its usefulness in our context (July 1986). Another projected digital base map at 1/5M scale is under way at IGN Paris, but this scale seems too small for most scientific purposes that we envisaged. Another possibility was the gridded data set of Global Topography with x-y-z values interpolated at 5' * 5' intersections but without rivers, coastlines, etc. The sources of this (US Defence) dataset are not attributable; furthermore, detailed examination seemed to reveal many inconsistencies. Finally, there is the commercial development, Mundocart, at 1/1M scale, an outline edition without relief, now available in CDRom form.

e) Digitising printed world map series. The choices here are, of course, wider. A grandiose plan for an International 1/1M Map of the World (IMW) was agreed by IGU before the First World War and revivified somewhat after the Second. The work to an agreed specification, in terms of classical cartography, was to be carried out by c. 20 national mapping organisations. In practice, many of the sheets were never drawn and other departed from the original specifications; initial enthusiasm for the task has evaporated and attempts to revive it found no appeal and sounded warning notes within our Group. Serious consideration was given to two post-war (1960-1970) map series that do provide consistent global cover and relief; both seemed to be candidates for the project. They were: Karta Mira 1/2.5M - produced by a consortium of East European mapping agencies; and Operational Navigational Chart series (ONC) 1/1M - produced and maintained by the Military Surveys of the Western Alliance.

The pros and cons of both the above options were fully considered and the final choice of the 1/1M ONC was made because of its inherently higher resolution and more direct reflection of e.g. 1/250k mapping, and because the series was deemed to be largely in the public domain, hence out of copyright.

IMPROVING ONC

While ONC 1/1M series is our principle source, there are as with any world map series - especially with one designed for air navigation and not for environmental science - grounds for criticism of ONC. Major editorial additions and improvements to it to create WDDES are envisaged.

a) Oceans are blank on ONC. However, faute de mieux, versions of the 18 sheets at 1/10M of the contoured General Bathymetric Chart of the Oceans (GEBCO) will be assimilated. These published maps are currently being digitised at the International Gravity Bureau in Toulouse (via IGN Paris) and an exchange of data has been agreed in principle and was demonstrated as feasible despite differences in resolution. New GEBCO regional compilations at 1/1M are in hand, and digitised versions of these can doubtless be used to improve the database over time.

b) Antartica is also unmapped on ONC. This area represents c. 10% of the land surface of the world and is of considerable scientific interest. A new ad hoc compilation of it (under the auspices of Dr. Swithinbank and the Scott Polar Research Institute (SPRI), Cambridge), will be undertaken for direct digital processing. This will assimilate the relatively small areas of 1/250k mapping that now exist and combine this with smaller scale, e.g. 1/6M, materials supplemented by reference to a complete set of cloud-free Landsat cover that is available.

c) Australia. Whilst ONC covers this continent (rather sketchily in parts), it has been established that National Mapping, Canberra, is currently in the process of producing its own national database at 1/1M scale and with closely similar objectives, features, etc. (including contours) to WDDES. This national database will, of course, take advantage of updating from current Australian mapping at 1/250k. Arrangements for the assimilation of this block of data into WDDES are being made, partly on merit and partly to explore future possibilities of exchanging national blocks of data, a prospect of importance to ICA.

d) Amazonia. The 10 or so sheets of ONC covering this area are in skeleton-outline form. Growing scientific interest in this region suggests that serious recompilation plus representation of relief should be given high priority. Recent Brazilian mapping is nearing completion and may be an important source.

e) Other gaps in ONC exist, for example in Arctic Canada and in smaller patches of Africa and S.E.Asia. These will also make claims on our attention - and on our budget.

f) Boundaries. ONC maps international boundaries on land but makes no attempt to represent internal boundaries or the Exclusive Economic Zones which are now becoming established in the oceans. Statistics relating to population and epidemiological distributions and to agriculture are referenced to such internal subdivisions, while EEZ boundaries have direct relevance to the exploration and development of submarine resources. Both sets of information are seen as relevant to WDDES insofar as they are known. In some instances these national subdivisions may be available in digital form but in other cases they will have to be compiled onto the ONC maps so as to be digitised and overlaid as sets of named polygons and centroids.

g) <u>Positional Reliability</u>. The sources used in small scale map compilation are liable to innate variations in reliability: these variations are often more discernible in printed cartographic form (e.g. at sheet edges) than within a digital database. WDDES will inevitably assimilate some data that have been derived from controlled local surveys and other data (e.g. in the Oceans or Antarctica) that represents lesser degrees of reliability; in some areas rivers may be more 'reliable' than contours, and contours than boundaries. In an ideal world these variations in reliability ought to be quantified but in practice only qualitative gradings seem feasible and useful in this project. They will appear as attributes to <u>each</u> line segment.

It should be noted that WDDES will omit, in the first instance at least, some ONC features (e.g. road/rail communications, minor towns) whose selection tends to be arbitrary, whose relevance to environmental science seems uncertain, and which date rapidly. Aeronautical data (beacons, landing strips, etc.) on ONC will also be omitted from WDDES. Nevertheless, ONC does provide a convenient starting point for WDDES.

In terms of production, editing - as above - and digitising - as below - will run concurrently on sheet by sheet priorities. Edits will then be digitised (a minor task) and merged with the structured data at the Quality Assurance stage of production. Once a DBMS is established we see that as having the capability of assimilating 'continuous improvements' of an editorial nature.

DIGITISING AND STRUCTURING THE DATA

ICA, as an international organisation, is uniquely placed to comment on those technical GIS aspects in which much recent development has been under way in national mapping agencies and universities. We have been fortunate in benefiting from this.

Two pilot exercises on sample areas (N.W. Sumatra and N. Kenya) of ONC have been undertaken as tests for this project (and are illustrated in the full report).

In the first (1986) pilot, expert held was provided by the firm Petroconsultants who undertook the digitising and computer processing and, moreover, funded the experiment. Other help on this project came from the Royal Geographical Society Map Room (map analysis), Institute of Hydrology (river structuring), Cambridge University Computer Laboratory (data structuring and database management), Nottingham University (digital terrain modelling) and Birkbeck College, London (GIS). The resultant data were tested at some eight international laboratories - USGS, World Bank, Goddard, Survey of Canada, Zurich University, Institute of Image Analysis (Graz), Landestopographie (Berne), IGN (Paris) - and it was discussed in detail at the Geneva Workshop. A technical account of this work is available.

The second (1987) pilot study was funded by Pergamon Press and was conducted by BKS Surveys. It was concerned to implement the precise GIS data structures as specified in detail in Appendices I and VI of the Report - q.v. It provided data used for the DBMS study noted below.

There are, of course, some heavy - and relatively novel - demands that the required logic of this project makes on the digitiser. Thus the map is made up of many areal features - lakes, islands, provinces, land above (or below) a particular contour: their boundaries need to be watertight, their insides have to be distinguished from their outsides, and each needs to generate its own centroid sometimes as a hook to other attributes (e.g. names). And logically it is desirable to identify how areas of one feature - say a province - are to be subdivided by overlapping areas of another feature - say a contour. Obviously many areas e.g. provinces, will have their own hierarchical pecking order that needs to be implicit and immediatly identifiable. Areal features are delimited by line segments but many line segments are also parts of linear networks (rivers and roads) with logical sequences of their own (downstream) that can be derived from the direction of digitising. The intersection of these line features (e.g. rivers with contours) enables desirable logical checking (e.g. via profiles) to take place. And some lines carry multiple attributes ("I am a thin single line river with this direction, also with this name, and that positional reliability category and coincident with the boundary between province X and Y which lie to the right and left respectively, and between this and that contour level; furthermore I terminate at another line section where I become the centre line through a lake whose left and right banks are other line segments to which I can point").

It has constantly to be reiterated to digitiser operators that the point of this exercise is <u>not</u> to reproduce the original colour separations with an eye to map printing but to provide logical data for a digital database where some relaxation in absolute accuracy levels may be acceptable so long as topological relationships are secure. (Indeed the absolute accuracy levels of compiled 1/1m mapping may not have great intrinsic merit anyhow). The lesson that we prefer logic to accuracy if we have to choose seems a difficult one for digitisers to learn. We believe they will have assimilated that after some 40,000 man hours on this job.

This logic, pioneered by USGS in their DLG formats, is complex to envisage and more so to apply consistently. Furthermore, additions to the dataset have to assume that a host of updating transactions can be carried out automatically and over a database of c. 3 to 5 gbytes.

QUALITY ASSURANCE

The anticipation and trapping of error in the digitising and structuring stages is obviously of high importance in a scientific database. These checks will be incorporated in the production flow line with inadequate results being returned for immediate correction. But some independent checks, probably on a random basis, are also necessary to fortify confidence in the data. Even so some errors will get through!

Traditional graphic methods (plots of data on transparent paper that can be manually overlaid on originals and checked by eye) are generally inadequate for checking data structures. They remain efficient for checking positional accuracy, and for identifying complete omissions of data. But they are inefficient, for example, in checking that <u>all</u> line segments in a river flow downhill, or that this polygon is 'watertight' or that higher ground lies on, say, the righthand side of this contour.

We see the process of quality control as a relatively new field in computer mapping. The data structures required are themselves complex but many of them can be examined (and in some cases automatically corrected) via batch programs. The architecture of the DBMS will assume that the sheet by sheet data it receives have been cleared up and will respond to logical manipulation that can reasonably be demanded of them. I suspect we may all have some way to go in developing appropriate software and even in being alerted to the kinds, frequencies and seriousness of problems that will arise. There is a production nightmare that the combinatorial problems inherent in our logical data structure will accumulate to a level where data are held captive in this Q.A. maze, unable to progress to the next DBMS stage.

DBMS

A database design for WDDES is presented as Appendix III of the Report. It assumes the handling of 'metadata' and indices under a modern database management system such as Oracle, but leaves the bulk data (coordinates etc) in separate magnetic tape or disc form. Following on from this, an arrangement was made with the (British) Natural Environment Research Council to mount a sample (Pilot2) of WDDES data on their Oracle system which is currently in use on several large databases in the field of environmental science. NERC had in 1986 selected Oracle as a result of detailed trials of database systems then commercially available; their 12 months experience of using it was a material benefit to us.

The experimental work carried out by NERC was demonstrated at a small technical meeting in January 1988: a full report on the findings of the scientist primarily concerned (Robert Sanderson) is in the press. Broad conclusions are as follows:

(a) There were no problems in transferring data from DLG structured form into Oracle files (organised into column and row form for SQL searches).

(b) Quite sophisticated searches on the cartographic data were possible, some of them (e.g. for names) at reasonably fast speeds.

189

(c) The experiment suggested that there seemed little merit in keeping the bulk data separate from the metadata. Most searches would, in fact, call on coordinate data which would then need retrieving more lengthily and expensively from tape or disc. It was concluded that the full data could and should be held within Oracle.

(d) Estimates - on the basis of Pilot2 - suggested that the full WDDES data might amount to between 3 and 5 gigabytes. Estimates for complete dumps of the entire database were the cause for considerable concern and cast doubt on whether e.g. a Micro Vax would provide adequate processing power. This implies the need for more expensive investment in computers than was previously contemplated. More expert study of this problem is necessary.

(e) Sanderson suggests that professional Oracle specialists might well be able to maximise the efficiency of his procedures. There is an equivalent need to predict more accurately the kinds and frequencies of searches; and what are variant end products required from this kind of database.

We hope this conference will have further constructive suggestions for us in this field.

PUBLISHING AND CDROM DEVELOPMENTS

Professional concern with 'marketing' is a new and important element in cartographic enterprises, whether in the public or private sector. The WDDES plan had assumed that the very considerable funds required to launch such a project were more likely to emerge from the private sector. In practice this has not been the case here, with support for the project from combined resources of Petroconsultants and of Pergamon Press. My own I.C.A. Commission is cast in the role of a relatively independent editorial board attempting to link God and mammon.

You will not, of course, expect me to reveal the business plan for this whole expensive undertaking. You will, however, not be surprised to know that a professional market research survey for the project has been undertaken. At the same time, Petroconsultants have been gaining market experience in selling their Mundocart product - itself a digitised map of outline elements (main rivers, coasts, international boundaries) taken from ONC. The latest version of this product is now on the market in CDRom form and will doubtless provide us with more evidence about how to package and distribute our much larger WDDES - or Mundocart II as they call it.

Our aim is to produce a CDRom version of WDDES for \1000. The number of CDRoms to provide global cover depends on convenient segmentations by geography and interest. In addition to the CDRom data - in whatever format seems most appropriate - there would be additional software intended only to extract data from CDRom: this software (possibly on floppy disk on the user's P.C.) would fetch and convert the data into a format of user's choice. Thus the user would have access to the full link/node, left/right areas, multiple feature coding and hierarchical structures incorporated into the database. This could be directly manipulated by the user's own GIS. There are clearly a number of variations on this theme and more market research should enable the large potential in WDDES to be used effectively, both in scientific institutes and more widely in developing countries.

POSTSCRIPT

During the recent history (October 1987) of this scientific project we learned of the decision of the American military also to digitise the ONC series. We initiated discussions about collaborative arrangements for this work, but unfortunately these have been negative. There will, however, be significant differences between the DMA digital copy of the present ONC maps and the ICA 'scientific' version as described here with its emphasis on editorial improvements, on independent quality control, on a DBMS, and on professional marketing.

THE ROLE OF THE WORLD METEOROLOGICAL ORGANIZATION IN DEVELOPING GLOBAL ENVIRONMENTAL DATABASES

V.G. Boldirev

The World Meteorological Organization (WMO) is an intergovernmental UN organization that has a long history since the establishment in 1873 of the International Meteorological Organization. Now 160 states and territories are Members of the WMO.

Undeniably, one of the reasons why meteorologists in 1873 agreed to co-operate in an international arena was a need to exchange data.

The principle of free exchange of data amongst meteorological services, established since then, is now included in the WMO Convention.

To solve their national problems, all countries need information about current weather, forecasts of weather, warnings of hazardous weather, data on climate, hydrological data, forecasts and warnings, agrometeorological data, etc. One unchallenged strength of the international meteorological system (involving national meteorological and hydrometeorological services) and the WMO is an ability to achieve, through co-operation of those national services, a daily worldwide exchange of weather data in real-time. The World Weather Watch (WWW), established 25 years ago, serves as the basic programme of the WMO and primarily provides Members with observational data and processed products for meteorological forecasting and warning purposes. The WWW also supports other WMO activities and the relevant programmes of other international organizations.

Among the main long-term objectives, the following should be mentioned with respect to the global databases development:

- To provide quality-controlled observational datasets with documented and consistent accuracy, with geographical distribution and with temporal and spatial

192

resolutions required for the preparation of all time-ranges of meteorological forecasts and severe weather warnings;

- To ensure highly reliable WWW data and product collection, dissemination and exchange;

- To support other WMO programmes and relevant programmes of other international organizations, in accordance with procedures agreed within WMO through the provision of quality-controlled data and the use of facilities for the collection, processing, management, dissemination and exchange of data as appropriate.

The WWW functions at the global, regional and national levels and includes three essential assignments:

(a) The Global Observing System (GOS), consisting of facilities and arrangements for making observations at stations on land and at sea, from aircraft, meteorological satellites and other platforms;

(b) The Global Data-processing System (GDPS), consisting of meteorological centres with arrangements for the processing of observational data and preparation of analyses and forecast products (real-time uses) and for the storage and retrieval of data and processed products (non-real-time uses). The network of GDPS centres comprises:

   - World Meteorological Centres (WMCs), located in Melbourne, Moscow and Washington;
   - Regional Meteorological Centres - 26 at present. Plans for the further development of the WWW envisage the establishment of Regional Specialised Meteorological Centres (RSMCs).
   - National Meteorological Centres or centres with similar functions (NMCs);

(c) The Global Telecommunication System (GTS), consisting of telecommunication facilities and arrangements necessary for the rapid and reliable collection and distribution of the required observational data and processed products. The GTS is organized into:

   - The Main Telecommunication Network (MTN);

   - The regional meteorological telecommunication networks;

WWW THE INTEGRATED SYSTEM CONCEPT

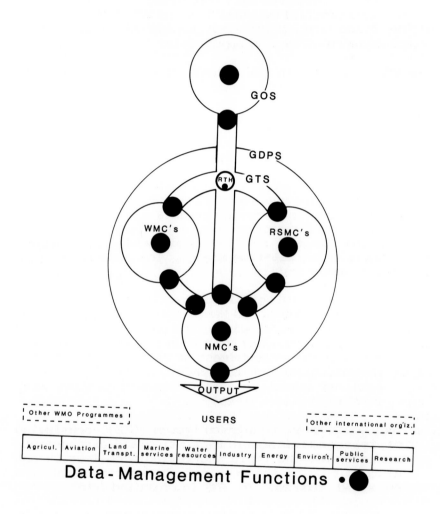

Figure 1

- The national meteorological telecommunication networks.

The concept of the WWW as outlined in the WMO Second Long Term Plan (SLTP) for 1988-1997 is presented in figure 1. The structure of the Global Observing System is shown in figure 2.

The highest priority of the GOS will be to meet global data requirements. Only part of the data obtained by systems shown in figure 2 is operationally circulating through the Global Telecommunication System. A data volume of observational data required daily by centres operating on a global basis is, however, very substantial: about 6 million characters in 1985 with a projected increase up to 10.5 million by 1990.

Data Archiving within the WWW belongs to the GDPS; the non-real-time functions of the GDPS include:

- Long-term storage in a recommended format and medium of GOS data and GDPS products, as well as verification results for operational and research use;
- Maintenance of a continuously updated catalogue of the data and products stored in the system.

It should be mentioned that the amount of the GDPS products provided from one global forecast centre was about 6 million characters daily in 1985. Plans for the implementation of the GDPS involve the concept of databases associated with the WMCs and RMSs/RSMCs. At World Meteorological Centres, global databases should have high speed communication links to regional, automated databases and communication centres.

At Regional/Specialized Meteorological Centres associated regional databases should ensure the access, delivery, coverage, content and frequency of data and products as agreed by Members to establish adequate access to global, regional and national databases through suitable automated terminals with monitoring functions, for data and product exchange with WMCs and other RSMCs.

WWW being the backbone of WMO activity, supports other programmes dealing with data acquisition, archiving and storage. Data handling components are included in the World Climate Programme (World Climate Data Programme), the Hydrology and Water Resources Programme, all components of the Applications of Meteorology Programme, and the Research

Figure 2:   The Global Observing System

SURFACE-BASED SUB-SYSTEM	SPACE-BASED SUB-SYSTEM
Meteorological and Oceanic Data provided by: Surface synoptic stations Upper-air stations Aircraft meteorological stations Aeronautical meteorological stations Research and special purpose vessel stations Climatological stations Agricultural meteorological stations Weather radar stations Radiation stations Atmospheric detection stations Meteorological reconnaissance aircraft stations Meteorological rocket stations Ozone sounding stations Background pollution stations Planetary boundary-layer stations Tide-gauge stations	Meteorological and Oceanic Data provided by: Polar-orbiting meteorological satellites Geostationary meteorological stations Environmental satellites Research satellites giving IMAGERY and QUANTITIVE DATA with near-global coverage

THE COMPOSITE OBSERVING SYSTEM

and Development Programme (especially the Environmental Pollution Monitoring and Research Programme).

Within the World Climate Programme, the World Climate Data Programme is aimed at ensuring the timely access to reliable climate data which are exchangable in an acceptable format to support climate applications, impact studies and research. The scope of the WCDP includes data from the entire climate system, being composed of the atmosphere, oceans, cryosphere and land surface (including the biosphere).

Two projects of the WCDP should be particularly mentioned in the context of developing global databases:

- implementation of the climate data referral system (INFOCLIMA); and

- development of the global/regional climate system datasets.

Within the WCDP, requirements for climate data are also being consolidated.

INFOCLIMA provides information on the availability of datasets and data summaries (where and in what media) and on station networks (including period of operation and other basic station history information). Input and output formats and access codes developed under INFOCLIMA for the computerized storage and retrieval of information will be the basis for guiding INFOCLIMA users and developing national referral services. Initial INFOCLIMA catalogues were published in 1986.

Based on 600 dataset descriptions from 82 countries (140 data centres) an updated computerized INFOCLIMA catalogue of climate system datasets was prepared, including new sections on satellite and remote-sensing data, hydrological data, historical and proxy data. The possibility of issuing the catalogue (over 550 pages) on computer diskettes is being considered.

The WMO INFOCLIMA Inventory of Climatological and Radiation Stations was prepared as a computerized databases, on the basis of information collected from over 100 countries. The issue of the station inventory computerized databases on diskettes is being considered, to reduce printing and distribution costs.

A specific project was initiated to promote the establishment of a network of reference climatological stations (RCSs) and datasets containing long-time series data from an RCS network (i.e. a reference global climate dataset). The project was expanded in scope in 1986 to promote the maintenance of a global climate database of which the reference global climate dataset would form a component. For the World Climate Programme, a variety of datasets will be required, comprising regular observations of surface and upper-air meteorological variables (including remote-sensed parameters), marine, oceano-graphic, cryospheric, land-surface and sub-surface vegetation, soil, topography and other variables. A commensurate international co-ordination effort will be required to prepare the required global datasets, through relevant international organizations, at international data centres such as WMCs and various World Data Centres.

·Some WCRP projects are already collecting and assembling global datasets while others are in various stages of planning. The following WCRP data projects are included in the implementation plan for the programme:

- International Satellite Cloud Climatology Project (ISCCP)
- Radiation Budget Climatology Project
- Global Sea Surface Temperature Data Project
- Atmosphere-Ocean Fluxes Data Project
- Ocean Circulation Data Project
- Tropical Wind Data Project
- Global Precipitation Climatology Project
- Continental Water Run-off Data Project
- Global Land Surface Data Project

The WCRP data projects are essential scientific tasks which must be performed by operational agencies or by operational teams set up within research institutions. It is expected that the fulfilment of WCRP data management objectives will be a major challenge in terms of both personnel and dedicated equipment, including worldwide communications or direct satellite read-out when appropriate.

Examples of implementation of the WCRP data projects are:

- Global Sea-surface Temperature Project: the USA Climate Analysis Center continues its work as the Data Centre for the project which began in January 1985. Monthly mean sea-surface temperature-analysed fields are produced on a 200 x 200 km^2 grid, using a technique which blends information from Voluntary Observing Ships,

198

drifting buoys and operational polar-orbiting satellite visible and infra-red radiometers. The fields are being archived in the World Data Centres for Meteorology;

- Global Precipitation Climatology Project: Formal commitments have been made by Japan, the USA and EUMETSAT to provide the geostationary satellite infra-red histogram data in the form required. Furthermore, the USA has agreed to operate the Geostationary Satellite Precipitation Data Centre, and production of monthly rainfall estimates for the zone $40^{\circ}N - 40^{\circ}S$ has already begun. The Federal Republic of Germany has offered to implement the Global Precipitation Climatology Centre which will collect surface raingauge data and merge them with satellite data to produce global precipitation fields;

- Radiation budget climatology: The Earth Radiation Budget Experiment (ERBE) data are being processed and analysed under the guidance of the ERBE Scientific Team made up of investigators from the Federal Republic of Germany, France, the United Kingdom and the USA. The information obtained provides fluxes of reflected sunlight and emitted thermal energy from the Earth and its atmosphere.

Surface radiation data are being collected and published by the WMO World Radiation Data Centre in Leningrad, USSR (the centre was established in 1964).

Another important kind of data is being collected and published by the World Ozone Data Centre operated jointly by WMO and the Atmospheric Environment Service, Canada.

The global ozone observing system consists of about 70 active stations, concentrated mostly in the northern hemisphere. The WMO Global Ozone Research and Monitoring project aims at maintaining, improving and expanding atmospheric ozone measurements.

Air pollution monitoring activities are carried out in a large number of Member countries. Many of these activities are on a continuous basis and contribute to the global WMO Background Air Pollution Monitoring Network (BAPMoN) and thereby to the Global Environment Monitoring System (GEMS) initiated by UNEP (a few years after the conception of BAPMoN). BAPMoN, however, constitutes the only real global and standardized network, linking existing activities and covering regions without national activities. From such monitoring comparable and representative information on

global and regional levels and trends of selected sub-
stances is expected to emerge. Much effort was made and
still is being made towards a better geographical coverage,
higher data quality and additional parameters.

Data collection schemes for application purposes exist and
are being developed as part of the WMO agricultural
meteorology programme and the Marine Meteorology and
Associated Oceanographic Activities programme. Within the
former, the objective is to help national Services to meet
national needs for agrometeorological data - climate,
recent weather and forecasts - and to collaborate with the
relevant agricultural services for the inclusion of non-
meteorological data in the establishment of agrometeorological data banks.

As for the latter, a marine climatological and related
ocean databases is being established to pursue the
collection, storage and retrieval of global marine
climatological datasets, in particular for the WCP and the
provision of marine services, and to continue and improve
the operation of the Marine Climatological Summaries
Scheme. This scheme was established in 1963 to provide a
comprehensive marine climatological databases and related
climatological analyses over the global oceans. Under the
scheme, eight Members of WMO were allocated areas of
responsibility for the collection of marine data and the
provision of summaries. Despite the inadequacy of the
databases, particularly for certain ocean areas and at
certain times, the scheme operates well.

For the next decade, the project "Marine climatological and
related ocean databases" is planned to:

-   pursue and expand the collection, storage and retrieval
    of the global marine and ocean climatological datasets,
    including data from remote-sensing technology, in
    particular global datasets with respect to support for
    the WCP and to the application of marine meteorological
    /climatological information to the provision of marine
    and ocean services, and to continue the development and
    operation of the Marine Climatological Summaries Scheme;

-   ensure the development and introduction of efficient and
    uniform quality-control procedures for the collection
    and processing of marine climatological data; and

- further the development of a sea-ice observational /climatological dataset, including data from remote-sensing technologies.

Unlike meteorological and oceanographic data, hydrological data are not generally exchanged globally. Therefore the WMO Hydrology and Water Resources Programme deals mainly with hydrological data management on a national basis.

In particular, main long-term objectives of the Operational Hydrology Programme (a component of the HWR) include helping in the establishment and improvement of national water-resources data banks, including both hydrological data and statistics on water use and to promote the integration of these with other environmental data banks. The following projects are being implemented:

- Collection and transmission of hydrological data: To make available technical support for the establishment of modern data collection and transmission systems;

- Primary processing and storage of hydrological data: To continue to provide assistance in improved primary processing, storage and retrieval of hydrological data, and in standardization of data formats.

Within the limits of this paper, only a rather sketchy presentation can be given of WMO programmes and projects relevant to the global environmental databases development. Many specific activities deserve more attention: traditional, such as issuing the so-called World Weather Records, that is carefully checked multi-year climatic averages of meteorological elements; historical, such as the unprecedented global data management effort and creation of comprehensive datasets within the Global Weather Experiment in 1978-79; perspective, such as compiling for the first time in history datasets on atmospheric pollution on a global basis (this is being done by the Background Atmospheric Pollution Monitoring Network - BAPMoN). These are only a few those which could be mentioned.

At this stage suffice it to say that in collaboration with other international agencies (UNEP, ICSU, FAO, Unesco and others), the WMO does and will promote international co-ordination of data management, including the development of global databases.

THE SHORELINE AS A BASELINE FOR GLOBAL DATABASES:
A PILOT STUDY IN CHINA

Chen Shupeng

INTRODUCTION

The diversity of geographical distributions of natural resources and the environment requires that the global database, viewed as part of a multi-dimensional geographical information system, must involve not only raster and polygon data structures, but also network and vector data structures.

For those geographical information systems (GIS) established in China, three database structures exist at present.

First are raster structures, such as digital terrain models, using the unique transit coordinate network, and a mapping grid system with a unified origin for local regions. Uses include terrain analytical models, registration of Landsat imagery, three-dimensional display, statistical analysis and computer-aided cartography. Second, are polygon structures, such as those relating to census and social economic statistics based on administrative divisions (provinces, municipalities and countries), as well as units in the form of a central / provincial level network. These create a sound scientific foundation for the establishment of a global database in the future.

This article lays stress upon the concept and design of the third type of database. Using 'dots' and 'arc lines' this type forms various 'chains', which are used to represent fixed spatial models of the physical environment and socio-economic activities, as well as the geographical zonal structure of flows of materials, so as to establish a multi-level information retrieval system, which can gradually be expanded from a simple to a comprehensive data network. This approach will provide a scientific basis for geographical location analysis and will reveal differences and progress within and between regions. It could be one of the feasible technical routes to the establishment of the global database.

THE SHORELINE AS A DATA CHAIN

Shorelines are the most essential and clear-cut of all geographical boundaries. Along them exist zones marked by the most vigorous human activity, with large flows of material and information.

Man's knowledge of the planet on which he lives began from observations made along the coastlines, then extended to the hinterlands via navigable water ways and roads, finally embracing the inner continents and the depths of the sea. To conform to the logical process by which Man came to know the world remains a valuable approach in the establishment of the global database.

In the past, China long regarded itself as a continental country, and national activities were forbidden along the coastlines. Nevertheless, their impact on Chinese culture could not be blocked. From the 19th century, colonialists broke into feudal China by way of the sea and exploited the resources along the rivers, although they could never wholly conquer the vast territory. Today, the Chinese people and their government have, with unprecedented enthusiasm, opened up their coastal cities, increasing their participation in the global cycle of science, culture, technology and economy, and thereby demonstrating the significance of coastlines in human development.

China has a total coastline of 18,000 km, with 158 important coastal cities and 315 seaports of varying size, of which 22 are capable of receiving ships of more than 10,000 tons.

These seaports can be represented by 'dots' for the purposes of dividing the coastline into three classes. On the basis of their economic connections and resource / environmental conditions, 21 shorelines fall into class III, nine into class II and four into class I. The resulting dendritic structure is shown in Table 1.

The database of the Chinese shoreline will then consist of three parts:

- data on coastline segments are taken as the base
- hinterlands are connected with seaports using economic data on town systems and traffic networks
- maritime environments and resources are divided according to their bathymetry and their distance from the seaports.

1	2	3
	- Dilian	- Dandong - Dalian
Tianjin -----	- Tanggu	- Yingkou - Qinhuangdao - Tanggu - Yantai
	- Qingdao	- Qingdao - Lianyungang
Shanghai ----	Shanghai	- Nantong - Shanghai --- - Jinshanwe
	- Xiamenn	- Ningbo ----- - Fuzhou - Xiaomen
Guangzhou --	- Huangpu	- Shanton - Hongkong --- - (Shenzhen) - Aomen (Zhuhai)
	- Haikou	- Xhanjiang - Beihai - Jilong ---- - Gaoxiong --

Table 1.

Acquisition of data elements should reflect local conditions as a way of portraying the characteristics of both
seaports and coastlines. For example, each of the four
Class I shorelines possesses a number of unique features:

1. The northern shoreline, with Tianjin as the centre, has
    an inner sea (Bohai Sea) and an arcurate trend, with
    alternating stretches of rocky and sandy coast. Good
    natural harbours are lacking in the two big deltas of
    the Yellow River and the Luan River, and most of the
    harbours suffer from large deposits of mud and sand,
    and may be blocked during the winter by thin ice.

2. The shoreline of south eastern China, with Guangzhou as
    the centre, has several good harbours. Its winding

coast is mainly rocky and almost 90% of Chinese islands are located here. Coral reefs and mangrove are among the tropical features.

3. The shoreline of the Yellow Sea, with Shanghai as the centre, is sandy, and comprises the deltas of the Yangtze River and the ancient Yelllow River, but it has few good natural harbours. Navigation of the Yangtze River into the hinterland is well developed. The flow of the Yangtze River is so powerful that river water reaches 300 km eastward into the sea.

4. The western shoreline of Taiwan, with Gaoxiong as the centre, is sandy and bordered by lagoons, while the eastern side faces the stormy Pacific Ocean, and comprises the gulfs at the northern and southern ends offer good conditions.

The database of shorelines comprises chains made up of dots and arc lines, where dots refer to the seaport cities and the arc lines refer to the intervening shorelines. Basic data items for each seaport include population, harbour conditions, grade of facilities, handling capacity, input and output of goods and the composition of commodity flows, passenger transport capacity, water and electricity supply and so on. Basic data items for the shoreline arcs may include the length of the shoreline, a classification of its nature, existing landuses (such as saltpans, enclosed tidelands for cultivation or a tourist site), environmental engineering condition and so on.

NETWORK PATTERNS IN THE HINTERLAND

China has approximately 6,686 small towns (based on figures for 1984), 2,738 county-level cities and 444 big cities. All of these are connected with the eastern coastal cities via a variety of networks such as waterways, railroads, highways, post and telecommunications. They have thus entered the global cycle of trade, commercial and cultural exchanges. As a result, they could be considered, from the perspective of the global database, as sub-systems dependent upon the aspect of the seaport cities.

The town system and traffic networks of the Chinese hinterland can be grouped into four models, described in the following sections.

The Dendritic pattern

The main course of the Yangtze River, with Shanghai harbour as the terminus, could be regarded as the most typical feature. Its central axis starts along the main course and runs through the cities of Nanjing, Wuhan and Chongqing to Dukou. Shanghai and these large cities are linked to a number of medium-sized cities in individual sub-classes, while those cities are in turn connected with many small towns.

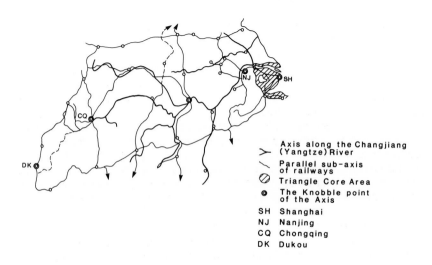

Axis along the Changjiang (Yangtze) River
Parallel sub-axis of railways
Triangle Core Area
The Knobble point of the Axis
SH Shanghai
NJ Nanjing
CQ Chongqing
DK Dukou

Figure 1: The Dendritic Pattern of the Shanghai Network

These large cities are the hubs of the economy, politics, culture and communication in the regions. Within the hinterland of each hub, its material and information flows, collection and distribution the industrial and agricultural products, trade and scientific and technological exchanges, are controlled in a concentrated way. The two banks of the main river resemble two opposing shorelines, along which industrial bases, commercial centres and river cargo traffic flourish. Since water transport in the Yangtze basin is not fully developed, two trunk railroads have been laid parallel to the river in order to speed up transport to and from outlying towns. In the southern part of the

Yangtze River Basin, the railroad ties together the provincial capitals, such as Hangzhou, Nanchang, Changsha, Quiyang and Kunming; in the northern part, it connects the cities of Lianyungang, Xuzhou, Kaifeng, Zhengzhou, Xian, Lanzhou, Xining, even stretching as far as Urumuqi. The two parallel railroads serve a dual purpose: on the one hand, with respect to the Yangtze River, they function as tributaries, for they help to reduce loads and speed up transport; on the other hand, with respect to the provincial state capital cities, they are considered as aids to the expansion of tributary areas or to the intensification of the collection and distribution of goods.

The Radial Arc Pattern

The two metropolises, Beijing and Tianjin, are the core within the Bohai circle and cities such as Dalian, Yingkou, Jinzhou, Qinhuangdao, Tangshan, Tianjin, Dezhou, Jinan, Zibo, Dongying, Weifang and Yantai constitute the inner ring. They have convenient communications both by sea and on land, tapping a vast hinterland in the northern and north-eastern China Plain, which provides the largest area in China of commercial cotton and grain production, livestock and forests, the largest industrial centres in China for coal mining, oil extraction and iron and steel manufacture. Moreover, the area within the circle has also the most concentrated railroad network in China and the largest harbour for the export of coal and petroleum.

The circle has four radial lines: the first line is the line Tianjin-Beijing-Datong; the second, Dalian-Shenyang-Changchun-Harbin; the third, Jinzhou-Tongliao-Baicheng-Qiqihar-Nenjiang-Mohe; and the fourth, Beijing-Shijiazhuang-Tiyuan and Xi'an. Of these lines, the first and second are major axes with double track railroads. Further plans are being made to build highways and to develop canals to strengthen transport along these two axes.

In addition, the circle has four unclosed railroad rings. The first ring, noted above, is the innermost. The second ring is made up of cities, such as Dandong-Benxi-Shenyang-Fuxin, Chaoyang-Chengde-Beijing-Zhangjiakou-Datong-Taiyuan-Changzhi-Jiaozuo-Xinxiang-Heze-Jining-Shichao. The most important Chinese bases for coal, iron and steel run through it.

207

The third ring is made up of two lines in north-east China. It goes from Yanji-Jilin-Changchun-Baicheng-Ulanhot-Yinshi. In northern China, it links Hohhot-Dongsheng-Yulin-Yanan-Tongchuan-Xi'an, but this line is not yet connected from within the boundaries of Inner Mongolia to Dongsheng and Yuan in Shanxi Province. Its eastern end is linked to Qingjin Harbour in Korea.

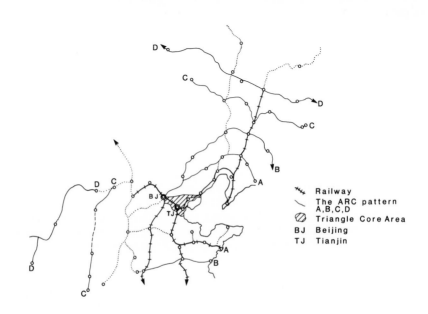

Figure 2: The Radial Arc Pattern around the Bohai Circle

The fourth or outermost ring refers to the combination of cities, such as Suifenhe-Mudanjiang-Harbin-Daqing-Qiqihar-Hailar-Manzhouli. Its eastern and western ends are both linked with the Soviet Union, its western part is in Inner Mongolia and links the cities of Hohhot, Bastou, Wuhei, Shizuishen, Yinchuan and Lanzhou.

In this network structured by radial lines and ring-arc segments, cities, such as Beijing, Shenyang, Harbin, Jinan, Zhengzhou and Xi'an form both the key pivots in the sub-class and the centres of history, politics and economy.

The truncated pattern

The 'Golden Triangle' formed by Guangzhou, Hongkong and Macao plans a pivotal role for the fan-shaped south-east coast zone of China. Its hinterland is rather small, the network of communications does not reach very far, and it has a well developed export orientated economy. Along the Dongjiang River, it reaches Shenzhen, Shantou and Xiamen, in the special economic zones. Along the Beijing River, and the Beijing-Guangzhou Railroad, it goes through Qujiang, interlinking Hengyang and Ganzhou, which in turn draw Xiangnan (southern Hunan) and Gannan (Southern Jiangxi), two special economic zones, into the third level.

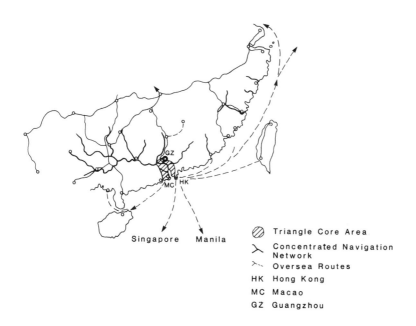

Singapore   Manila

⊘ Triangle Core Area
⋏ Concentrated Navigation Network
⋋⋅⋅ Oversea Routes
HK Hong Kong
MC Macao
GZ Guangzhou

<u>Figure 3</u>: The Truncated Pattern of the Guangzhou Network

The zone extends far along the Xijiang River, through Wuzhou, Liuzhou, Guiyang and Kunming, and there is a strong tendency for it to capture the hinterland of the upper and middle reaches of the Yangtze River basin, and particularly the output of raw materials, such as ferrous and non-ferrous metals, and agricultural and animal products.

Its export-orientated economy is the most distinctive feature of the Guangzhou model. It greatly attracts foreign funds and technology through the free port. It also offers facilities for the processing of imported materials that will be sold back in the world market. Its foreland is far more extensive and active that its hinterland. To the east is Taiwan, whose economy is highly developed and to the west is Hainan, where great economic potential exists and which will soon become a new special economic area. Furthermore, international sea lanes fan out to link it closely with the most prosperous Asian countries such as Japan, Korea, Thailand and Singapore. Great inputs and outputs make its economy full of vitality. Being one of the centres of global economic activities, Guangzhon is also a centre and source for overseas Chinese activities.

The enclosed circle model

The model often occurs in the islands where sea transport is well-developed. Generally it is limited in scope but it has enormous capacity for change and rapid development. For example, Hainan began development as a number of seaport cities and towns with navigable circular links, which were then replaced by highways and railroads, and ended with high-speed central lines through the mountains and deserts, modern bridges linking the other islands and the mainland.

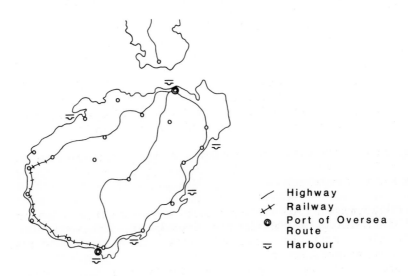

Figure 4: The 'Closed Circle' Pattern of Hainan Island

These various patterns are evidently restricted by the geographical environment and shaped in co-ordination with the network of waterway systems. The dendritic pattern, for example, is often based on water-transport and well-developed river basins; the radial-arc pattern always has a large lake or gulf as the core, while its hinterland belongs to arid or semi-arid plains or plateaus. The enclosed circle pattern, such as the Guangzhou model, is blocked by parallel mountain ranges along the seashore, its hinterland is narrow and its river system short, but there are numerous coastal islands and flourishing sea transport.

Thus it can be seen that these models objectively exist and develop in an orderly fashion. It has a global nature in line with location theory in geography. As a result, it has great value with reference to the establishment of a global database of shorelines.

BELTS OF ACCESSIBILITY

In view of imbalances in regional development and understanding, minimum items of basic data at various levels should be taken into account for the global database, as well as some additional items suitable for distinguishing belts. In essence, when rates of use of data items are considered, unnecessary increases in storage may be avoided. With shorelines as the baseline, hinterland and foreland are divided into several belts in line with considerations of accessibility. A general stipulation of the geographical density and precision of data should be made with reference to international norms, which were set for map compilation at a scale of 1:1m, and also by the World Meteorological Organisation for station networks. This is necessary for construction of global databases, and regional pilot projects should be undertaken to check and revise such international agreements.

Currently China can acquire a fairly rich harvest of statistical data. At county level, about 180 items can be obtained, including:

- Geographical base - co-ordinates, geographical names, settlements, topography and drainage systems.
- Natural resources - climate, water, land, sea, minerals, biology and tourism.
- Socio-economy - population, traffic and transport, factories, agriculture, fisheries, animal husbandry, forestry and administrative divisions.

- Eco-environment - pollution, natural calamities, land deterioration and nature conservation.

These items are available from original sources with spatial coding whose mode and structure are well adapted to a polygon-based approach. If agreement is reached on a pilot project for the global database, China will be able, given all the work accomplished, such as compilation of detailed classification and coding system tables, the design of the nation-wide map projection system, controlling grids and transfer standards, a database through a micro-index for topographic maps, thematic maps and aerial and Landsat images, as well as a database for the oceanographic environment and resource documentation since the year 1850, to meet all the needs for data items equivalent to those of the international maps at 1:1m or 1:2.5m scales and to handle the requirements by computer-aided cartography.

In terms of the design and pilot study for the global database, the crux lies in the principals and standards defined for screening or combining data items in order to enhance their practical value and their rate of utilization, and at the same time, to reflect fully their resource and environmental characteristics and regional differences in developments (while not neglecting differences in survey and investigation).

Again, to take China as an example, three belts of hinterland could be defined from east to west:

1) The eastern coastal belt. It needs particularly to show the structure of the export-orientated economy, with emphasis on seaports and sea transport, open cities and special economic zones, tourist resources and facilities and updating of data items. Notice should also be taken of thermal power stations, heavy chemical bases, electronic and other light industries, which embody a rather high degree of regional development, and land reclamation, canals, municipal water supply and modern environmental engineering projects.

2) The central belt. Stress is put on featuring resource - model states of agriculture, forestry, energy, heavy chemical bases, such as grain, oil, cotton, hemp, coal and petroleum of the export commodities, hydro-power, thermal power and natural gas of the energy supply, and of frequent natural calamities of drought, flood, wind, sand, hail, salinization, water and soil loss, which affect the stable

212

yield of agriculture, landslides, and mud flows which threaten the security of traffic and the working of cities.

3) The western belt. Special interest is given to the weakness of the eco-environment caused by water-shortages, low carrying capacity for both humans and livestock, the instability of agriculture and animal husbandry, the scarcity of forest and pasture land, and the low elemental biomass, but in this belt there is also great potential for gold and other minerals, and geo-thermal, solar and wind energy.

The three longitudinal belts mentioned above differ greatly owing to their distances from the shoreline, and the impact of the monsoon climate intensifying the differences in aridity as a result in large-scale disasters.

The Chinese maritime areas facing the Pacific could also be divided into four belts:

1) The offshore islands. Within 100 km of the sea, there are about 6,500 offshore islands, 90% of which are located on the South and East Seas south of Shanghai. Provinces are established for each of the two big islands, Taiwan (35,780 sq. km) and Hainan (32,300 sq. km), each with a coast line of more than 1,500 km. Counties are set up on the islands of Chongpeng, Zhoushan, Pingtan, Nanao, Penghu and Jinmen. Hongkong, Macao and Xiamen comprise groups of islands.

2) The shallow sea. Adjoining the continent and islands, the area of shallow sea (with a depth of less than 20 m at the low tide line) is a base for oceanic-ecological agriculture, such as breeding and fishing, and also gold and tin. Harbour construction and engineering projects are greatly influenced by the sea and turbidity currents, by tides and storms, as well as by coral reefs and mangrove swamps.

3) The continental shelf. With the development of petroleum and gas fields and the discovery of mining deposits, more and more knowledge has been gained of the geological structure of the sea bed and of the continental shelf with water depths of less than 200m. Systematic observations have also been made for monitoring and tracing fish migrations, ocean currents, sea ice and of the chemical composition of the water.

4) The ocean basin. By prospecting for ferro-manganese modules and other minerals, by an increase in deep-drilling and by discoveries such as the El Nino phenomenon and deep volcanoes, thermal water and biomass, the volume of data on the ocean basin is being greatly increased.

CONCLUSION

In addition to the existing polygon and raster bases of the Global Database, the writer suggests that a vector database, with shorelines as a baseline, be designed. Such a database would not only be a necessary supplement, but also a new development in favour of the analysis of geographical location and the use of a realistic base of the data sources.

The database envisaged is based on dot items located by the existing geographical coding in a multi-level network structure. The 'dot' position is the base point of the seaports, cities or islands. The network is formed by traffic lines, such as navigable rivers, railroads, highways and air routes.

The hinterland and the sea area are divided into belts according to their accessibility from the shoreline. Standards of density and precision for the basic data items and the dot net are set so as to improve the rate of utilisation of data items and to mirror accurately the imbalences in regional development research.

From a consideration of the reality of the natural resources and the geographical environment of China, the writer draws attention to information services for management and decision-making for giving priority to the development of the coastal belt, the opening up of coastal cities and the development of an export-oriented economy, thus providing an environmental background for investment by international co-operation and enterprises. Such an experimental programme will obtain support from Chinese governmental authorities.

The writer noticed in addition that the basic concept of coastal data chains, hinterland models and continental belts with shorelines as the baseline, may be used as a basis for the design of the global database.

Experts from other countries throughout the world are invited to join in a pilot project in China. We greatly hope that the project will be listed as one of the case studies for the global database of shorelines in an effort to promote regional co-operation in South-east Asia and around the Pacific.

REFERENCES

Chen Shupeng, 1987. 'The development and application of remote sensing information in China'. Selections from the Bulletin of the Chinese Academy of Sciences, 3, 47-53.

Chen Shupeng, 1987. 'The development and application of geographic information systems in China'. Asian Geographer, 6(2), 1-7.

Chen Tian, 1987. 'A preliminary analysis of the system of influence regions of China's urban economy'. Acta Geographica Sinica, 42(4), 308-318. (Abstract in English).

Lu Dadao, 1987. 'The macrostrategy of regional development in China'. Acta Geographica Sinica, 42(2), 97-105. (Abstract in English).

Marble, Duane F., 1987. 'Design and implementation of a master spatial data indexing system: an international case'. Proceedings, International Workshop on GIS, Beijing 1987 (LREIS). 1-14.

State Population Census of China, Institute of Geography, Chinese Academy of Science and State Commission of China, 1987. The Population Atlas of China. The Oxford Press. (English edition).

Zheng Hongyi and Gu Chaolin, 1987. 'A study of the coastal urban system in China'. Journal of Natural Resources, 2(3), 213-228. (Abstract in English).

GLOBAL DATABASES: A NOAA EXPERIENCE

David M. Clark and John J. Kineman

INTRODUCTION

The National Oceanic and Atmospheric Administration (NOAA) was established in 1970 as part of the United States Department of Commerce. The purpose of forming NOAA was to create a civil center of strength for expanding the effective and rational use of ocean resources, for monitoring and predicting conditions in the atmosphere, oceans, and space, and for exploring the consequences of natural and manmade environmental change. Since its inception, NOAA's role in environmental science has gradually evolved and strengthened, and presently covers a wide range of environmental science from the core of the Earth to the surface of the sun.

Because NOAA is involved in such a wide spectrum of Earth related science, the development of diverse environmental data bases has naturally been required in support of its mission to monitor, research, assess, evaluate, analyze and predict our natural environment. It was recognized long ago that these tasks could not be effectively accomplished for the United States without the compilation of supporting global data bases. Therefore, NOAA has addressed the problems of global data bases since its formation.

NOAA'S OPERATIONAL STRUCTURE

NOAA's strength as a scientific agency is due, in part, to its diverse make-up. There are five major operational components that make up NOAA. The National Ocean Service (NOS), the U.S. government's oldest scientific and technical organization, surveys and charts the rivers and coasts of the United States, and also the oceans of the world. The National Marine Fisheries Service (NMFS) supports the commercial fishing of United States waters by establishing sound fishery management and research. NOAA's Office of Oceanic and Atmospheric Research (OAR) conducts environmental research at numerous laboratories, and

216

supports university research on national and global problems of the oceans and atmosphere. The National Weather Service (NWS) monitors and predicts the weather and issues warnings which are vital for the protection of life and property. Finally, the National Environmental Satellite, Data and Information Service (NESDIS) operates the U.S. civilian operational satellite system and the national environmental data centers.

Each of the major components of NOAA generates large quantities of environmental data. NWS's observational network provides tens of thousands of global weather observations in order to formulate daily weather predictions. NOS surveys of the inland, coastal and ocean waters generate a significant amount of bathymetry, bottom characteristics, and navigational hazards data. In addition, NOS maintains the nation's geodetic reference network which requires the collection of land and satellite data. NMFS collects information on the yields of the U.S. coastal fishery, the status of marine mammal populations and other information affecting the oceans' living resources. OAR collects a wide range of environmental data related to their research. Examples of the types of data collected include global baseline measurements of atmospheric carbon dioxide, space environment (upper atmosphere), ozone, and acid rain. NESDIS operates two satellite systems, the geostationary and the polar orbiters. There is at least one each in operation at any one time, and ideally two. This results in an enormous amount of satellite data.

NOAA'S ENVIRONMENTAL DATA CENTRES

NESDIS operates three environmental data centers for NOAA. In addition to the observational data generated by NOAA's operational components, much data are compiled from numerous external sources and used by these operational components. As an example, NWS uses various observational data from other U.S. federal, state, and local sources and from foreign countries to make their daily weather predictions. After these data are used by the operational component, both the NOAA data and the acquired data are often sent to one of the NOAA environmental data centers for archival and subsequent retrospective use by the scientific community. In addition to these data, the data centers often compile other data, which are not used operationally by NOAA components, to enhance the data base. This additional compilation of data is usually a result of an interagency or international agreement, project, or program, and the data are from numerous national and international sources. Ultimately, this compilation of disparate data sets makes the resulting final data base much more comprehensive and thus more useful to the scientific community. This is truly a case of the sum being better than the parts. The following description of each of the data centers illustrates the amount and breath of the data bases at the National Centers.

National Climatic Data Center

Located in Ashville, North Carolina, the National Climatic Data Center (NCDC) is responsible for collecting, archiving and publishing data from national observational networks and environmental satellites that have enduring value to the United States and are sufficient to describe the climate of the United States. It also archives data collected through international agreements and under the responsibilities as a World Meteorological Center and World Data Center - A (Meteorology). The Center is also charged with the responsibility to disseminate or furnish information to users through routinely scheduled publications or by extracting microfilmed records, digital data files, etc., in response to unique requests.

NCDC annually receives, processes, and archives over 30 million conventional meteorological observations comprising surface, marine, upper air and solar radiation data. Data are gathered from the National Weather Service, NOAA's satellite programs, military services, the Global Telecommunications System, and other national and international sources to provide a national climate data base in digital, analog, microfilm, photo imagery, and manuscript forms. NCDC provides data summaries and related products to a large and diverse user community. The data and publications are used by planners, designers, engineers, lawyers, academic groups, government agencies and the general public.

National Oceanographic Data Center

The National Oceanographic Data Center (NODC) is located in Washington D.C. NODC develops and maintains a national marine environmental data base, including acquisition, processing, storage and retrieval of marine data and information generated by domestic and foreign activities. NODC provides products and information derived from these data to the federal, state, academic and international marine science community; manages and operates the World

Data Center-A (Oceanography); maintains liaison with federal, state and industrial oceanographers, and provides data management services, as requested, for various marine programs.

In addition to the data acquired from NOAA and other federal agencies, a large volume of data is acquired through international exchange agreements. Data holdings at the end of 1987 include over 1,610,000 bathytherm-ographs, sea-surface to bottom or near bottom records from 860,000 stations containing temperature, salinity, and in many instances, nutrient chemistry data; 18,000,000 surface and selected subsurface current measurements; and 400,000 surface temperature and salinity records. Data from automated ocean buoys include more than 16,500,000 records. Holdings also include more than 7,000 other automated data sets containing approximately 15,000,000 records from special projects or surveys such as the Marine Ecosystems Analysis Program. Measurements of ocean temperature, salinity, currents, waves, nutrient and pollutant chemicals, and marine biota are the primary types of data managed by NODC.

National Geophysical Data Center

The National Geophysical Data Center (NGDC), located in Boulder, Colorado, conducts a data and information service in all scientific and technical areas involving solid earth geophysics, glaciology (snow and ice), marine geology and geophysics, and solar-terrestrial physics. The scientific specialities treated include seismology, geomagnetism, gravimetry, earth tides, crustal movement, geothermics, marine geology and geophysics, glaciology, ionospheric phenomena, solar activity, and related areas. The services are provided for scientific, technical and lay users in government agencies, universities, and the private sector in the U.S. and their counterparts in foreign countries.

The Center prepares systematic and special data products and performs data-related research studies to enhance the utility of service to the users. NGDC performs all functions related to data acquisition, archiving, retrieval, indexing, quality assessments, evaluation, synthesis, dissemination, and publication. NGDC also operates the World Data Center-A for its respective scientific areas and performs necessary liaison with other NOAA components and with national and foreign contributors and users of data and information. Data holdings at the end of 1987 included well over 300 data sets, some of which

are very large. For example, NGDC has microfilmed and
archived over 2,500,000 magnetograms and 50,000,000
ionograms; it holds marine geophysical data collected on
nearly 11,000,000 miles of ship tracks and aeromagnetic
survey tracks consisting of 35,000,000 observations.

NESDIS Environmental Data Holdings, the Challenge

In a study of the present and future data holdings of the
NESDIS Data Centers (NOAANET Technical Working Group,
1986), the true magnitude of the "data explosion" was made
apparent. The current (1986) volume of digital data at the
data centers amounted to 63,159 gigabytes (GB), and the
average size of each data base is 290 GB. The annual
projected growth for all the Data Centers is 15,514 GB.
This projects that in 1998, the total volume of data in the
NESDIS Data Centers will be 264,846 GB with the average
size of a data base to be 963 GB. Many of these data bases
are global in nature. Of course, one must realize that the
numbers are skewed by the vast amount of satellite data
that will be a result of the Polar Platform and the Earth
Observation System.

NGDC'S GLOBAL DATABASE EXPERIENCE

Starting in the mid-1970's, NGDC was concerned with the
efficient compilation, inventorying and retrieval of
digital global data. Our experience was somewhat different
than most other Earth science organizations since our data
sources were very numerous and ranged from technologically
sophisticated to very simple. This resulted in the data
being in numerous and difficult formats. Many were very
poorly documented and many had magnetic tape "read" errors
in addition to data errors. The preponderance of data
sources and the sheer amount of data exacerbated the
situation. The situation today has not greatly improved.
These problems must be recognized in any project-oriented
compilation of global data bases, for example, the
International Council of Scientific Union's (ICSU)
International Geosphere - Biosphere Program (ICSU, 1986;
NRC, 1986).

NGDC response to the above problems was to begin a series
of experiments with data management systems. The results
of two are described below. The two data bases discussed
represent only a small fraction of the data archived at
NGDC.

Geophysical Data System

The Geophysical Data System (GEODAS) was developed at NGDC starting in 1977 (Hittelman and Metzger, 1983). GEODAS is a computer system that processes underway marine geophysical data (tracklines of bathymetry, gravity and magnetics) into a data base with a common format and provides inventory and data retrieval capabilities.

The inventory portion of GEODAS allows searches on specific geographic areas and the result is a summary of the marine geophysical data in the area. The output is broken down by institution, legs (individual surveys), type of data found in the search for the area, and the number of digital records. Table 1 is a search on the entire world and is a summary of the total content of the data base. The GEODAS data base contains 26,000,000 observations and represents 11,000,000 miles of ship tracks.

In addition to the listing of the data in the search area, an option allows the plotting of an inventory map of the data in the selected area. Figure 1 is a "quick look" plot of the contents of the entire GEODAS data base.

After the inventory search, a decision is made as to whether the data are appropriate for the requester's needs. If so, the system will generate the necessary archival magnetic tape numbers on which the data are located, and proceeds to select and output the data onto a magnetic tape.

In this brief outline of GEODAS, it is apparent that it is a powerful system and has many of the desirable characteristics needed for global data systems. The major drawback of the system is that all of the data must be in a common format in order fully to utilize the system.

More recently, NGDC initiated the compilation of a global aeromagnetics data base. This multi-format survey data base was the subject of a prototype inventory development using a Geographical Information System (GIS). The complete aeromagnetic database contains 37 million observations from 286 surveys, covering 3 million flight line miles. The information is stored on 370 computer tapes holding 3 gigabytes of data.

221

Total Holdings   *** GEODAS SEARCH ***   88/03/31

institution	legs	geophysical data summary in nautical miles				seismics	sscan/refrac	dig recs
		navigation	bathymetry	magnetics	gravity			
01 LAMONT (LDGO)	542	2252443.0	2131120.5	1898047.1	1675713.1	1739225.2	284806.8	3916382
02 WOODS HOLE O.I.	186	651138.3	599863.2	362671.7	326810.7	269087.3	19662.7	1241890
03 NOAA	130	722885.2	704110.2	671093.9	484900.7	254596.3	8198.3	779244
04 US ARMY	12	3836.7		0.0	0.0	3836.7	0.0	0
05 NEW ZEALAND	42	62290.2	26345.4	56158.1	17306.5	0.0	0.0	250369
06 US GEOL. SURVEY	200	370467.8	205633.7	159309.1	168710.7	117110.6	12460.7	2421005
07 OREGON ST. UNIV	69	163069.4	151080.0	115533.6	106283.1	59511.8	27493.1	325658
08 HAWAII INST GEO	149	535652.2	506281.1	334275.6	366564.0	383999.0	86216.9	2584345
09 US NAVY	292	1110705.5	895137.6	465941.7	77777.9	675036.9	0.0	3329266
10 UNIV OF TEXAS	19	50695.8	41982.6	41700.6	0.0	48284.4	0.0	97546
11 RICE UNIV.	2	7680.6	7680.6		0.0	0.0	0.0	3558
12 CANADA	109	520001.7	491149.0	35729.3	4478.6	0.0	0.0	672353
13 UNIV OF CONN.	5	5308.4	3884.0	0.0	5306.9	0.0	0.0	3424
14 U.MIAMI (RSMAS)	21	46531.6		41784.0	0.0	30917.0	0.0	0
15 SCRIPPS INST.OC	508	1927843.1	1698118.1	1382469.7	71212.8	682439.1	0.0	4137718
16 CHINA	1	2142.5	2008.1	39129.0	2142.5	0.0	0.0	645
17 U RHODE ISLAND	33	115655.5	111401.5		0.0	32282.0	0.0	492465
18 DUKE UNIVERSITY	1	3381.0	3381.0		0.0	0.0	0.0	0
19 UNITED KINGDOM	45	178940.4	169549.2	133426.2	121465.5	0.0	0.0	539692
20 U.WASHINGTON	9	12768.2	8221.0	0.0	0.0	4925.4	0.0	13128
22 WESTERN GEOPHY.	1	440.8	440.8	0.0	0.0	440.8	0.0	0
23 TEXAS A+M UNIV.	16	25105.5	14239.5	8969.0	0.0	21780.8	0.0	57717
24 AUSTRALIA	5	48449.8	21262.9	44580.8	9243.3	5959.3	0.0	311498
25 MONACO	1	5959.3	0.0	0.0	0.0	0.0	0.0	0
29 USSR	22	247936.2	219536.1	0.0	188447.8	32426.8	0.0	77555
35 DEFENSE MAP.AG.	86	376728.6	374556.3	0.0	0.0	0.0	0.0	703580
56 JAPAN	145	743433.1	659359.2	365766.2	476142.9	0.0	0.0	618435
58 NETHERLANDS	1	715.3	715.3	715.3	715.3	0.0	0.0	0
60 MIN MANAG SERV	22	85713.2	84266.4	0.0	0.0	85713.2	69041.3	670918
63 ISRAEL	1	437.9	0.0	0.0	0.0	437.9	0.0	0
67 FRANCE	168	415363.6	374965.1	268502.2	151171.5	0.0	0.0	2705144
71 SOUTH AFRICA	16	47252.4	40578.6	44936.8	0.0	0.0	0.0	57993
77 INT. GRAV. BUR	9	59762.0	58993.3	0.0	59751.6	0.0	0.0	30171
84 NEW CALEDONIA	15	49353.7	47784.0	37831.0	28448.9	0.0	0.0	70846
grand totals	2883	10850087.0	9653644.0	6508571.0	4342594.5	4448012.0	507879.8	26112545

Table 1: Inventory listing of the entire GEODAS data base.

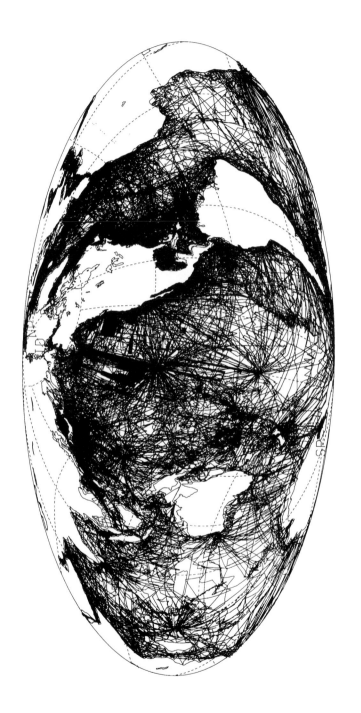

Figure 1: Global inventory plot of the contents of GEODAS.

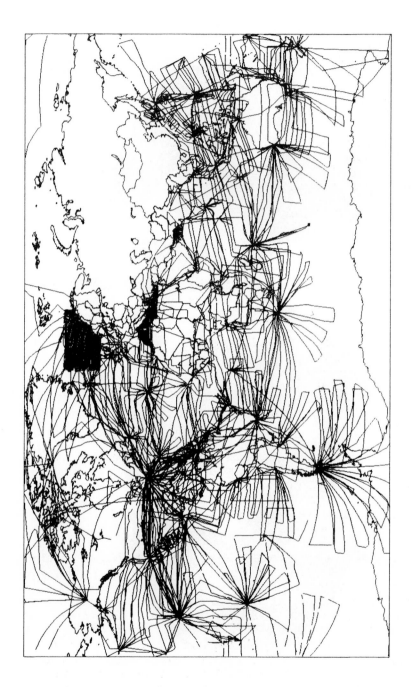

Figure 2: Global aeromagnetic flight lines.

The flight line navigation data were sampled at a ratio of
about 100 to 1 to produce a global inventory of the flight
paths. The generalization procedures used a modified triad
algorithm to reduce the number of navigation points. A
portion of this inventory - the Project Magnet data base --
is plotted in Figure 2, which represents less than a
quarter of the inventory.

The attribute capabilities of the system were used to
provide statistical and labeling information, as well as to
provide Boolean search and retrieval functions on flight
line data. Table 2 shows 9 of the 24 variables created in
the attribute file.

KEY   DESCRIPTOR

FLT_LINE   SURVEY FLIGHT LINE IDENTIFIER
CREAT_DATE   GENERALIZED FLIGHT LINE CREATION DATE
MEAN_ELEV   MEAN ELEVATION FOR SURVEY FLIGHT LINE
MEAN_MAG   MEAN TOTAL MAGNETIC FIELD FOR THE FLIGHT LINE
STDEV_MAG   STANDARD DEVIATION OF THE MAGNETIC FIELD
MIN_MAG   MIN. MAGNETIC FIELD VALUE FOR SURVEY FLIGHT LINE
MAX_MAG   MAX. MAGNETIC FIELD VALUE FOR SURVEY FLIGHT LINE
SAMPLES   NUMBER OF SAMPLE POINTS FOR FLIGHT LINE ARCHIVED
THATATTR   LENGTH

Table 2. Examples of attributes in the aeromagnetics
          flight line inventory

By structuring an inventory in this manner, we have
available the normal GIS capabilities for geographic
searching and windowing, plus the ability to search and
select by attribute. For example, Figure 3 shows a sample
retrieval by Boolean search for flight lines with a high
average aeromagnetic total-field strength. As one would
expect, flight lines are retrieved in the vicinity of the
geomagnetic poles.

This project was successful in demonstrating the potential
of using a GIS for a sophisticated inventory system, but
not in making the inventory operational. The missing
elements were (1) a high-level language interface to set up
smooth and friendly operations for non-technical users, and
(2) speed of retrieval, which is sacrificed for analytical
capabilities in a GIS. Variations of the GIS concept,
streamlined functions, and perhaps integration with other
methods, could solve these problems. An important point to
stress, however, is that by structuring data for GIS,

little time is lost in systems development and the entire inventory can be transferred with ease as systems improve.

Global data bases will grow to such size in the near future that even summary and inventory information will require special-purpose, spatial display systems, such as demonstrated in this global aeromagnetics inventory project.

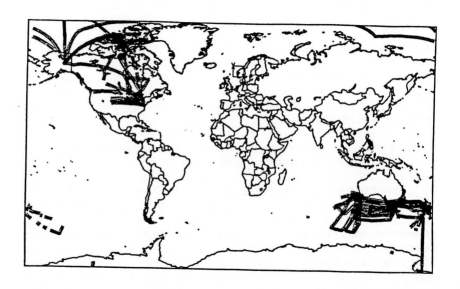

Figure 3: Search for flight lines with high average aeromagnetic total-field strength.

FUTURE CONSIDERATIONS

NGDC has begun to develop plans to integrate existing and future programs into the NOAA Climate and Global Change Program. Since NGDC is a national and international data center, the development of global data bases and the data management systems to utilize them is a high priority.

INTEGRATED GEOGRAPHIC INFORMATION SYSTEM/IMAGE PROCESSING
SYSTEM

NGDC became involved with Geographic Information Systems
technology in 1985 with the acquisition of the Department
of Interior's MOSS/MAPS family of software. This system
was used for research and development of GIS applications
in graphical inventories, environmental mapping, and data
quality control. We are now convinced that the
evolutionary descendants of present-day GIS, integrated
with Data Base Management Systems, statistical graphics,
Image Processing Systems and Artificial Intelligence, are
inevitably linked to the future of data-dependent
applications in global studies (Hastings and Moll, 1986;
Kineman and Clark, in press). GIS will be important for
data management applications as well as for verifying
models through data-model intercomparison on time-dependent
spatial dimensions. Furthermore, the potential of GIS-like
analysis for creating virtual representations of systems
characteristics, and performing near real-time "what-if"
modeling is rapidly becoming feasible and may soon result
in sophisticated ways of representing systems behavior for
hypothesis testing.

Adopting GIS methods for Global Studies

GIS have been primarily designed for resource management
and regional planning applications. The use of such
systems for Global Change studies, however, implies certain
requirements that are not always standard in GIS software.
Global data management in particular, places unique demands
on these systems. It is clear that data and systems will
have to be designed to work together. Based on our
experience, we have identified those essential GIS
functions needed for global studies:

- Ability to work with global (360 degrees) latitude /
  longitude coordinates, as well as projected coordinates
- Complete range of cartographic projection capabilities
- Ability to input random and gridded point data for large
  geographic areas (up to global)
- Ability to convert random or gridded data to different
  grids using a variety of algorithms (in various
  projections) and export these as new data sets
- Ability to produce contours from gridded data
- Ability to edit vector and raster data using
  DBMS/spreadsheet algorithms and/or AI procedures

227

- Full functionality of "standard" GIS functions, such as Overlay, Merge, Statistics, Reports, Search by attributes, etc.
- Cartographic output, including shade and fill, attribute placement, contour labeling, legends, annotation, scaling, etc.
- Conversions for all major data formats, for both input and output
- Integration with Image Processing Systems
- Integration with Data Base Management Systems
- Integration with Statistical and Statistical Graphics Systems
- Integration with Expert Systems and Artificial Intelligence

DEVELOPING A GLOBAL ENVIRONMENTAL DIGITAL ATLAS

The integration of existing data sets into an easily used digital "atlas" for evaluation purposes is an essential stage in defining the status, design and development of data for future synthesis efforts (Kineman et al., 1986). Furthermore, such a product would find immediate use in global modeling and descriptive studies, as well as education and general public interest. The atlas should be distributed on CD-ROM and published in book form. This product would contain global digital reference data, including gridded topography and linear boundary data, as well as a variety of thematic data related to the Earth's environment, systems, and resources. The data would be integrated into a compatible form for easy use by software that is readily available for display and geographic analysis. Selection of data for the "atlas" will be based on four criteria: (1) global coverage, (2) current public domain availability in digital form, (3) potential usefulness for modeling global change, including geographic reference, and (4) interdisciplinary significance for living Earth systems.

The initial compilation would be accomplished relatively quickly using only EXISTING data. The primary purpose of this compilation will be to stimulate an assessment of the present status of digital global data sets in terms of their usefulness and overall completeness for anticipated needs. By distributing these data in an integrated and accessible form (CD-ROM) with full documentation and extraction software, a community-wide evaluation can take place while the opportunity for creative applications will be maximized. Publication and distribution will result in useful feedback, which will assist in planning an overall program for contemporary data bases.

Time scale and thematic variables

The initial atlas project would involve quality control of the US Navy's 10 minute elevation and terrain characteristics data (available through NGDC) as well as the addition of available surface environmental data (mostly at 1/2 to 1 degree resolution) such as soil classifications and chemistry, terrain and ground cover classifications, surface temperatures, historical rainfall averages, etc. The data sets can be divided into "long-term reference data," which do not change rapidly, and "thematic reference data" which may have to be updated periodically. The data can be arranged according to time variability, as indicated below:

- Reference data (Long Term)

    - Elevation and bathymetry data, merged from 10' and 5' data
    - Terrain characteristics (number and direction of ridges, terrain classifications)
    - WDB-II boundary files
    - Coastal elevation and bathymetric contours
    - Geophysical fields (e.g. gravity and magnetics)

- Thematic data (Annual to Decadal)

    - Natural hazards (e.g. earthquakes, volcanoes, tsunamis)
    - Soils classification (dominant, associated, slope, texture, phase)
    - Soil Chemistry (nitrogen, carbon, etc.)
    - Ecosystem and ground cover classifications
    - Average annual land and ocean surface temperature
    - Hydrology (surface, groundwater, etc.)
    - Average annual rainfall and insolation
    - Agricultural, land use, and urbanization data
    - Vegetation index averages from AVHRR 16 km global area coverage (GAC)
    - Sea height and ocean flux averages
    - Permanent ice thickness
    - Global energy budgets

- Thematic data (Sub-annual)

    - Aerosols
    - Rainfall and temperature summaries (annual and monthly)
    - Vegetation index summaries (weekly)
    - Insolation, and cloud cover summaries
    - Evapotranspiration
    - Net Primary Production
    - Biogeochemical data

Spatial scale

Since global resource and environmental information systems will ultimately serve as the integration tool for studies that span a wide range of information sources, they will need to be designed to integrate data from multiple levels of remote sensing and direct observations, e.g. satellite, aerial, and low-altitude sampling, and conventional data gathered on the ground. To incorporate these concepts into the atlas project, integration software will allow data to be stored in a hierarchy of grid scales such as:

- 1 degree (most global environmental databases at present)
- 1/2 degree (best resolution of majority of available global environmental data)
- 10 arc-minute (approximately matching 16 km global vegetation index coverage)
- 5 arc-minute (9 km at equator, matching topography data for parts of world)
- 2 arc-minute (approximately matching 4 km AVHRR Global Area Coverage (GAC) data)
- 30-second (approx. 1 km, matching AVHRR Local Area Coverage (LAC) data and reference data bases under development; also matching topography data for parts of the world)
- 3-second (90 m at equator; matching the DMA Digital Terrain Elevation Data)
- 1-second (approx. 30 m; matching Landsat Thematic Mapper data)
- 1/2 second (15 m at equator; approximately matching Spot data)

INTERAGENCY COORDINATION

Finally, in order to coordinate the efforts of NGDC, other NESDIS data centers, and other US Government agencies that are concerned with environmental data, there has been established the Interagency Working Group on Data Management for Global Change (IWGDMGC). Formed in 1987, it initially consisted of representatives of NOAA, the National Science Foundation, National Aeronautics and Space Administration, the U.S. Geological Survey, the U.S. Department of Navy, and the U.S. Department of Energy.

The charge of this working group is to make it as easy as possible for scientists and others to get data appropriate to the study of global change. The goal of the working group is a virtual national data system by 1995 that is consistent across agencies and involves and supports university and other user communities. Current activities of the IWGDMGC are broken down into four areas: a) directories, catalogs, and inventories; b) status of data observation, collection, archiving, and distribution; c) data pricing and policies; and d) international data exchange agreements.

CONCLUSION

NASA's Earth System Sciences Committee summed up the considerations of global data bases and Global Change by stating: "On the basis of our experience, the Earth System Science initiative will founder on the rocks of indifference to data information management unless an aggressive and supportive new approach is taken - beginning now...At the center of a long-term program for the study of Global Change must be the immediate development of an information system for Earth system science designed to facilitate the acquisition, reduction, and analysis of integrated data sets and to make both data and suitably analyzed products readily available for current and future research." (Earth System Sciences Committee, 1988)

REFERENCES

Earth System Sciences Committee, 1988. Earth system science, a closer view. NASA, Washington D.C. 208 p.

Hastings, D.A., and Moll, S.H., 1986. 'Using geographic information systems as an initial approach to artificial intelligence in the geological sciences'. Proceedings, First Rocky Mountain Conference on Artificial Intelligence, Boulder, Colorado, BREIT International, Boulder, 191-200.

Hittelman, A.M. and Metzger, D.R., 1983. 'Marine Geophysics: Database management and supportive graphics'. Computers and Geoscience, 91, 27-33.

ICSU Ad Hoc Planning Group on Global Change, 1986. The International Geosphere-Biosphere Program: a study of global change. Prepared for the 21st ICSU General Assembly, Berne, Sept. 14-19. ICSU, Paris, France. 21 p.

Kineman, J.J. and Clark, D.M., 1987. 'Connecting global science through spatial data and information technology'. Proceedings, International Geographical Information Systems Symposium, Crystal City, VA, 1987 [in press].

Kineman, J., Hastings, D. and Colby, J., 1986. 'Developing global data bases for the environmental sciences'. Proceedings, 20th International Symposium on Remote Sensing of Environment, Nairobi, Kenya, December, 1986.

NOAANET Technical Working Group, 1986. NOAANET functional requirements. National Environmental Satellite, Data and Information Service, Washington D.C. 126 p.

National Research Council Committee for an International Geosphere-Biosphere Program, 1986. Global change in the geosphere-biosphere: initial priorities for an IGBP. National Academy Press, Washington, D.C. 91 p.

INFORMATION ABOUT THE NATURE OF THE USSR AND ITS POSSIBLE USE IN THE INTERNATIONAL GEOSPHERE-BIOSPHERE PROGRAMME

Alexander V. Drozdov

The efficiency of the "Global Change" Programme in its parts directed to the study of changes in the state of the biosphere during a hundred-year span directly depends on the possibilities for a comparative analysis of the accumulated information on the state of the biosphere's components.

A purposeful collection of such information in Russia was initiated at the end of the last century because of the need to make an inventory of resources in vast areas. Under the leadership of V.V. Dokuchaey, systematic studies were undertaken of the state of the soil cover. Forest management included a careful assessment of the state of forests with descriptions of particular sample areas. Still earlier materials of the "Master Surveying", beginning with the eighteenth century, also often contain quite objective and valuable information, from the present-day point of view, at least on some regions.

The work on the inventory of natural resources was particularly intensive in the 1930's. In the studies, comparable methods were used covering nearly the whole country. Particularly consistent were the studies of the structure and productivity of forests, pastures and soils. Studies were carried out not only on economically important objects, but also those areas where possibilities for the use of natural resources were extremely limited. A typical example of such kind of information collected in the course of such studies were schemes of description of forests worked out under the leadership of V.N. Sukachev. The descriptions included the following: an exact location, characteristics of relief (mega, macro, meso, micro and nanoforms), of soil-forming rock, and of humidification conditions, descriptions of soils by horizons, a detailed characteristic of all the stages of vegetation cover with a special description of species composition, thickness, viability, age, height and diameter of stands. Naturally, the volume of descriptions was somewhat different in different studies, but on the whole they were quite comparable with each other.

In the 1930's through the 1950's the results of these studies were published in numerous regional summaries on vegetation. In fact the whole territory of the USSR was covered by highly qualified investigations of this type. In many cases studies of such kinds may be fully reproduced now.

In the same way special information was also accumulated about the soil cover. In the 1960's much attention was paid to the study of the numbers of animals (mammals, birds, soil invertebrates, etc.).

The information on the state of the nature's components, collected for scientific purposes, served as a basis for national economic information services. For instance, in forestry, forest taxation developed based on the typology of forests worked out in the process of research. Depending on the complexity of this work and on the role of regions, forest taxation was done on three levels of precision, mainly by deciphering aerial photographs combined with some field studies. Each forest portion was plotted on forest taxation plans, and its detailed characteristics were entered into special forest taxation books. According to the regulation in force, forest taxation is repeated every ten years.

Similar work was done for inventorying land resources, game animals, etc. For most regions there are published materials giving detailed characteristics of the agrochemical properties of soils.

Beginning with the 1930's, continuous studies have been undertaken in the State Reserves of the USSR on the programme called "Chronicle of Nature". They include counts of animals, phenological observations, repeated careful studies of changes in vegetation within permanent sample areas, etc. This work has continued up to the present (Opyt raboty i zadachi zapovednikov SSSR, 1979). Unfortunately, the sequence of observations in some Reserves is not as detailed as it should be. In some of them part of the materials have been lost. The quality of the collected materials is not homogeneous. Still the analysis which we have just undertaken shows that all this material is of great and diverse value.

234

Practical needs of economy determined the intensive development of the theory and practice of thematic mapping. Much attention was paid to the working out of uniform typological schemes and genetic legends, of the systems of multilayer plotting of several variables on one map, to differentiated mapping of very different components of nature and to the problems of co-ordinating information on maps of difference scales. In the final instance, the uniformity of approaches provided for comparability of maps (of different scale and on different components of nature) compiled for quite different regions of the USSR. At present for the most part all components have been reflected on maps with scales 2,500,000 and over. For many components there are maps of 1:1M and larger. Maps used for economic purposes directly have been made on larger scales. All these materials on individual regions have been brought together and generalised in regional atlases (Kompleksnye regional'nye atlasy, 1976).

The International Biological Programme has become a qualitatively new stimulus for collecting scientific information, and promoted the development of research at experimental stations. Such research in the USSR was initiated back in the 1950's (Remezov et al, 1959). Still their "boom" may justly be accountable to this International Programme.

Within the IBP framework, stations in different natural zones of the USSR - from tundra to deserts and mountains - collected information on biological productivity and the cycle of chemical elements. Continuous studies on biophysics and biochemistry, which at that time were begun at experimental stations of geographical institutions, have continued till the present in biosphere reserves (there are twenty-two such reserves in the USSR now). These reserves were organised within the framework of one of the projects of the "Man and Biosphere" Programme. In most cases they represent research sites not only for investigators of the reserves themselves, but also for groups of specialists from large research centres. As for the early 1980's the most complete review of the national network of reserves and special stations carrying out continuous integrated research was published by the Institute of Geography of the USSR Academy of Sciences in a special report (1984). It was in the 1960's and 1970's that observations and studies at experimental stations were especially intensive. In the 1980's the interest in such studies began to decline. The development of a new stage of such research at stations, but done on a higher scientific-methodological and technical level, in the USSR is directly associated with the implementation of the IGBP and with the new tasks of nature conservation, environmental improvement and collection of integrated information on the functioning of natural and anthropogenically transformed geosystems.

Most of the accumulated information is contained in accessible numerous publications and maps as well as in the funds of different departments in an uncirculated form. In the recent decade, with the development of computerisation, the work has begun on the creation of data banks. This work is still mainly of an experimental character, although some services have already created specialised data banks, embracing individual areas or objects.

At the present time the largest databases on nature are available in specialised national services, such as the Ministry of Geology of the USSR, the State Committee on Hydrometeorology, the All-Union Board "Lesproyekt" and some others.

In recent years numerous databases have been created by research institutions. For instance one hundred and twenty-three institutions from forty-nine cities of the USSR presented their results in this field at the recent All-Union Conference on Ecological Data Banks (Printsipy i metody ekoinformatiki, 1986). Among geographical and ecological research institutes and higher educational bodies of the USSR the following have in their possession special data banks: the Pacific Institute of Geography of the Kazan' State University, the Institute of Evolutionary Morphology and Ecology of Animals of the USSR Academy of Sciences (Moscow), the Institute of Geography of the USSR Academy of Sciences (Moscow), the Geophysical Committee of the Presidium of the USSR Academy of Sciences (Moscow) and others (Banki geograficheskikh dannykh, 1987; Koshkarev and Karakin, 1987; Trofimov and Panasyuk, 1984). The Institute of the Problems of Management (Moscow) is one of the co-ordinators of the geoinformational studies within the framework of the Academy of Sciences of the USSR.

Just to illustrate the existing and the planned geographical and ecological data banks of national and global scales, let us describe data bases of two academic institutions - the Institute of Geography and the Institute of Evolutionary Morphology and Ecology of Animals named after A. N. Severtsov.

236

Information about the USSR and its use in IGBP

The USSR Catalogue of Glaciers (The Institute of Geography of the USSR Academy of Sciences)

The USSR Catalogue of Glaciers was published at the end of 1982. On the whole the work on the Catalogue continued for twenty years. The series on the Catalogue consists of one hundred and eight parts in sixty-nine books. The Catalogue provides data on twenty-six thousand, seven hundred and seventeen out of twenty-eight thousand, seven hundred glaciers situated within the USSR. It gives the ordinal number of a glacier, its name, location, morphological type, exposure, length, area, heights of the highest and lowest points, altitude of the firn line, area of accumulation and ablation. The location of glaciers in respect to each other and their hydrological type are shown on the schemes of regions. Tables give data on hydrometeorological stations, storage gauges and snow sampling points in the glaciation areas. The Catalogue also supplies physico-geographical descriptions of regions, various total and average characteristics of glaciers, peculiarities of their plan and altitude, location, exposure, moraine distribution within them, information on climatic conditions, ice accumulation and ablation, ice formation zones, ice movement, temperature regime, mass balance and direction of glaciation development, and ice runoff.

The data on glaciers have been tape recorded and are suitable for computer processing. Copies of the magnetic tapes were sent to the World Data Centre A on Glaciology (Boulder, Colorado, USA) and the World Glacier Monitoring Service (Zurich, Switzerland). In the latter Centre analogous data on glaciers of other countries are collected constituting the World Glacier Catalogue with the USSR Catalogue of Glaciers as part of it.

The World Atlas of Snow and Ice Resources (The Institute of Geography of the USSR Academy of Sciences)

The principal aim of the Atlas is to make a global assessment of natural ice as a potential source of fresh water and a regional assessment of resources, regime, variability and possibilities for using snow-ice resources and phenomena. The Atlas will also help understand the role of snow cover and glaciers in climate formation and, especially, in the evolution of nature in polar and high-mountain regions.

237

The maps of the Atlas contain materials on the conditions of formation, regime and variablity of all types of snow and ice and on all the natural objects and processes accompanying them: precipitation, snow cover, snow avalanches and glacial mudflows, glaciers and ice sheets, subsurface ice and aufeises, sea, lake and river ices, snow and ice melt runoff. The total number of maps in the Atlas is 1,250 and the scales from 1:25,000 (individual glaciers) up to 1:90M (the whole world).

Preparing the Atlas for publication the Institute of Geography simulataneously carries out the work on converting the information contained in it to the computer data-storage medium using personal computers of the Apple Macintosh type. In addition, an original integrated program package for computer processing of cartographic information is being prepared: an assessment of the resource and statistical characteristics of separate maps, their conversion, as well as an assessment of informational and statistical characteristics of the field links represented in the maps.

World Economy and Population (The Institute of Geography of the USSR Academy of Sciences)

Data bases on the world economy and population are the components of a geographical automatised system (GAS) "DASPOG" and a geoinformation system "VM-COUNTY". The latter system is realised on a virtual computer with 6 megabytes, while GAS "DASPOG" is implemented on a professional computer with the on-line storage of about 200 kilobytes. The data bases of both systems are compatible and can partially be multiplied on magnetic tapes. The managing system of geographical data bases is not multiplied.

GIS "VM-COUNTY" is intended for processing spatially distributed data and for mathematical geographical modelling. Numerical retrospective data bases within the framework of GIS are referred to a file type. Each figure, characterising a system of spatial objects of one hierarchical level, corresponds to its file. The features describe spatial objects or their relationships. The data bases are created for the areas of the USSR and USA.

In the data base on the USSR there are three principal territorial levels: administrative regions (4213), districts and territories taxonomically equal to the latter (174), and cities (231). Information on smaller areas includes population size, area and the distance to the nearest regional centre. For an urban system demographic indices are used, such as employment structure of aggregated industries and the distance matrices. The greater part of information in the data base concerns units of regional levels in particular, characteristics of different population structures, population migration, indices of social sphere development, natural habitats, etc. The total number of features used in the data base on the USSR is about 150.

In the data base on the USA so far we have only one type of basic spatial objects - counties (3145). It is presupposed that any other objects consisting of the totality of the initial (basic) ones may be reproduced with the help of the GIS control system. The indices characterising the counties are grouped in 3 blocks:

- demographic and social characteristics of population;

- distribution of population among the types of settlements;

- the employment structure of the main activities.

The total number of indices is over fifty. Moreover, in the structure of the data base there is a proximity matrix and a matrix of distances between one hundred and seventy-five most important agglomerations. The data are collected from statistical reference books. In a number of cases expert estimations have been used.

The GAS "GASPOG" system is intended for an imitation system-dynamic simulation of spatial objects and for dissemination of geographical knowledge. The data base is of a documentary type. Corresponding documents are collected on territorial objects, their totality, characteristics, object features and other information indices. Geographical taxa of different hierarchical levels are the main objects of the inquiry. Each object is correspondingly supplied with one or several documents of a numerical, and/or textual-numerical and/or textual and/or graphical content.

The data base retrospectively embraces the territory of the USA, Canada and some West European countries. Four spatial levels are distinguished: agglomerations, regions of the first, second and third order (for the USA they include correspondingly: metropolitan areas, States, 9 regions of the Census Bureau and the grid of a trinominal division). The total number of agglomerations is about four hundred, of the regions of the first order - seventy-nine, of the second - eighteen. All the other objects are outside the main hierarchical levels and their presence in the base is due to the work of individual scholars.

Information on the main spatial levels includes data on population and areas (also on urbanised areas), employment structure of the main economic activities, manufacturing and individual industries and subindustries. At present the total number of indices used in the data base is four hundred and ninety. A group of forty characteristics reflecting the state of natural environment, the availability of natural resources and the most important ecological parameters is being additionally formed for characterising the natural-resource potential.

The total number of documents in the data base is about 3000. The data is collected from statistical reference books, from special literature and through telecommunication channels. The missing data is supplemented by methods of calculation and expert assessments.

In the future the above bases of data on economy and population should be included as components of geoinformation systems of a much broader profile, whose creation has already been initiated in the Institute of Geography (see below).

The World Atlas of Natural Environment and Natural Resources (The Institute of Geography of the USSR Academy of Sciences)

In two or three years the work will be finished on the compilation and editing of over 350 maps on nature, population and economy, which will then become part of this new integrated atlas. The creation of the Atlas was initiated by the Institute of Geography and most of the work on it is done by the staff of the Institute. The world maps on the scale of 1:60M or 1:80M, as well as some maps of the Continents on scales from 1:10M to 1:40M, completed by the staff of the Institute prior to the compilation of the Atlas, will be used for building a global geoinformation system in order to make a substantial contribution to the IGBP.

The following thematic sections are foreseen in the structure of the Atlas (Gerasimov et al, 1985: the history of the formation of biosphere (22 maps); relief, geological structure, mineral resources (ten maps); climate and waters (40 maps); soils, vegetation, animal population, biological and land resources (40 maps); global factors of an anthropogenic modification of the environment (30 maps).

In the last section there will be maps of manufacturing and mining industries, as well as of the state of the environment in the regions of their intensive development, maps of agriculture, transport and population. It will also include maps of recreation resources, of natural and socio-economic factors leading to the spread of diseases, maps of production and consumption of energy, and those of desertification processes.

Thus, the materials of the Atlas highlight the present-day natural conditions of the existence of mankind, the distribution of the resources of its development, and the areas of different forms of economic activity. In totality, they may be used for analyzing (probably) global and macroregional changes of the geosphere-biosphere system, if one assumes that the evolved spatial relationships among its natural components are in the state of equilibrium, while the distribution of areas with different types and intensity of economic activity is the factor which disturbs these balanced relationships.

The structure of the database presupposes that it may be supplemented by spatially-distributed parameters, characterising the now-recorded or expected changes of the biosphere and of its components. The availability of paleogeographical maps will make this database stronger as regards its prediction abilities.

The scales of the maps in this database for the most part correspond to the scales of maps from the 'Physico-Geographical Atlas of the World' (1964), which provides for a continuity of these two world summaries.

The Biological Productivity of Terrestrial Ecosystems of the World (The Institute of Geography of the USSR Academy of Science).

The created and now computerised database will be of two forms - the first a series of small scale maps and the second a body of local conjugated characteristics of the store and production of phytomass, its chemism, parameters

241

of climate, soils and a number of other components of local geosystems.

The cartographic presentation of this database will for the most part be included in the GIS based on the materials of the World Atlas of Natural Environment and Natural Resources. The initial cartographic basis for this purpose will be the world geobotanical map from the Physico-Geographical Map of the World (1964). Materials on soil and climate parameters from other world cartographic publications, as well as materials characterising the biological turnover of oceanic ecosystems will be an addition to the geobotanical map.

Descriptions of over 4000 definite terrestrial phytocenoses were taken as a basis for a localised reference realisation of the database. They included characteristics of the reserves of living and dead phytomass by different functions (underground and overground, assimilating organs, etc.), its annual growth, the amount of chemical elements involved in the biological cycle, the species composition of plants-edificators, and the type of phytocenosis (Bazilevich, 1986). Most characteristics have been obtained by direct measurements, but some parameters are calculated. Published materials are used for the description of other components of biota, as well as of climate and soils. Such materials are reference books containing results of many years observations at meteorological stations, special large-scale maps, material of the land evaluation (cadaster) and others. The block of 'climate' includes the following groups of characteristics: (a) solar radiation and temperature of air and soil, (b) precipitation, runoff, soil humidity, (c) hydrothermal indices, wind and other parameters. All in all, there are about 50 parameters of climate (with their intra-year varients taken into account). In the block of 'soil' there will be characteristics of the parameters of humus condition, physical properties, reserves of mineral elements, morphology of the profile and the genetic type of soil. The total number of all parameters in all blocks will be about 150.

At present all the collected materials on biological productivity concern natural phytocenoses. In the next stage, the database will be supplemented by indices of the biological cycle and by agrochemical parameters characterising simple agricultural or forestry ecosystems, which by the properties of climate and soils are analogous or similar to the already systemised 4000 natural phytocenoses.

The structure of this database foresees the possibility of transition from its localised variant to the cartographic version mentioned above.

Thus, in the Institute of Geography of the USSR Academy of Sciences, in the first stage (1988-1990) it is planned to create databases of cartographic data for the world as a whole, for the USSR with its European part taken separately, and for individual regions. All this will be done on the basis of created and accumulated atlases, maps, tabulated numerical information and territorially coordinated qualitative descriptions. During the next stage, it is planned to detect and assess spatial interrelationships among the types and parameters of geosystems in order to specify the knowledge accumulated in the geographical science and to apply it in the matter of resolving the tasks of a rational use of natural resources.

The scientific basis of the cartographic modelling will consist of the theory of a cartographic symbol system (the language of a map) worked out in the Institute of Geography and its practical supplements - recommendations on the prevention of errors in the systems of map symbols, which are quite common in the world cartographic practice, concepts and methods of a cartographic imitation experiment and others.

The work will be based on the use of mini- and micro-computers produced both in the USSR and abroad (compatible with the DEC system and IBM PC) supplied with the corresponding peripheral equipment for input and output of graphic information and the available and still to be developed software.

Database of a statistic simulation of the Forest Vegetation in the USSR (The A.N.Severtsov Institute of Evolutionary Morphology and Ecology of Animals of the USSR Academy of Sciences)

This database of a statistical simulation has been organised on the basis of a small-scale empirical model of the vegetation of the USSR forest zone with the use of an information-statistic analysis of a spatial realisation of observations over the state of vegetation and edaphoclimatic parameters of the environment. The database consists of matrices of transitional states between the characteristics of the vegetation and environmental parameters, which are stored on the outer accumulations of information in computers. The database is of an open type and may be both corrected by new data and supplemented by parameters of different ecosystems' components. When applied to the database in accordance with the given environmental conditions on the basis of the method of a threshold logic, a synthesis of the matrices of transitional states is performed and on its basis a decision is made about the state of the vegetation. The database is organised in two versions of programmes, which allow to make an active dialogue in the regime 'man-machine' and to perform an automatic compilation of computer maps for any territory within the forest zone of the USSR and also for the whole zone. An approximation of the state for the present climate gives satisfactory results. Correspondingly the input of the known and supposed changes of climate makes it possible to estimate the sales and the character of changes in the background state of forest growth conditions. And here the reliability of decision-making determines the stability of vegetation, whose assessments are output as computer maps. Automatic superimposition of computer maps for different states of the environment allows the detection of areas of potentially unstable forest growth conditions. The above estimations may be effectively used when creating a system of biosphere stations for monitoring the natural environment.

An analogous database is created for an individual region (the Middle Sikhote-Alin') on the basis of a large-scale empirical model. Thus, within the framework of one approach there is a possibility to organise a multilevel hierarchical database of an ecological monitoring with the income of information to its lower level taking place on a real time scale from automatised systems of monitoring.

Zooarealogical Database of the World Fauna (The A.N. Severtsoz Institute of Evolutionary Morphology and Ecology of Animals of the USSR Academy of Sciences).

The formation of this kind of database is a recent undertaking. Data about an area are presented in the form of a graphic image - a closed line which is kept in a cartographic database of a relative type. In it, in separate tables there accumulates information about location of the areas of animal species by their belonging to a certain continent. The tables themselves contain graphic information in the form of a sequence of coordinates about the location of the area's boundary and its attribute - the name of the species. The software allows the following operations: input of graphic contours or dots with the help of a digitiser which works with the precision of +/- 0.1mm; input of Latin and Russian names of species; formation of the database on the outer accumulators of information; performance of scale transformations and transition to different kinds of projections; compression of the graphic information in the computers memory; and graphic and alpha-numeric output.

The database has a convenient interface of connection with the application programmes. To make a zooarealogical analysis, a problem-orientated system of software, AREAL was created. The system consists of such programmes which provide for a choice of graphic information from the database by attributes, by geographical coordinates or by a given region; for rasterisation of the graphic information with any given level of resolution; for output of a list of species for any given point or region; for estimation of the size of areas; for building of the function of the distribution of areas' sizes for a given group of species; for determination of a minimal distance from the given point to the border of the area of any species; for the formation of a file of maps of areas in a discrete form. Through this, an arealogical analysis may be done including a zoogeographical regionalisation for any group of species; for the typology of areas with the use of different means of similarity and with the output of the results onto a plotter in the form of computer maps with an automatised compilation of their legends. There are a number of programs for resolving special tasks when substantiating the choice of an area for protecting the gene pool of animals and rare species, for instance, a program of a search for a minimal number of locations which represent the fauna of the given regions in a maximal degree, etc.

At the present time, the database includes areas of mammals of the USSR, Mongolia and North America. On the basis of the AREAL system a zoogeographical analysis was made of the mammals of the USSR and Mongolia.

However, it is necessary to admit that the majority of these databases have been developed in different systems of management, on different computers, with different ideas, and consequently, do not connect well with each other. Elaborations of uniform conjugated databases are still in the design stage.

245

At the same time in the USSR, much attention is being paid to the methods of generalisation and analysis of background, tabulated, textual and cartographic information. These works are also of an experimental character and, on the one hand, are directed to the revealing of fundamental relationships between components and their properties and, on the other, to the working out of effective methods for classifying and approximating the properties of objects in space. Within the programme of these studies over a thousand descriptions of forest vegetation were generalised and compared with climatic variables (Puzachenko and Skulkin, 1982). On this basis, methods for compiling maps of resistance of the vegetation cover to the changes of climate or to a wider scope of other variables were worked out. Regional schemes have also been worked out, which reconstruct the natural vegetation cover, give methods for defining unstable biosphere regions and planning the location of a network of observation stations providing for a maximum sensitivity of integrated research to global changes of the biosphere processes.

Soviet specialists working with computers of an early generation with a small storage capacity and operative memory have to make great efforts for providing a good quality of software and a sufficient utilization of the computers' capacity. The use of an irregular net for introducing information from maps, as well as of parameters determined at the most informative points, helps to economise the time and effort. For instance, the required precision of the input of relief from a topographic map is provided for by information only by the points of bends in the surface, thalwegs and watersheds. Interpolation procedures allow to reproduce an initial relief in horizontals practically without errors (with the precision of 10%). Original elaborations concerning both the input of cartographic information and the methods for analysing tabulated and cartographic information and methods for its presentation are made practically in all research fields and all centres of the USSR.

Much attention is being paid to determination of a system of uniform databases with account not only of current needs, but also of future prospects for the development of the information system. In computer cartography special attention is paid to the analysis of the conjugation of components, to the detection of their balanced relation-ship, of regions with a disturbed equilibrium which require special study for constructing factor-genetic maps, etc.

Much attention is paid to the methods of presentation of cartographic information. The initial principle is its rapid transformation on computers correspondingly with the requirements of a consumer and his thesaurus. Information should generate new questions and effective solutions.

Thus, at present, a gradual transition from traditional means of information storage to the modern ones is under way. The accumulated experience shows that practically all the information contained in literature and on maps may effectively be transferred into an active state on modern computers.

We believe that on this basis, within the framework of the IGBP programme, the following fundamental tasks could be resolved:

- Creation of the model of a 'balanced biosphere' characterising the most probable correlation of the states of different components in a wide scope of features of every component. Such a model, reflecting correlations between components, which existed in the interval between the 1930's and the 1970's, could serve as a specific reference point when estimating changes observed at the present time.

- Determination of the regions, in which balanced relationships are disturbed and identification of the reasons for it. In particular cases, these may also be errors in information. In those cases when information is reliable, discrepancies may be connected with differences in the characteristic time of the processes of components' transformation, with the current processes taking place in the biosphere, and with historical pecularities in the development of nature on different continents. All these aspects seem to be important both when organising a system of observations and when interpreting their results.

- Promotion of the organisation of ecologically substantiated economic activity, taking into account the regional sustainability of the biosphere.

To solve these tasks we shall have to overcome considerable methodological and technical difficulties.

The main problem here is coordination of diverse information on the state of components on the biospheric level. At present, it has been solved for hydrometeorological variables, for seismic variables and for a number of other physical and, to a lessor extent, chemical processes. However, coordination of data on relief, soils, and vegetation is very difficult methodologically. The task is further complicated because of the necessity of a hierarchical information arrangement, of making a uniform scheme of cartographic, tabulated and sometimes even textual information. The work done by Bukh may in this respect be considered as an important experiment, which shows that the problem can be resolved, but at the same time it is very complicated. It is obvious that the amount of work to be done is huge indeed. Strictly speaking, the input of information on a national level is expedient only after the elaboration of a single international system, which would provide for a sufficient coordination. Naturally, there may be intermediate solutions corresponding to the current needs, but still it is desirable that they coordinate with a uniform general plan and transform in accordance with the changing goals.

None the less complicated is the task of working out uniform mutually coordinated methods for processing and interpreting information. It is important to find such forms of data presentation which would correspond to national interests and possibilities of the projects participants, being at the same time sufficiently generalised.

Of great significance is also the task of the input of initial information. Unfortunately the input of most cartographic information may be done only from a digitiser. For that cartographers and editors should be well qualified. The use of a great amount of reference and tabulated material also requires considerable efforts. In our country we have started solving these tasks, but it is obvious that a purely national approach will inevitably lead to an undesirable limitation for use of the information. So all the above problems should be carefully considered within the framework of IGBP, for which a special subcommission of the Programme should probably be created, which would include scientists with a wide range of interests who are acquainted with the structure of information in different countries, but specialising in a certain component (for instance soils or vegetation) and united by specialists in the field of database management and control systems, of expert systems and cartography. Technically advanced national and/or regional centres should probably be created which would provided for a coordinated input of basic information and its continuous expansion. Such centres should undertake elaboration of methods for processing and presenting information and select the best solutions for a uniform international system.

REFERENCES

Bazilevitch, N.I., 1986. 'Bank dannykh pokazatelej biologitcheskoj produktivnosti nazemnykh ekosystem mira (The Database of Indices of Biological Productivity of the World Ground Ecosystems)' in Printsipy i Metody Ekoinformatiki, pp. 52-53, Moscow.

Gerasimov, I.P., Ilyina, L.N., Liouty, A.A. and Narskikh, R.S. Prirodnaya Sreda i Estestvennye Resursy Mira (Tasks, Structure and Contents of the Atlas 'The Natural Environment and the Natural Resources of the World'). pp. 7-20.

Kompleksnye regionaljnye atlasy (The Integrated Regional Atlases). Moscow, Izdatel'stvo, 1976. 638 pp.

Koshkarev, A.V. and Karakin, V.P., 1987. Regional'nye geoinformatsionnye systemy (Regional Geoinformational systems). Moscow, Nauka, 126 pp.

Opyt Raboty i Zadachi Zapovednikov SSSR (The Experience and the Tasks of the USSR Reserves). Moscow, Izdatel'stvo Nauka, 197 pp.

Printsipy i metody ekoinformatiki. Materialy Vsesoyuznogo Soveshcaniya (The Principles and the Methods of Ecoinformation Science. The materials of the All-Union meeting). Moscow, 334 pp.

Puzachenko, Yu.G. and Skulkin, V.S., 1981. Struktura rastitel'nosti lesnoj zony SSSR (The Vegetation Cover of the USSR Forest Zone. Systematic Analysis). Moscow, Nauka, 276 pp.

Remezov, N.P., Bykova, L.N. and Smirnova, K.M., 1959. Potrebleniye i krugovorot azota i sol'nykh elementov v lesakh Evropeiskoi chasti SSSR (The Consumption and Rotation of Nitrogen and Ash Elements in the Forests of the European part of the USSR). Moscow.

Salischev, K.A. and Serbenyuk, S.N., (eds.) 1987. Banki geografitcheskikh dannykh dlya tematicheskogo kartograph-irovaniya (The Geographical Databanks for Thematical Map-making). 187 pp., Moscow.

Statsionarnye issledovaniya geosistem (The Geosystems Investigations at Stations). Moscow, Institute of geography, 1984. 271 pp.

Trofimov, A.M. and Panasyuk, M.V., 1984. Geoinformat-sionnye sistemy i problemy upravleniya okruzhayuschei sredoi (The Geoinformational Systems and Problems of the Environment Management). Kazan, Izdateljstvo Kazanskogo Universiteta, 142 pp.

ACTIVITIES ASSOCIATED WITH GLOBAL DATABASES
IN THE NATIONAL AERONAUTICS AND SPACE ADMINISTRATION

John E. Estes and Joseph H. Bredekamp

INTRODUCTION

The National Aeronautics and Space Administration (NASA) was established by the National Aeronautics and Space Act of 1958. This legislation was enacted to provide for research into the problems within and outside the earth's atmosphere. The objectives of the NASA program of research and development are to expand our knowledge of the Earth, its environment, the solar system and the universe; to expand the technology for practical applications of space technology; to develop and improve manned and unmanned space vehicles; and to assure continued development of the long-term aeronautics and space research and technology necessary to accomplish national goals.

Within NASA, the Office of Space Science and Applications (OSSA) further these objectives by (1) conducting a broad spectrum of scientific investigations to advance our knowledge of the Earth, the Sun, the planets, interplanetary and interstellar space, the stars of our galaxy and the universe; and (2) identifying and developing the technology for the useful applications of space techniques in the areas of advanced communications satellite systems technology; materials processing research and experimentation; and remote sensing to acquire information which will assist in the solution of earth resources and environmental problems.

These objectives are pursued through an integrated program of ground - base laboratory research and experimentation; suborbital flight of instruments on airplanes, balloons, and sounding rockets; and the development and flight of automated Earth - orbiting and interplanetary spacecraft.

A major research emphasis within the overall OSSA science program is in the area of Earth Sciences and Applications. The overall goal is the investigation of the Earth as a system from its interior through the oceans and atmosphere

251

and out to the magnetosphere boundary. Recent research has made it clear that land, atmospheric, oceanic, and biospheric processes are strongly coupled. To come to an improved understanding of our environment, and ultimately to predict global change induced either naturally or through human interaction, it is important to study the Earth as a single coupled system as well as to answer questions arising in such separate disciplines as atmospheric chemistry, climatology, biology, ecology, geology, geography, meteorology, and oceanography.

The scientific productivity of NASA basic and applied research programs is very dependent on the use of advanced information technology. OSSA is working towards a coordinated data management program to provide the research community access to data and information about data acquired from space flight experiments and observations. An integrated OSSA approach is being established to ensure the orderly flow of mission data into archives, along with master directories and interoperable catalogs to provide a consistent user view across the various science disciplines. This is especially important to support the interdisciplinary research objectives associated with global change.

In particular, OSSA is very interested in global data base technology from both an analytic and a data management perspective. NASA space and aircraft systems have the ability to acquire large volumes of data in both digital and and analog formats. We need to improve our ability to integrate these data into data/information systems wherein one particular component is a GIS. These data combined with other more traditional data can then be used to inventory, map, monitor, and model important components of the global system. The key is to integrate these data so that they may be manipulated, integrated, and processed in such a fashion as to improve our fundamental understanding of the rates, directions, and magnitudes of environmental processes and changes.

OSSA currently supports numerous global databases. The primary archival site for these databases is the National Space Science Data Center (NSSDC). Over the past several years, OSSA has also developed data management and distribution systems centered around specific scientific disciplines. These have generally been initiated as pilot efforts and evolve to become operational systems as they prove to be successful. The pilot approach is conducted to provide a sound technical foundation for future operational systems or components of operational systems. In addition, these pilot activities typically are limited in scope and directed towards the identification and solution of important technical problems.

In addition to the discussion of the NSSDC data archives, this paper will then briefly describe the discipline of data systems of most interest which apply to global change. These include the NASA Oceans Data System, the Pilot Climate Data System, and the Pilot Land Data System. We then conclude with a brief summary of other relevant current and future directions in NASA data systems activities.

NATIONAL SPACE SCIENCE DATA CENTER

The National Space Science Data Center (NSSDC) is the principal depository for NASA data acquired from space flight experiments and observations. NSSDC was established in 1966. For approximately the next 10 years of its existence, it concentrated on establishing an archive of off-line data and associated documentation, along with a homegrown information system to permit internal operations and the generation of data catalogs. NSSDC continued to mature through the late 1970's and early 1980's, as the design and implementation of the Coordinated Data Analysis Workshops (CDAW) system epitomized the expansion from data archiving and disseminating to the development of tools to exploit the data archive. With the implementation of recent community recommendations regarding data management, NSSDC has restructured to serve its user community more effectively. This evolution is continuing.

Today NSSDC activity collects, organizes, stores, announces, disseminates, exchanges, and refers to a wide variety of science data that are obtained from spacecraft and ground-based observations. Discipline users come from a wide variety of disciplines including:

* astronomy and astrophysics
* atmospheric sciences
* ionospheric physics
* land sciences (e.g., ecology, forestry, geography and geology, among others)
* magnetospheric physics
* ocean sciences
* planetary sciences
* solar terrestrial physics

Data are contained on more than 100,000 magnetic tapes and tens of thousands of film products, and optical, video and magnetic disks. NSSDC also publishes information catalogs and data inventories for the whole archive of data. A subset of this information is maintained on line and is accessible over many international computer networks.

The NSSDC is primarily responsible for providing an interface to the scientific community and for data service operations. In addition, NSSDC pursues advanced topics in computer science research in areas that are likely to contribute to more effective data management.

In the past, NSSDC has been given responsibility for archiving and disseminating data from all NASA scientific missions. This includes the full range of space and Earth science missions with the exception of Landsat data. Recent recommendations from NASA advisory groups, particularly the Committee on Data Management and Computation (CODMAC) of the National Academy of Sciences, have stressed the merits of the development of a distributed data archiving system - a system in which the data reside in close or virtual proximity to active users. For instance, Space Telescope data are to be archived and disseminated by the Space Telescope Science Institute in Baltimore. Details of the implementation of the CODMAC recommendations remain to be determined. However, it is likely that in the future NSSDC will be a principal archive for some disciplines. In addition, NSSDC may do long-term archiving for most disciplines; provide the central directory for the whole system; and will continue to provide overall leadership in the development and implementation of the hardware, software, and communications approaches need for effective data management in this distributed environment.

NASA OCEANS DATA SYSTEM

The NASA Oceans Data System (NODS) began as a pilot data system activity in 1980. NODS became operational in 1986. The objective of NODS is to archive data sets from spaceborne ocean viewing sensors, together with the required supporting data and metadata, and to distribute these data sets in efficient and convenient forms to the ocean research community.

The primary user community of NODS consists of ocean researchers supported or approved by the NASA oceanic processes program management, researchers in academic and government laboratories and approved foreign researchers. NODS does not support commercial users, but directs such users to the National Space Science Data Center (NSSDC) or to the National Oceanic and Atmospheric Administration (NOAA) to purchase the data. If data at those centers is missing or corrupt, NODS provides those centers with updated copies for general distribution.

Data can be obtained from NODS by any bonafide scientist if this data is used in a research application. Potential user of NODS are required to complete an application form and attach a one page summary of the research work they intend to address using the data they obtain from NODS. User are also requested to send us reprint of publication resulting from the use of data obtained from NODS. Users are free to redistribute data obtained from NODS.

The types of data handled by NODS are seen in Table 1. NODS also archives ancillary data from these sensors as well as the supporting in situ data. These include:

Table 1:   Examples of Data Sets Held Within NODS

1. NODS Holdings
       GEO-3 Altimeter
       Seasat Altimeter
       Seasat Scatterometer (SASS)
       Seasat Scanning Multichannel Microwave

2. RADIOMETER (SMMR)
       Atlas Dealiased Seasat Scatterometer Winds
       West Coast Level 1 AVHRR
       West Coast Level 1 Nimbus CZCS
       West Coast Color/Temperature Time Series
       Tropical Heat Exchange Project (THEP) - FUTURE
       Defense Meteorological Satellite Program (DMSP-F8)
          Special Sensor Microwave

3. IMAGER (SSM/I) JASIN in situ data sets
       Gulf of Alaska NDBO Buoy data sets for Seasat period
       Navy GEOSAT Altimeter (unclassified, exact repeat
          mission)
       Ocean Topography Experiment (TOPEX)

4. Altimeter - Future
       Poseidon Altimeter - future
       NASA Scatterometer (NSCAT) - future

NODS provides a catalog of data sets; supporting data and information about data; a bibliography of abstracts of documents relevant to the catalogued and archived data sets; data selection requests in a data archive; and, browse file display capabilities in an archive and in inventories. These functions are available interactively.

The NODS Catalog contains information about the platform, sensor, processing level, parameter, temporal and spatial resolution, and accuracy and precision of each data set. The catalog may be searched by project, platform, sensor, parameter, region or time. The following table (Table 2) describes the data maintained in NODS today, and future data holdings envisaged in 1995.

Table 2:   Present and Future (projected) NODS Data Holdings

Type	No. of Bytes Now	1995
Number of Directory and Catalog Entries	90	hundreds
Number of digital Data Sets	23	100
On-Line Directory/Catalog volume (bytes)	0.3M	1M
On-Line Accessible Data Volume (bytes)	1.5G	5G
Digital Data Tape Storage (bytes)	145G	500G
Number of Tapes	4189	10,000

NODS is a historical data archive, not designed to provide data in real time. Data delivery is in minutes if under data requested are 1 MB. Other requests are serviced in less than a week in general. Very large requests (e.g., whole Seasat level 1) are accommodated by special arrangement. All NODS data are loaded into our archives with no backlog (faster than they arrive). Data availability for the current Defense Meteorological Satellite Program is several months after collection due to constraints involved in the processing of the data and its transmittal to NODS. Within NODS, data on magnetic tape is renewed every four to six years. Regeneration of higher level products using updated algorithms is done occasionally, but this is generally done by a special project (e.g. CZCS Global Processing at GSFC), or by a PI (e.g. West Coast Time Series by Mark Abbott). Data compression has not been applied to data sets archived by NODS. The on-line data sets that held by NODS have been reduced in volume by removing intermediate parameters stored with the GDRs.

The usage and performance of all NODS functions (catalog, bibliography, archive and inventory) are kept track of by accounting functions which collect data and produce reports. Usage and performance data are collected by dedicated accounting programs and are also provided by the computer operations system as well as by the operations staff. Information compiled, per user, in report form are: the number of tapes sent, numbers of observation extracted form the archive, number of plots generated, number of disk files created, number of Bibliography requests made, and the number of documents sent from the Library. In addition, a careful compilation is made of papers (journal articles and technical reports) and abstracts which make use of NODS data or NODS computer facilities.

Digital data is kept in swath (spacecraft crosstrack and along-track geometry) and gridded forms in binary formats. For swath data the data base is indexed by time. An orbit and sensor scan geometry model is used to map requests for data from specific geographic locations into the data time segments that are extracted form the data base. Gridded data is indexed by time only. Data is presented to the user as scaled positive binary integers format or in an ASCII characters format. Both formats are machine independent.

In the future, the functions of the catalog, bibliography, archive and inventories will all be performed in a distributed environment where specific data sets will be managed and distributed by the institutions possessing the unique expertise pertaining to a data set. In this context, NODS will become a "federation" of cooperating "open systems" consisting of data centers connected via wide area networks such as the Space Physics Analysis Network (SPAN) or the NASA Science Network. An "open system" is a data system which interacts with other data systems using published protocols. A "federation" of such systems has no hierarchical structure, and no system wide control function; rather, each participating system is a peer of the other, with respect to communication.

The following represent a number of problem areas and key issues related to current NODS operation:

-   Source Material - In almost all cases the data NODS receive are from data producers. These data require editing to ensure that NODS is protected against the "garbage in - garbage out" problem. Also, data generally arrive in a variety of formats that require

257

special attention. NODS management has addressed these problems by building special purpose loaders to edit and reformat input data. Many, but probably not all, of these data ingest problems could be resolved if the data producer were to provide well documented data in a well publicized standard format.

- Integration - NODS can take swath data and grid it onto a user specified level 3 product; thus data from several different data sets can be presented on a common grid. In the future we would like to see the community served by NODS agree on common a set of grids and resampling techniques for the presentation of data that is destined to be combined with other data sets.

- Data Loss - Data loss has been avoided by re-recording data sets onto newer storage media. Data set accountability has been achieved by keeping trace of the elements (granule of the data sets) through the use of inventories.

- Data Volume - NODS management feels that they must continue to improve data handling efficiency if we are to cope with increasing data volumes. This can only be achieved by sorting through the experience gained in the past decade and using that as a bases for future work. NODS has been working with NSSDC, ESA and others to formulate a data management model that standardizes many of the metadata management procedures and allows as much flexibility as is needed to deal with data from a variety of different data sets.

PILOT LAND DATA SYSTEM

Beginning in 1983, initial plans were developed for a Pilot Land Data System (PLDS). PLDS is intended to improve the ability of NASA and NASA sponsored researchers to conduct research on land processes. The goal of the Pilot Land Data System (PLDS) activity is to establish a prototype state-of-the-art data and information system to support research in the land-related sciences that will lead to the development of a permanent research tool. PLDS is designed to be a limited scale, distributed information system that can be employed to explore scientific, technical, and management approaches to satisfy the needs of the Land Science community now and into the next century.

Land scientists currently experience varying degrees of difficulty accessing, processing, transferring, and analyzing remotely sensed and other scientific data required in their research activities. PLDS is being developed on the premise that current technology advancements in data management, networking, and analysis techniques makes it possible to develop a land data system that meets the information needs of the land scientists. To the degree that this is correct, it should also be possible to significantly reduce the burden on scientists who are forced to spend long periods of time and effort searching, acquiring, and analyzing data. PLDS is managed within the NSSDC with the Ames Research Center, the Jet Propulsion Laboratory, and a number of researchers at universities actively participating.

The initial PLDS concept was to develop an advanced information system that would employ existing, along with new and emerging technologies to achieve levels of operational performance that, until recently, were felt to be unachievable. PLDS system design was based on a distributed architecture that would utilize powerful microcomputer workstations, supercomputers, and high-speed digital communications to form an operational capability with intelligent value-added services. It was the one expectation of the PLDS design architecture group that such services would allow system operations to be goal-oriented rather than procedure-oriented, thus freeing the scientist from spending a disproportionate amount of data processing and data manipulation time and effort. It was felt that a PLDS based on such a concept would be able to support the most technically demanding computer operations with minimal user knowledge of, or experience on, the system. The overall goal was to reduce the time and effort spent on locating, accessing, ingesting, and otherwise processing data, thereby reducing this burden on scientists without compromising their ability to conduct scientific investigations. In essence, to let scientists be scientists, not librarian data base management experts and so on.

A preliminary system design was formulated based on existing technologies and resources that supported several land processes research projects. This preliminary system design concept has evolved into what is currently termed "BUILD 1". The current BUILD 1 System Concept is aimed at the development and implementation of a system that can demonstrate aspects of a long-term system concept in a limited fashion (in terms of time, cost, and performance), while providing operational support to selected science projects. BUILD 1 was implemented, then, to provide direction for the development and implementation of the long-term operational system.

Specifically, the BUILD 1 System Concept included the following:

- A data/information system capability that supports land science research for a limited set of research projects
- A database that manages both metadata (i.e. data about data) and spatial data at more than one site
- A limited capability for ingest of spatial data
- Communication capabilities to support both local and remote access for interactive operations based on the available line and communication services
- Communication support services that allow limited interaction between all PLDS users
- On-line support and advice on system services and operations for all PLDS users on an as-needed basis
- Software for analysis of specific data types
- Availability of a number of data analysis services to users on an as-needed basis
- User-friendly interfacing to allow easy access to system services and operations by both local and remote users

Although the above BUILD 1 capabilities and functions do not express the complete overall system concept, they do provide a foundation upon which an improved system can be designed and developed. Using testbedding and rapid proto-typing concepts, then, PLDS has focused its developmental efforts around two on going Land Processes research projects. The two projects are:

- Land Surface Climatology
- Multispectral Analysis of Sedimentary Basins

Land Surface Climatology is supported by the International Satellite Land Surface Climatology Project (ISLSCP), a long term research initiative to develop techniques for determining quantitative information about land surface climatological conditions from satellite observations of the radiation reflected and emitted from the Earth. NASA's portion of ISLSCP is planned to be made up of many research activities of which there are presently two: the First ISLSCP Field Experiment (FIFE) and the ISLSCP Retrospective Analysis Program (IRAP).

The First ISLSCP Field Experiment (FIFE) is an initial project designed primarily to produce the data necessary to meet ISLSCP objectives for the development of calibrated long term reflected and emitted radiation sets. FIFE is being conducted on a 15 x 15 test site in the Flint Hills region just south of Manhattan, Kansas. The following two types of measurements are being made:

- Monitoring of basic meteorological observations at approximately 20 locations over the site
- The Intensive Field Campaigns (IFC) include more extensive surface and aircraft measurements during two-week period distributed over a growing season

Data-gathering activities for FIFE were largely confined to FY78, with analysis phase activities extending an additional two years through FY89.

GSFC is providing the central repository for most of the data associated with FIFE. GSFC's FIFE responsibilities include providing an information system to support both the data-gathering and analysis-phase activities. PLDS is being used to provide partial information system support for FIFE. In this context, PLDS is facilitating the acquisition of FIFE-related data by the investigators and will expedite the exchange of information between principal investigators.

The ISLSCP Retrospective Analysis Program (IRAP) is examining existing historical records of satellite data for evidence that changes in the land surface of the Earth, either natural or anthropogenic, have had or are having an influence on weather/climate on local, regional, continental, and global scales, or vice versa. IRAP's objectives are to determine the extent to which changes have taken place in climatologically important properties of the land surface, to quantify these changes in terms of physical and biological parameters, and to determine the impact of the changes on the coupled land-atmosphere-ocean-cryosphere (i.e. climate) system. To accomplish these objectives, IRAP investigators are analyzing existing data sets, including more than a decade of Landsat MSS/TM data and more than five years of NOAA AVHRR data, which provide repetitive measurements of the land surface at various times.

PLDS will be used to provide GSFC's information system support for IRAP. In this context, PLDS will provide data management, networking and communications, analysis software, and system access support to IRAP investigators.

The Multispectral Analysis of Sedimentary Basins project at NASA Jet Propulsion Laboratory is an outgrowth of the GEOSAT project, in which a few test sites were studied with a variety of remote-sensing systems and techniques to assess their utility for geologic remote sensing. Instruments and techniques for analysis of remote-sensing data have improved over the last few years, but there have been few concerted efforts to apply the variety of new techniques to specific geologic problems. The sedimentary basins project is designed to use new techniques for analysis of remote-sensing data obtained by a variety of sensors at many wavelengths for geologic analysis of a major sedimentary basin (e.g. the Wind River Basin in Wyoming).

Sedimentary basins are large (>100 sq. km) structures that occur throughout the world. Such basins often contain economically significant amounts of oil, gas, coal, and other resources. Sedimentary basins also provide a record of the depositional and tectonic history of an area. Key to efficient exploration of the nonrenewable resources of a sedimentary basin are knowledge of the distribution of geologic units both at the surface and within the basin; and, an understanding of the evolution of the basin. Therefore, the objectives of the Sedimentary Basin research project are to:

- evaluate the utility of remote-sensing data for mapping subtle variations in sedimentary lithology
- compare and evaluate remote sensing data to conventional field mapping data of the Basin
- combine remote-sensing data of surface properties with subsurface geophysical data to generate a 3 dimensional representation of the basin
- employ findings to constrain models of basin formation and evolution

The Multispectral Analysis of Sedimentary Basins project involves a number of NASA-funded investigators at both JPL and the University of Montana and Hawaii. Spacecraft and aircraft remote-sensing data, geophysical field and seismic data, and field and laboratory spectral reflectance measurements have been acquired, calibrated, and are being registered to digital topographic base map to provide a Geographic Information System capability to project scientists. This preprocessing has placed a very heavy load on PLDS in terms of preprocessing functions such as calibration, registration, and overlay. With existing resources, analysis tasks must be performed separately at

262

the research nodes, often with inconvenient transfer of data and intermediate results by mailing of magnetic tapes. Interactive processing between nodes is highly desirable but presently not available. Routine transfer of text and newly developed algorithms is also necessary.

At present, then, the Pilot Land Data System (PLDS) consists primarily of two nodes: one at the Jet Propulsion Laboratory (JPL) and one at Goddard Space Flight Center (GSFC). Work on Networking and on workstation development has also occurred at Ames Research Center (ARC), but ARC is not, at this time, a science node on PLDS. Development of the two primary nodes, although conducted cooperatively, has proceeded at differing paces, and the resulting capabilities at the two nodes have not been identical or fully compatible. Incompatibilities between the two nodes have been (and are being) reconciled after their initial implementation. In general, it is felt that in order to PLDS to be successful, it must become a capable, functional system which can be exercised in a significant fashion by the Land Processes Program's research community. PLDS BUILD 1 provides basic capability , but PLDS, however, must continue to evolve if it is to be productively exercised by a significant portion of the land processes community.

As can be seen from this material, PLDS is continuing to evolve revision and is under the active evaluation by NASA Headquarters personnel at this time. We believe we have made a beginning in this area and that continued work is needed to determine the full system's needs of the Land Processes community. The lessons being learned here, however, are valuable and the need to incorporate those lessons into future systems such as the EOS data and information system is great. In this respect, PLDS has been a very beneficial project.

PILOT CLIMATE DATA SYSTEM

An early technical decision made in the late 1970's and early 1980's in the development of the Pilot Climate Data System (PCDS) was to use already existing software packages wherever possible. Therefore PCDS solutions have typically been implemented by integrated general purpose software packages - some commercially available, others developed by the PCDS or other NASA projects - with specialized software for accessing the appropriate supported data sets. General purpose packages available include a database management system for storing information about the data, a user interface package providing uniform interface to the tools provided by the other packages, and graphics and statistical packages for browsing data. PCDS's developers also defined a special self describing data construct (much more than a format) accessible to all of these tools. These existing systems packages have been integrated in a manner which allows the PCDS to be easily expanded, either to provide support for additional data sets or to provide additional functional capabilities.

The current PCDS database management system is Oracle. Oracle is a relational system providing a highly flexible method of storing and retrieving information about data. To improve performance, PCDS databases have migrated to a Britton-Lee Intelligent Database Machine using the OMNIBASE interface. This was accomplished in a manner that did not impact the user's view of the system. PCDS uses the TEMPLATE graphics package which is easily called from high-level programming packages and provides support for a number of devices, not tying the PCDS to any one output device. User interface to the PCDS is accomplished via the Transportable Applications Executive (TAE). TAE provides a user friendly interface to all system capabilities.

Functionally, PCDS capabilities are provided via five subsystems. Each subsystem is listed below with a description of its function. These subsystems include:

- Catalog - provides a comprehensive parametric set of descriptions of climate data sets and the associated sensor measurements from which they were derived
- Inventory - provides detailed information concerning the temporal coverage and data volume of each of the data sets which are readily accessible via the PCDS or other application systems with which it is interfaced
- Data Access - extracts portions of a given data set using criteria such as time range and geographic location, and outputs the data to on-line disk files in a self describing data format, to a user terminal, a system printer, or a tape
- Data Manipulation - accesses and manipulates PCDS data stored using the self describing data format, performing such functions as combining the data, creating a subset of the data, or averaging the data
- Graphics - can be used to create various graphical representations of the data stored in the self describing format

It is a basic philosophy of PCDS that data characteristics are a driving force behind the design of a scientific information management system. PCDS must be able to incorporate a variety of instrument measurements and derived geophysical parameters - maintained at various levels of data reduction (at different spectral, spatial, and temporal resolutions), in various formats, and at various archival locations or investigator files. Performance, volume, and their associated budget problems prohibit actually putting major portions of the data in a conventional database. Table 3 lists information about the data sets currently supported by the PCDS. Data listed in Table 3 accounts for only a small portion of the data sets available for scientific research.

Table 3: PCDS Data Holdings (05/08/87)

Data Set	# of Tapes	Time Span Start Time	End Time	Size in MB
ACRIM	N/A	1980-02-16	1985-06-30	<1
ANGELL	N/A	1958-01-01	1983-01-01	<1
BANAT	58	1978-11-01	1983-10-31	409
ERB-MATRIX	89	1978-11-16	1986-05-05	492
ERB-SAVER	29	1978-12-02	1986-03-01	12
ERB-SEFDT	61	1978-11-01	1984-11-01	881
ERB-ZMT	14	1978-12-01	1985-12-06	11
ESAT	1	1978-12-01	1986-03-30	4
ESMR3DAY	1	1972-01-01	1974-03-13	1
FGGE2B	90	1978-12-04	1979-12-01	2639
FGGE3B	82	1978-12-01	1979-11-30	2665
ISCCP-B3	142	1983-06-30	1984-07-31	17639
LIMS-LAMAT	8	1978-10-25	1979-05-29	151
LIMS/FGGE	8	1978-12-01	1979-05-30	75
NMCGRD	18	1973-01-01	1981-12-31	1222
NOAA-HB	47	1974-06-01	1985-05-31	727
OZONE-S	16	1978-10-31	1983-05-08	1176
OZONE-T	89	1978-10-31	1983-11-05	8855
SAGE-PROF	33	1979-02-21	1981-11-18	185
SSCLIMATE	3	1738-01-01	1982-12-31	2

Totals: 20 Data Sets;   789 Tapes;   Size 37 GB

Other data characteristics which must be considered and which involve information management problems include: (1) the complexity of the relationships within and among the data sets, (2) the significance of spatial attributes (e.g. a large proportion of the data sets consist of maps or images), (3) the chronological storage of data as sequential files on magnetic tape, and (4) the type of data values (mainly numeric and some text data).

Because of the unique data characteristics, scientists cannot always be expected to know which data sets they need to access for a given problem. The information management system helps the scientist determine what PCDS data exist for supporting their research efforts, and the characteristics and condition (quality, usability, etc.) of these data. This means that PCDS must not only manage the data, but also information about the data. PCDS also takes into account the fact that the most data requests are ad hoc, and that the requests vary widely. Scientists must be able to request data and obtain them in a reasonable time, and in a readily usable form.

Generally, data management systems within NASA have been developed for one mission (such as one satellite, one instrument, or one experiment). For PCDS to achieve its goals it could not have such limitations. PCDS provides extensive data management and analysis capabilities for use by climate researchers. These capabilities have been packaged into a system that is extremely easy to use and is very flexible. Researchers using PCDS need no knowledge of data formats or programming languages.

With specific reference to the data in PCDS, each data set is essentially treated as its own database, with each of the different types of data in a data set handled as a separate table of the database. Functions which users need to work with a data set (database) correspond to those of a typical DBMS: Select, Project, Delete, Join, and Union. Also included are a number of mathematical functions such as Sum and Mean, and qualifiers such as Group By, Order By, and Where. In addition, for each data set database to be of full utility, it must have a complete data dictionary. Also, owing to the large number of potential databases, there is one database which contains the metadata that points users to the databases (data sets) of interest. Data Dictionary Tables list characteristics of the data variables: full name and description, units, minimum and maximum value, and fill or exceptional values. These tables provide users with information required to understand and interpret the data.

Gathering the information for tables described above and writing specialized software for translating the data into usable forms are often the most time consuming tasks which

266

must be accomplished as data are located, understood, and validated. (Occasionally documentation may not exist, or is poorly written or incorrect). In an effort to reduce the time required in this task, PCDS staff actively encourages data producers to provide data set descriptive information in machine readable form with, or as part of, their data sets. Once the recording, documenting, and formatting of a data set is complete, PCDS can allow users to specify subsets of interest via a user-friendly interface. User specifications direct the PCDS to select the variables/columns/fields desired from the tables /records of interest, using the where conditions qualified on the primary keys (usually the temporal and spatial domains). The result of this are additional tables which are stored in a user's personal database. Such a database may be stored on media such as magnetic tape or magnetic disk.

PCDS graphics utilities are supported on a wide variety of hardware. Users can employ low cost graphics terminals for quick-look displays or more expensive terminals for complex data representations. Histograms, panel plots, two dimensional, three dimensional, and pseudocolor representations of the data are also supported by the PCDS.

Tape output is generally provided in the same format as provided by the producer (e.g. in the same DBMS as the original data, with the same underlying DBMS structure), keeping PCDS out of the time consuming, format writing business. Output to disk is to a self describing, data independent construct called the Common Data Format (CDF). This construct (much more than a format) and an associated software package for storing and accessing data in this format provide the PCDS with a variety of DBMS capabilities, including a full data dictionary, without the major overhead currently associated with most commercial products.

ISSUES AND LESSONS LEARNED

NASA is working towards the development of data and information systems capabilities which can enhance the productivity of both the fundamental and applied Earth Science communities. Through the efforts discussed above, NASA is gaining experience in handling a wide variety of data management systems. As a result of this experience, a number of issues appear and reappear with regularity.

These major issues can be grouped into three overlapping categories.

These categories are:

- User Interaction
- Interoperability
- Performance

In terms of user interaction with and access to NASA's data and information systems a sample of our problems range from defining user requirements to providing better network access to distributed sites. Too often as we have attempted to define user requirements for a given system we have run into the circular questioning of what do you need? And, the reply comes back what can you give us? It is imperative that we break this cycle whenever it occurs as quickly as possible. Through the close involvement of science steering and advisory groups, we are attempting to improve communications between our discipline scientists and our information systems scientists and technologists.

With respect to improved network access issues range from the development of intelligent user friendly interfaces; to improved connectivity; to system loadings. The latter is particularly important to this meeting. Moving large spatial data sets such as those produced by NASA satellite sensor systems over networks creates very large load factors. Indeed, Federal Express, DHL, or Postal overnight delivery (no endorsement intended) has a very high band width and is still a good way to go in the near term.

Interoperability covers a multitude of topics from standards; consistent user interfaces; connectivity of heterogeneous computing environments; and, generic analysis tools. In the area of standards, there is significant ongoing activity. The challenge is to integrate these activities. NASA is currently concentrating on developing master directories and interoperable data catalogs.

Issues associated with systems capability include both functionality and performance. Further research into cost effective techniques and methodologies for operating large spatial databases is needed. Improved access to and better methods for browsing large spatial databases are other issues which must be addressed.

CONCLUSIONS

NASA is actively involved in planning for the upcoming Global Change program. Activities associated with interoperability include:

- Internal NASA research and development
- Federal Agency Working Groups and Task Forces
- Cooperation with international partners and scientific societies

An important goal of all of these activities is to promote cooperation and improved sharing of data. Data/information is the common resource required for an improved understanding of the Earth as a Global System.

In planning for the Earth Observing System, with its four polar platforms and complex sensor and information systems capable of producing one terabyte of data per day, we recognize the Earth science community has identified the development of an integrated data and information system as its number one requirement for an effective program to study global change. This overall system will evolve in a modular, incremental fashion.

We appreciate the efforts of the International Geographic Union in bringing this group of distinguished data and information systems specialists together. Data bases designed and structured in a fashion which can increase the speed and efficiency of our interactions with spatial data at scales from local to global are needed. Improved methods of acquisition, encoding, storage, retrieval, manipulation, analysis and output of spatial data for the study of the Earth as a System and for the Analysis of Global Change is central to NASA's overall mission.

ACKNOWLEDGMENTS

This paper has used liberally from source material provided by personnel of both GSFC and JPL. Material used in this paper has been taken from NASA scientists and researchers including: Victor Zlotnicki, Diane Wickland, Paul Smith, Bill Campbell, Jim Green, Blanch Meeson, and Mary Reph, among others. We are especially indebted to Ms. Kathleen J. McCarthy for all her efforts and significant editorial contribution in the preparation of this paper.

THE IGU INFORMATIONAL SUPPORT TO IGBP:
A CONCEPTUAL APPROACH

S. A. Evteev and S. B. Rostotsky

INTRODUCTION

Before one starts doing something in one's everyday life, the first thing to do (even if it is a subconscious process) is to fix the goals and as a follow-up there will be a decision of how to achieve these goals and what is needed to achieve them. In most cases, preference will naturally be given to the simplest, the cheapest and the most prompt method. It is obvious. And we are all acting in just this way, when our personal interests are concerned. The opposite can be seen in the field of science, especially in the sphere of a wide international co-operation. You would probably agree, that quite often one can witness a situation when a process of some activity or its imitation turns out to be an end in itself or something absolute, while the purpose for which one is working may seem to be without shaped and unimportant even to oneself.

So, the very first thing to do for our meeting here to be sensible and useful; for our "World Digital Database Planning Project" to turn into "World Digital Database Creation Project" in the forseeable future; and for our Information Bank to be, hopefully, created at last, is to answer the main question, maybe an ideological one, which is: 'what are we willing to have in the end and for what reason?' i.e. what should be the character of the Information Bank, its orientation, and who will be its customers? And the answer should be sufficiently distinct and logical. Otherwise all our efforts will be in vain, and our Project, although important, will remain theoretical.

Having an answer to this main question we shall be in a position to reply to the question of what data is needed, i.e. to solve the second, less important, though maybe the most difficult strategic problem.

270

Only after these key questions are settled, shall we be able to solve the third level problem, a tactical one - in the working out of a plan of action, after which concrete practical matters of planning, designing and organisation of the Database may be undertaken along the lines indicated in the Project Description.

To discuss all these problems now is not only desirable, but very timely. Besides all other reasons, this need is further stipulated by the progress made in the creation of geoecoinformation systems (GEIS) in different countries, though it may seem strange on the face of it.

On the one hand, people having some experience are usually prone to idealise it. On the other, the important and highly valuable world digital topographic base on 1:1M scale made by the IGU/ICA Working Group on Environmental Maps and Atlases may be filled with anything you care to put in it; that seems hardly efficient, as even ordinary Banks have specialised sections dealing with trade, credit and building.

Having an Information Bank we shall be able to determine correctly what data is needed. As a result, the whole system will be more logical, more effective, much simpler, and consequently more accessible and cheaper.

The development of a perfect collector programme - the main stem of research and activity planning - will guarantee not less than 50% of the success.

This is theory, of course. Nevertheless, with its perfect development and realisation, the planned database will become not only a kind of support rendered by geographers to IGBP, but a real scientific base of the whole Programme, if not its brain. For the present, it is only one of the contributions of geographers to IGBP. It will be a substantial contribution, but not sufficient for such science as geography, since Geography being a unique integrated science with two wings - natural and socio-economic - is in the position to determine most comprehensively the main global problems of the world, to choose the right approaches in research, to ensure the necessary links with other sciences and to interpret the gained results correctly.

What are our practical proposals? Let us consider them in the same order as above, following the proposed relative levels.

THE IDEA.

The creation of a database is planned as an informational support to IGBP, i.e. we can consider IGBP as a customer. What are its requirements? They have not so far been defined with a sufficient precision though social demand is real. Thus we may have to define the essence of the Programme ourselves, as well as our attitude to it, and to act accordingly. What is "Global Change"? Life is impossible without changes. But living in the 'changing world' we are prone to admit only those changes that are vital for us and which can change our mode, way, quality or level of life. So any change should be considered only in relation to its possible influence upon the life-support system of mankind - its survival. Thus mankind with all its needs for resources to support its being and development should be the focal point of both IGBP and relative IGU programmes.

Dr. T. Rosswall - the IGBP Executive Director - making a speech at the Institute of Geography of the USSR Academy of Sciences last March said: "We are trying to understand the Earth as an ecosystem with interactions of all processes... The questions of man's impact on the environment should be studied by the 'Human Response' Programme, but not by IGBP". So if this statement refers only to 'pure' sociological or 'pure' economic aspects of man's activity, it may be acceptable, but we are afraid that he was referring to other additional aspects.

To understand the Earth as a single ecosystem, without its 5 billion population, as well as without the results of the activities of all the previous generations, is just impossible. Moreover, it is not so necessary during the coming twenty years to study abstract 'pure' natural ecosystems (which hardly exist) functioning without interrelationships (both direct and feed-back) with real processes taking place on the Earth. It is most likely that in the course of the next twenty years the last remnants of tropical forests will disappear, the greater part of genetic heritage of the planet will be lost, virgin lands will be cultivated and arable lands turned into badlands if not occupied by polluting towns. Even now desertification, deforestation, soil erosion, and environmental pollution are problems on a global scale and as a result, the soil and vegetation cover, as well as wildlife, become qualitatively different. The chemical composition of water bodies and the atmosphere have been changed and river flow is regulated. The change of global atmospheric circulation is underway - one can recall the impact of the Great Sahelian drought. All of this is as a result of human activity.

Our approach to research within the framework of IGBP according to which the proposed data bank should be built is shared by many Soviet scientists. Thus, one of the principal long-term interdisciplinary programmes adopted by the USSR Academy of Sciences, is the Programme of biosphere and ecological investigations of the USSR territory which will embrace the period till 2015. It is not by chance that the Programme was set up. Its second part deals with the problems of interaction between society and the environment, advocating the minimilisation of negative trends affecting the environment as consequences of this interaction. The following sections are considered: industrial ecology, agricultural ecology, human ecology, economics of nature management and others. An integrated analysis of the data on biosphere and ecological investigations will be considered in the section on regional ecocrisis situations.

The GRID system (UNEP) is built using an approach similar to ours. Although it has not yet achieved a desirable level of development, the experience accumulated by it should be thoroughly studied.

The knowledge we seek will be really useful if it can be used as a base for determining limits of anthropogenic pressure on ecosystems, standards for economic activities corresponding to these limits, and similar problems. Then we shall really be able to forecast the state of the environment not only for a million-year period - which is of theoretical interest - but for our lifetime, and surely everyone would like to live in a healthy environment. For all this the above problems should be recognized in advance.

If the "Global Change" Programme ignores man and his impact on the environment, it will impoverish itself and the interest in it will diminish (initially the interest of the decision-makers, which will then cause further worsening of the situation) while a considerable number of sciences and scientists representing them will turn aside.

Thus if there is no disagreement with the above in principle, the idea of creating a Global geoecoinformation system can be identified as follows:

To create an integrated and complete geosphere-biosphere database able to simulate and predict the trends of natural processes which are of vital importance for the wellbeing of mankind, as well as possible changes of these trends under human impact.

With such an approach the interest to the planned database may become very great indeed. Among its potential customers there will be not only 'pure' scientists, but decision-makers, politicians, managers, etc.

STRATEGY

Now on the basis of the identified idealogical 'filling', we are in a position to determine our strategic tasks. So what information do we really need? We believe it is as follows:

Integrated geographical information on the elements of natural, natural-economic, territorial-production and settlement systems. This will help us to understand the self-development of these systems, as well as their inter-relationship and interdependencies.

The problem of deriving comprehensive integrated characteristics of geoecological systems ranks as one of the highest priorities of contemporary fundamental natural studies. The world of science suffers much from the deficit of such knowledge, though modern methods of scientific research using remote sensing, computerisation, and mathematical modelling in combination with more traditional methods give us a good opportunity not only to derive the required characteristics, but also to determine them qualitatively. In this context we would like to stress that traditional methods of geoecological studies are not dying off, as one sometimes hears, but are passing on to a new qualitative stage of development. Without them all space-computerised-mathematical systems are worthless and vice-versa.

The most readable and obvious form of storage of geoecological information is a geographical map. This is suitable for practically all scientific purposes, as certain information on some regions being plotted on different sheets, say with different time and problematic parameters, can be compared, analysed and integrated according to the requirements of some specific research in the most convenient and prompt way.

Computerisation of databases requires transformation of existing information into digital form. That in principle, is not a great technical problem but it raises a number of problems mainly of a methodological character. First of all, it is a matter of information structuring. Even using a computer storage of information it seems expedient to take advantage of a multi-sheet structure of national atlases. This will facilitate the identification of particular inter-relationships both within and between sheets.

The possibility of tying objects to a definite geographical environment and the open character of a geoecological information system by itself, i.e. its nearly unlimited ability to expand due to the inclusion of new information 'sheets', are among the unquestionable benefits of such structural organisation of all geoecological information.

TACTICS

The next problem is to work out the general plan of action for the realisation of the main idea and the goals being determined. As set out below they are:

i)   inventory of existing geoecological information

ii) the establishment of the data selection criteria and the selection itself

iii) organisation of the monitoring of modern geoecological processes or identification of guaranteed sources of such geoecological information

iv) information processing and 'compression', including provision for data comparability

v)   storage, distribution and exchange of information with allied databases.

One of the main items of the Agenda of this meeting, the reason why we are all gathered here, is the first of the above points - the problem of an inventory and integration of the existing geoecological databases. There is no need to dwell on this question in detail, because a good part of Dr. Drozdov's paper submitted to this meeting is devoted to it. We shall just say that a number of different departments and agencies in the Soviet Union are engaged in creation of their own databases which give integrated or

275

component descriptions of geoecological situations in the USSR and abroad. One of the functions of the Interdepartmental Geophysical Committee within the framework of cooperation with IGBP is the collection of information about databases existing in the USSR. So far the Committee has received and systematised information on more than forty such databases with the total amount of computer-readable information exceeding 1.2 gbytes. A special catalogue on these databases is planned to be published this year.

The creation of a single geoecoinformation research centre within the USSR Academy of Sciences is envisaged as an All-Union database for ecological expertise and forecasting. According to the current Programme of the USSR Academy of Sciences on biosphere and ecological research, by 1995 a system of district, region, all-union and international (member countries of CMEA) geoinformation centres will cover some 30% of the area of the USSR and CMEA countries and, by the year 2000, up to 100% of this area and 30% of the worlds oceans.

A major source of data in the establishment of a GEIS is that of remote sensing and space monitoring. However, although data received from space, as well as aerial photography, is extremely valuable for monitoring large-scale changes in geosystems, it cannot provide for the level of monitoring of quantitative changes of the environment which is needed. Moreover, whilst there are now few technical problems in the receipt of remotely-sensed data, the problem of the sound exploitation of remote sensing techniques is still a serious one. Before making measurements one should at least realise the degree of representativeness of objects chosen for observation from space or air. The measurements taken without account of the above condition will produce an immense amount of data than can hardly ever be used. In this connection, space and air sensed data should be supplemented by ground observations, including those fulfilled at the stations and during field expeditions.

The undeniable advantage of the ground observations at stations is the possibility of providing their integrity, continuality, duration and reliability. So the proposal to organise within a framework of IGBP a network of the geosphere-biosphere observatories is an excellent one.

The question of the establishment of these observatories, the programmes of research and so on need a special study

276

and special discussion. It is obvious that besides 'standard-type' stations, which should be located in the regions the least changed by man and the most resistant to his impact and thus the most stable, we need a network of 'indicator-type' stations on the boundaries of different ecosystems for recording the changes that are most apparent there.

However, establishment of an absolutely new network of field stations (observatories) is not only an extremely labour-consuming, long-term and expensive task, but it will not provide us with retrospective data and will not give us any information about former trends, as the research at these stations will be starting from scratch.

To estimate the network which we already have, the International Union for the Conservation of Nature and Natural Resources (IUCN) have prepared a special list of National Parks, and UNESCO a list of biosphere reserves. Geographers, in their turn, should catalogue all kinds of stations including field stations at their disposal and initially all those at which integrated geographical research is made. The abundant scientific material collected at geographical stations during a long period is invaluable for IGBP research development. In this context not only research stations, but also training grounds are of great importance. There, students of Universities, Institutes or Colleges are doing their practical work on a regular basis adding geoecological data, analyses, generalization and mapping.

As a rule, geographical stations are engaged in the working out of methodological aspects of geoecosystems monitoring. Geographical stations can be used and are used as a base for case studies for the whole complex of geosphere-biosphere inter-relationships at a local level. They serve as field laboratories for conducting different geographical experiments over a small area and on the basis of these they can then study and develop a theory of geographical forecasting. Here one can support conclusions received with the help of mathematical modelling and computer processing. Scientific data received at the stations can be extrapolated and sent to corresponding regions.

Taking all the above into consideration, it seems expedient to include the network of geographical field stations, training grounds, biosphere reserves and so on into the proposed Global Database. It is evident that the existing network of such kinds of observation sites will not be satisfactory for solving all current problems of organising the ground survey - new field stations will have to be established and new scientific expeditions organised. Nevertheless, the existing network of stations taking into account their qualitative characteristics should initially by plotted on a map to provide the required minimum for starting research within the framework of IGBP and to facilitate the filling in of gaps in the system in the most optimum way.

One of the proclaimed goals of our Commission - the IGU Commission on Geographical Monitoring and Forecasting - is to make an inventory of geographical stations existing in the world. Last year a special questionnaire was mailed to the national committees for IGU, to Chairmen of IGU Commissions as well as to some other organisations. The first responses to this questionnaire have already been received. Although the results of the enquiry are still rather modest, it seems advisable to discuss the problem itself within the framework of one of the working groups envisaged at this meeting.

FEATURE BASED SPATIAL DATA MODELS -- THE CHOICE FOR GLOBAL DATABASES IN THE 1990'S?

Stephen C. Guptill and Robin G. Fegeas

INTRODUCTION

National mapping agencies, including the U.S. Geological Survey (USGS) have been producing digital cartographic data for over a decade. The data structures and underlying data models (some utilizing topology, others not) used in collecting this information, for the most part, have not changed since they were developed in the late 1960's or early 1970's. However, during this time, the tasks for which the data are being used have become increasingly sophisticated, placing information demands on the data that were not planned for in their initial design.

In the case of the Geological Survey, one of the sources of these demands arises from the Survey's National Mapping Division (NMD), which is undertaking a major system development activity called Mark II. Mark II will be a digital cartographic production system with the National Digital Cartographic Data Base (NDCDB) at its hub. Information in the data base will reflect the data content of the National Mapping Program's standard map series. This information will be periodically revised and new graphic products generated using computer-assisted cartographic methods. Maintaining the information required to support these processes is a driving force behind the design of a more comprehensive data model (Guptill, 1986; Callahan and Olsen, 1987.) Additionally, the growing sophistication of geographic information systems (GIS's) and the increasing diversity of applications involving GIS and spatial data are beginning to demand a more flexible and comprehensive model for spatial information. This linkage between advancing GIS capabilities and need for more advanced data structures has been explored by Goodchild (1987).

In response to these demands, the Geological Survey (as both a data supplier and data user) has begun the design of an enhanced version of the digital line graph, termed Digital Line Graph - Enhanced (DLG-E). Several other major agencies collecting digital cartographic data are also considering (or have implemented) new feature based spatial data model designs. These agencies include the U.S. Bureau of the Census, U.S. Defense Mapping Agency, the Institut Geographique National (France), Landesvermessungamt Nordrhein-Westfalen (W. Germany), and the military geographic services of the NATO allies. The Proposed Standard for Digital Cartographic Data (The American Cartographer, 1988) accommodates the representation of features in the Spatial Data Transfer Specification (SDTS). This trend toward feature based data models should be noted in the design of any future global data bases.

In this report, the general characteristics of DLG-E provide an example of a feature based approach to modeling digital spatial data. An outline for implementing DLG-E in SDTS is given. This is followed by a discussion regarding agreements on a common exchange specification within the framework of SDTS and how this might foster data exchange and creation of global data bases.

DLG-E DATA MODEL

Overview

In simple terms, the DLG-E begins with the topological model used in the Survey's present DLG format (USGS, 1986) and builds a cartographic feature layer upon the topology. The feature definition is open-ended, allowing users to define additional features of interest. Cartographic entities will be described using objects, attributes, and relationships. In addition, recommendations contained in the Proposed Standard for Digital Cartographic Data regarding data quality information, and formatting will be followed. Details on the DLG-E design are given in the paper "Designing an Enhanced Digital Line Graph" (Guptill, Fegeas, and Domaratz, 1988).

Levels of Abstraction

To translate a set of data requirements into data model or data structure constructs first requires that we define these terms and place them in context. The framework given below itemizes levels of data abstraction (based on Peuquet, 1984). These levels can serve as steps in progressively refining the process of translating these requirements.

- Reality is the total phenomena as they actually exist.

- Data Reality is an abstraction of reality that includes only those entities thought to be relevant to anticipated needs. It is a definition of the scope of the data.

- A Data Model specifies the sets of components and the relationships among the components pertaining to the specific phenomena defined by the data reality. A data model is independent of specific systems or data structures that organize and manage the data.

- A Data Structure specifies the logical organization of the components of a data model and the manner in which relationships among components are to be explicitly defined.

- A File Structure is an implementation of a data structure in a computing system environment.

Note that the data model is concerned with defining components and relationships among those components. The next level down, data structuring, defines how these components and relationships are organized in a particular environment.

An important point to note is that many different data structures may be developed based upon one model. If we expect to support the wide range of user requirements expected of the NDCDB, we must try to develop a comprehensive data model.

Spatial Data Model, Overview

The phenomena of our data reality are considered entities. An entity and its digital representation define a feature. Features are the sum of our interpretations of phenomena on or near the Earth's surface. Often features are identified by a name, such as Goose Creek, Lookout Mountain, or Washington, D.C., but any set of attributes and relation-ships may be used to define a feature.

The spatial components of our data model are limited to two dimensions upon a surface. Data for the third dimension are limited to the spatial definition of the surface. Other third (heights of objects above the surface) or fourth (temporal) dimensional data are relegated to nonspatial attribute status. These constraints bound the data modeling task.

The components of the digital representation of features are termed objects. Cartographic data are considered to be composed of objects, attributes, and relationships. Objects are the basic units of representation of the encoded phenomena. Attributes are the spatial and nonspatial characteristics of the entities represented by the objects. Relationships are the spatial and non-spatial links between the objects. Note that relationships may be modeled as attributes.

Objects are of two types: feature objects and spatial objects. Nonspatial attributes and relationships are associated with feature objects. Spatial attributes (for example, location) and relationships are associated with spatial objects. A given feature object is defined as consisting of other feature objects and/or spatial objects. A given entity may always be represented as one feature object. However, for the feature to be complete, one or more spatial objects must also be associated with the feature, either directly, or through other feature objects.

Data Model Definitions

The definitions given below briefly describe the components of the DLG-E data model. More extensive definitions are given in Guptill and others, (1988). These definitions further refine the definitions of cartographic objects given in "The Proposed Standard for Digital Cartographic Data".

Entity: A real-world phenomenon that is not sub-divided into phenomena of the same kind.

Object: A digital representation of all or part of an Entity.

Feature: A set of phenomena with common attributes and relationships. The concept of feature encompasses both Entity and Object.

Feature Object: A digital representation of an Entity to which only non-spatial attributes and relationships are associated. Feature Objects may be composed of other Feature Objects and/or Spatial Objects. For the

representation of an Entity to be complete, however, a Feature Object must be
composed of one or more Spatial Objects,
either directly or through other Feature
Objects.

Spatial Object: An Object to which spatial attributes and
relationships are associated. Spatial
Objects are defined for 0, 1, and 2 dimensions. Data for the third dimension are
limited spatially to the definition of a
surface upon which the 0, 1, and 2 dimensional objects occur. The remaining third
and fourth (time) dimensional data are to
be considered nonspatial attributes in the
context of this model.

Linear Graph: A set of Nodes, Chains, and Areas all
occurring upon a defined surface such
that: (a) each Chain is bounded by one (in
the case of a single Chain forming a ring)
or two Nodes and, except at the Nodes,
each Chain does not intersect itself or
any other Chains; (b) each Area is bounded
by on or more Chains, and is exclusive of
all other Areas; (c) the set of Areas
completely exhausts the surface; (d) each
Node bounds one or more Chains; and (e)
each Chain is either a Bounding Chain (it
bounds two Areas) or a Singular Chain (it
is wholly contained within one Area).

Node: A zero-dimensional object bounding on or
more Chains of a Linear Graph. A Node may
be part of (that is, the location of) any
number of Features.

Chain: A one-dimensional object of a Linear
Graph, bounded by one (in the case of a
single Chain closed upon itself) or two
Nodes. A Chain may describe all or part
of the extent of a linear Feature(s)
and/or the limits of an areal Feature(s).

Bounding Chain: A Chain bounding two and only two Areas of
a Linear Graph.

Singular Chain: A Chain contained within one Area of a
Linear Graph.

283

Area: A two-dimensional object of a Linear Graph. Each Area can be a "component of" (be used to describe) any number of Features.

Point: A zero-dimensional object within a Linear Graph but disjoint from the Chains of the Graph. A Point may be part of (that is, the location of) any number of Features.

Data Model Description

In DLG-E, features have attributes and relationships as follows:

- Attribute - characteristic of an object or attribute value;

- Attribute Values - measurement assigned to an attribute; and

- Relationships - linkages between objects.

Additionally, there are two kinds of attributes and relationships: spatial and nonspatial. Spatial attributes describe an object's geographic location or geometric characteristic. Nonspatial attributes give us a generic description of the feature object, such as the number of lanes of a highway. Spatial relationships include the topological relationships among objects. Nonspatial relationships between feature objects can be used to describe situations such as administrative hierarchies (the Town of Vienna, spatially contained within Fairfax County, is not part of the county's police jurisdiction). Nonspatial relationships can also be used to define the classes of objects that represent cartographic features.

It is also noted that relationships can have attributes. Such attributes might be used to describe the state of a given relationship (for example, the University of Michigan is definitely composed of Rackham Hall and Michigan Stadium and probably composed of unnamed buildings #101 and #189).

Another usage of attributes of relations would be to describe the set of members included in the relation; particularly if those members were to be considered in an ordered or directed sense. The representation of flows through a network may require such facilities. For example, given feature objects composed of chains, the

284

chains are to be considered as an ordered set having uniform direction. The direction is indicated by an attribute describing the direction for traversing the chain. In addition, a real-world (ground) significance to this ordering is indicated by attribution of the feature object. Under the present design, this is the only case that utilizes attributes of relationships. All other cases requiring attribution of relationships are proposed to be handled by attributes of feature objects.

The following attributes and relationships are defined for use in the DLG-E model:

1. Locational attribute - a specific type of spatial attribute that describes the geographic location of a feature; locational attributes are assigned to a spatial object.

2. Nonlocational attribute - characteristic of a feature object or attribute value other than location.

3. Topological relationships - boundary/co-boundary relationship between spatial objects

4. Nontopological relationships - relationships between feature objects and/or feature objects and spatial objects.

The various logical components of DLG-E are shown diagrammatically in figure 1. The spatial components of a feature are described by the spatial objects: points, nodes, singular chains, bounding chains, and areas, or some combination of these. The nonspatial components of the feature are described by a set of feature objects. The feature objects have nonlocational attributes. The spatial objects have a set of locational attributes, typically a set of coordinates that characterize their location in space. These consist of x,y and optional z coordinates.

All of the relationships between model components are listed in table 1. The feature relationships are further described as follows:

> "feature composed of/part of *" : describes the formation of feature objects from feature objects and/or spatial objects. Can be used to aggregate either disjoint or adjoining spatial objects or feature objects. For example: Green Bay is part of Lake Michigan.

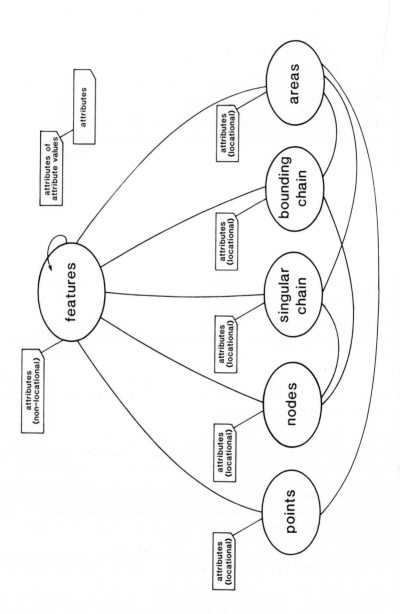

Figure 1: Logical components of the DLG-E data model.

"feature bounded by/bounds feature" : describes the
limits of the contiguous spatial extent which are all
or part of a given areal feature. This relationship
references a "boundary feature" that is an outer ring
of bounding chains containing the feature and inner
rings that bound areas that are not the feature.

Table 1. Relationships between the components of the DLG-E
data model

ELEMENT	LINK	ELEMENT
feature	----composed of---> <---part of-------	*
feature	----bounded by----> <---bounds--------	feature
point	----within--------> <---contains------	area
node	----bounds--------> <---bounded by----	chain
singular chain	----within--------> <---contains------	area
bounding chain	----bounds--------> <---bounded by----	area

* means that any of the model components (feature, point,
node, singular chain, bounding chain, or area) can be used
in this relationship.

The model also accommodates additional relationships, such
as follows:

"feature - any named relation-feature" : allows for
user-defined feature object relationships. For
example: West Virginia "was previously part of"
Virginia.

This relationship is not utilized in the current DLG-E
design and is noted here for possible future use.

The relationships between spatial objects consist of the boundary/co-boundary topological relationships. These were defined previously.

It must be mentioned that the topological relationships of the spatial objects do not reflect any feature relationships. For example, the fact that a singular chain (representing a landing strip) is contained in an area (representing a park) does not define any feature relationship between the features that those spatial objects represent. Nothing should be assumed about the relationship between the landing strip and the park unless a specific feature object relationship gives the information (for example, saying that the landing strip is operated by the park).

Representation of Features

The model allows a wide variety of representations of features to be formulated. In order to enhance the value of the model as a vehicle for data exchange, however, rules must be established for the representation of occurrences of the features, or "feature instances". Some general guidelines include:

- Consistency between the definition and nature of the feature and the representation of the feature instance.

- Consistency between the detail of information known about a feature from the source materials and the detail of information provided in the feature instance.

- Consistency in the representation of like features.

- Simplicity in representation.

These guidelines are achieved through the formulation of rules for the representation of feature instances. Three rules have been identified to be used in formulating the description of a feature instance:

- Rules for defining feature instances -- include the definition of the domain of features to be represented, and rules used to delimit the individual occurrences of features.

- Composition rules for representing feature instances -- govern the selection of feature and/or spatial objects to be used to represent an instance of a feature.

- Rules for aggregating feature instances -- govern the creation of instances of higher-level compound features from simpler feature instances.

An initial domain of approximately 200 features (with associated attributes and attribute values) has been defined to be used with DLG-E. Future plans include development of the other rules described above.

SPATIAL DATA TRANSFER SPECIFICATION IMPLEMENTATION

The components of the DLG-E data model may be implemented within the constructs of the Spatial Data Transfer Specification (SDTS). SDTS has its own set of data model components (primarily defined in Part I of the Proposed Standard for Digital Cartographic Data). The components of DLG-E must first be mapped into SDTS model components. Only then can an SDTS data structure and file structure be selected.

For the most part, DLG-E data model components have direct counterparts in SDTS. SDTS is more general in that it deals with graphic vector data, raster data, as well as topologically structured vector data. The DLG-E model is a clear topological vector data sub-set of SDTS. In only a few cases do we have to qualify the definitions of SDTS components to match DLG-E.

The data mappings outlined in Table 2 do not include Global (i.e. header) data. The DLG-E data model does not explicitly include them. Once the data model mappings have been performed, actual file structures can be outlined that will include SDTS Global modules.

Table 2: Summary Data Mapping Equivalence Table, DLG-E and SDTS Model Components

DLG-E Objects	SDTS Objects
Feature Object	Feature implemented as a Composite Object
Linear Graph/Spatial Objects	
Node	Node
Chain	Chain
Bounding Chain	Complete Chain
Singular Chain	Complete Chain (qualified as left ID = right ID)
Area	Polygon (with Rings created from chains) - qualified to represent only topological "2-cell" areas
Point	Entity Point (qualified as wholly contained within 1 Area)

DLG-E Attributes	SDTS Attributes
Locational	Location coordinates (often termed Spatial Addresses)
Non-locational	
of Feature Object	Attribute
of Attribute Value	Not explicitly included in the SDTS model - to be implemented as Secondary Attributes

Table 2 cont'd.

DLG-E Relationships	SDTS Components
Topological	
Point-within-Area	Attribute with Polygon Foreign ID a Attribute Value
[All others]	[Included in Node, Chain and Polygon object definitions and defined relations]

DLG-E Relationships	SDTS Components
Non-topological	
Feature composed . . . . . . of Element	Composite-composed of Element relation
[all others]	[Attribute implemented with Foreign Identifiers as Attribute Values]

OTHER FEATURE BASED DATA MODELS

Over the last several years, various mapping agencies have been designing data models for use in their current or future information systems. Much of this work is still ongoing and few references to the published literature are available. In those cases without published references, either agency representatives or internal reports are cited. In any case, it seems clear that the trend is towards a data model built on a basic set of topological elements and superimposed with a set of cartographic features.

U.S. Bureau of the Census

The U.S. Bureau of the Census has developed the Topologically Integrated Geographic Encoding and Referencing (TIGER) system for its use in automating the geographic support system required for the 1990 Decennial Census. The

291

geographic data contained in TIGER consists of a set of topological elements with a set of feature directories and lists. The topological elements are represented by 0-, 1-, and 2- cells. Feature lists (containing items such as landmarks, road names, and county names) reference the appropriate set of topological elements that make up the features (Marx, 1986; Kinnear, 1987).

U.S. Defense Mapping Agency

As part of its Mark 90 modernization effort, the United States Defense Mapping Agency (DMA) has developed a new data structure called MINITOPO (also referred to as its "Advanced Mapping Charting and Geodesy" (MC&G) format). The data model underlying the MINITOPO structure consists of the following elements: nodes, edges, faces, point feature components, line feature components, area feature components, and features. The nodes, edges, and faces correspond to 0, 1, and 2 dimensional topological objects. The point, line, and area feature components are groupings of topologic objects of the same dimension. Features are collections of feature components or of other features. Attributes are associated with either the features or feature components (C. Kottman, DMA, pers.comm.).

NATO Military Geographic Services

As part of the efforts to enhance the exchange and use of geographic data among the various commands of the North Atlantic Treaty Organization (NATO) a group called the Digital Geographic Information Working Group, composed of representatives from various NATO Military Geographic Services, has developed a Digital Geographic Information Exchange Standard. The data model used in this standard is basically the same as that of MINITOPO except for the fact that feature components are considered the same as features (J. Garrison, DMA, personal communication).

Institut Geographique National

The Institut Geographique National (IGN), France, is in the process of creating several digital cartographic data bases, one with data commensurate with 1:25,000-scale mapping, and the other with 1:100,000-scale mapping. The data model used in these consists of a set of "elementary objects" corresponding to topological elements and a set of "complex objects" made up of the elementary objects. Descriptive information is associated with the complex objects (Benard and Piquet-Pellorce, 1986; Salge, 1986 and Salge, IGN, pers.comm.).

Landesvermessungamt Nordrhein-Westfallen

The Landesvermessungamt Nordrhein-Westfallen is designing both a digital cadastral map data base and a Digital Land Model (with data appropriate for mapping at scales from 1:5,000 to 1:1,000,000). These activities in the North Rhine - Westfalia region are part of a nationwide project to create the Official Topographic-Cartographic Information System (ATKIS). The Digital Land Model consists of objects that were classified into "point-shaped, line-shaped and area-shaped objects" and are further characterized with attributes. An object has pointers to other objects and to object parts. For each object there may be defined several attributes of different attribute types and references of different types to other objects (Barwinski and Bruggeman, 1986; Bruggeman, LVA, pers.comm.)

COMMONALITY VIA SDTS

Using DLG-E as an example it has been shown how SDTS can be used in the transfer of spatial information that is described in terms of a feature based data model. It is postulated that other feature based data models can be implemented in a similar fashion within SDTS. Indeed a common implementation of SDTS is one mechanism to foster (or promote) exchange of global data. It is through a common implementation of SDTS (along with common definitions of features) that USGS and DMA are endeavoring to define a baseline specification that will allow them to provide uniform data (with respect to structure and content) to their joint user communities. The first candidate data base to conform to this proposed baseline would be DMA's Digital Chart of the World (a digital representation of all of the features shown on the 1:1,000,000-scale Operational Navigational Charts). If others can follow this example and agree on such a common implementation, then the promise of transparent data exchange and the construction of global data bases may be much closer to reality.

SUMMARY

The DLG-E design provides a flexible framework for modeling spatial data. The model builds a feature layer upon a foundation of spatial objects that conform to the principles of graph theory and topology. It is believed that DLG-E can readily accommodate present and future requirements for a comprehensive model for information supplied by the Geological Survey.

DLG-E also serves as an example of the type of feature-based data models that are being developed by various other mapping agencies around the world. Since SDTS provides a mechanism for transfer of this data, a common implementation of SDTS could foster global exchange and use of data sets from various producers of feature based data. This would expedite both: 1) the panelling of data sets of the same phenomenon, but of less than global extent into a data base with global coverage; and 2) the merger of data sets of related phenomenon with global extent. Developers of future global databases should note this apparent trend towards the use of feature based spatial data models and consider it in the design of their system.

ACKNOWLEDGMENT

This paper draws upon the work of an ad-hoc National Mapping Division study team consisting of the authors and Michael A. Domaratz, Kenneth J. Boyko, and David E. Hair. Their contributions to the development of the DLG-E data model design are gratefully acknowledged.

REFERENCES

Barwinski, Klaus, and Bruggeman, Heinz, 1986. 'Development of Digital Cadastral and Topographic Maps - Requirements, Goals, and Basic Concept'. Proceedings, AutoCarto London, ed. M. Blakemore, Vol. 2, 76-85.

Bernard, Antoine and Piquet-Pellorce, Daniel, 1986. 'A Workstation for Handling Located Data : PISTIL'. Proceedings, AutoCarto London, ed. M. Blakemore, Vol. 1, 166-174.

Callahan, G.M., and Olsen, R.W., 1987. 'Digital Systems Development at the U.S. Geological Survey'. Proceedings, International Cartographic Association Conference, Morelia, Michoacan, Mexico, October 12-21 [in press].

Goodchild, Michael F., 1987. 'Towards an Enumeration and Classification of GIS Functions'. Proceedings, International GIS Symposium, Arlington, Virginia, November, 1987 [in press].

Guptill, S.C., 1986. 'A New Design for the U.S. Geological Survey's National Digital Cartographic Data Base'. Proceedings, Auto Carto London, ed. M. Blakemore, Vol. 2, 10-18.

Guptill, S.C., Fegeas, R.G., and Domaratz, M.A., 1988. 'Designing an Enhanced Digital Line Graph'. American Congress on Surveying and Mapping, 1988 ACSM-ASPRS Annual Convention, Technical Papers, Vol. 2, 252 - 261.

Kinnear, C., 1987. 'The TIGER Structure'. Proceedings, Auto Carto 8, Baltimore, MD, 249-257.

Marx, R.W., 1986. 'The TIGER System: Automating the Geographic Structure of the United States Census'. Government Publications Review, 13, 181-201.

Peuquet, Donna J., 1984. 'A Conceptual Framework and Comparison of Spatial Data Models'. Cartographica 21(4), 66-113.

Salge, Francois and Piquet-Pellorce, Daniel, 1986. 'The I.G.N. Small Scale Geographical Data Base (1:100,000 to 1:500,000)'. Proceedings, Auto Carto London, ed. M. Blakemore, Vol. 1, 433-446.

The American Cartographer, 1988. The Proposed Standard for Digital Cartographic Data. Vol. 15(1), 144 p.

U.S. Geological Survey, 1986. Digital Line Graphs from 1:24,000-Scale Maps. U.S. Geological Survey Data Users Guide 1, 109 p.

GLOBAL DATABASE PLANNING EFFORTS
BY THE U.S. GEOLOGICAL SURVEY

Gary W. Hill and Ronald J. Walton

INTRODUCTION

The United States Geological Survey (USGS) is the Nation's principal earth-science agency whose basic mission is to provide geologic, topographic, and hydrologic information that contributes to the wise management of U.S. natural resources. The information resources to support this mission consist of maps, databases, and descriptions and analyses of the water, energy and mineral resources, land surface, underlying geologic structure, and dynamic processes of the Earth.

The management of these information resources effectively requires the use of appropriate computer technology. Technologies to create, manipulate and disseminate earth science information are being applied by USGS scientists to help them accomplish their research mission. The application of these technologies in the USGS is directed to allowing us to integrate our earth-science data and to allow interpretation of spatial and temporal processes for our earth-science studies. Tools for handling the large volumes of spatial data are being developed for researches to allow more effective use of our data. Significant contributions have already been made and additional studies planned are relevant to global change. USGS Director, Dallas Peck, is chairman of the Committee for Earth-Sciences of the Federal Coordinating Council for Science, Engineering and Technology (FCCSET). FCCSET is directly under the President's Office of Science and Technology Policy, which has been the primary focus for U.S. interagency coordination of global change.

Currently an Interagency Work Group on Data Management for Global Change is developing a strategy and implementation plan for an Earth Science Information System. Members include representatives from the USGS, National Oceanic and Atmospheric Administration (NOAA), National Aeronautics and Space Administration (NASA), Department of Energy (DOE),

National Science Foundation (NSF), Department of State (DOS), and the Department of Defense (DOD). The charge for this interagency work group is to make it as easy as possible for scientists and others to access or acquire data appropriate to the study of global change. The goal is to develop a national data and information system for global change research that is consistent across agencies and involves and supports university and other user communities. Work has already begun in developing directories, catalogs, and inventories of data. The strategy of the work group is to use existing mechanisms to achieve their goals by demonstrating successes when possible through prototypes and to develop a system consistent with the evolving international framework. Advisory groups will also be employed for guidance and oversight.

The study of global processes will require an integration of all of our solid Earth geoscience data. A key factor in their integration is standard data formats and structures for earth-science data. Data from different sources at different sites and with different resolutions requires a standard method of reporting. An example of this type of data standard is the geographic point location standard developed by the USGS in cooperation with other agencies and now in use throughout the U.S. Government as a Federal Information Processing Standard (FIPS). Other data standards have been developed with USGS as lead agency as designated by the National Bureau of Standards (NBS). The ability to transfer spatial data from different systems without conversion requires a data exchange standard. The U.S. National Committee for Digital Cartographic Data Standards (NCDDS) is promulgating the Spatial Data Transfer Specification (SDTS) for this purpose. The SDTS is an attempt to meet the recognized need for easy transfer of spatial data whether in raster or vector form from one spatial data handling system to another.

New technologies and tools are being developed and applied to the collection, storage, analysis, and display of earth-science data at the USGS. Similar tools and technology will be required for global change studies in order to identify, analyze, and observe both natural and anthropogenic changes that are occurring over time and space and to understand their implications for the future of our planet's ecosystem. These technologies and tools include geographic information systems (GIS), supercomputers, artificial intelligence (AI) and relational database management systems (RDBMS).

APPLICATION OF COMPUTER TECHNOLOGIES IN GLOBAL DATABASE PLANNING

The concept of global change is a theme that cuts across many disciplines to look at the potential consequences of man's activities superimposed on natural changes. The USGS has much to offer in the study and documentation of global change. The USGS mission is a national mission, but one which extends to a global perspective as well. To accomplish this mission, the USGS pursues and applies new technologies to collect, integrate, and interpret earth-science data.

One of the new technologies, which the USGS has placed a great deal of emphasis on, is the Geographic Information System (GIS). A GIS is a computer hardware and software system designed to collect, manage, analyze, and display spatially referenced data. GIS project funding by the USGS Director over the last three years has been substantial, about $3.2 million, supporting 20 projects. A new GIS lab has been established at USGS headquarters in Reston, Virginia, and new GIS labs are in the process of being established at our western (Menlo Park, CA) and central (Denver, CO) region centers. These labs will provide shared facilities for GIS equipment and software for interdisciplinary application development. Application specialists in geology, geophysics, hydrology, geography, cartography, and computer science will have access to a full range of GIS hardware and software when these labs are fully operational. These GIS efforts have led to a substantial enhancement of methods for representing spatial information and exchanging digital data among various systems. In addition, recent results from cooperative application projects (e.g. National Coal Resources Data System) are enabling the USGS to make appropriate responses to digital earth-science data users at the local, state, national, and international levels.

Other technologies being applied for the interpretation of earth-science data include expert systems and supercomputer(s). Active Artificial Intelligence (AI) Special Interest Groups (SIG) exist in each of the regional centers and promote the application of expert system technologies to the analysis and understanding of integrated earth-science data. Current efforts are underway to develop memoranda of understanding(s) (MOU) with three major supercomputer centers in the United States for use of their supercomputers. Supercomputers are expected to foster advances in computational analysis applied to geologic modeling. Plans are to develop sharing of supercomputer capabilities at Florida State University, University of California-San Diego (National Science Foundation-NSF Center) and at Los Alamos National Lab (Department of Energy-DOE). Earth scientists at each of these centers will benefit from increased access to and use of USGS data in their computational geoscience research.

A common Relational Data Base Management System (RDBMS) is planned for the Office of Energy and Marine Geology (OEMG) to allow integration of various minicomputers and microcomputers. OEMG has an assortment of DEC/VAX, Data General and PRIME minicomputers and SUN workstations. Microcomputers include IBM PC/XT and AT (or compatibles) and APPLE PC's. A common RDBMS will permit sharing of data and integration of our databases that reside on a network of different vendor's machines.

The INGRES RDBMS by Relational Technology Inc. (RTI) was chosen as the standard for storage, retrieval, and manipulation of data on OEMG minicomputers and microcomputers. The database plan will integrate our five types of data for broad geologic studies: (1) geological, (2) geophysical, (3) geochemical, (4) cartographic and digital spatial, and (5) image-related data.

DATABASES IN OEMG AND PROBLEMS IN THEIR USE

Geological data in our office includes data stored as point-source interpretations and summaries of energy-related and marine-related data observations. Summaries of oil, gas, and coal resources related to fields or counties of the U.S. predominate these holdings. The marine data is organized on the basis of oceanographic cruises or voyages. The marine program has three major elements: (1) Regional Geologic Framework, (2) Marine Deposits and Sedimentary Dynamics, and (3) Formation of Marine Energy and Mineral Deposits. The Continental Margin Mapping (CONMAP) and Geological LOng-Range Inclined Asdic (GLORIA) programs are a part of these marine programs. The CONMAP project to prepare a series of maps of the United States Exclusive Economic Zone (EEZ) is in response to a need to reference and disseminate geographically oriented marine data and information. The CONMAP project will characterize, at a reconnaissance scale, the geological framework, mineral resources, geohazards, and offshore geological and geophysical processes of the U.S. EEZ. This map series will provide continuous coverage at a scale of 1:1Mof the areas covering the EEZ of the U.S. and is being prepared by computer, using an Albers conic equal-area projection.

A computer software system for MAP GENeration (MAPGEN) processes the thematic data sets for each map sheet into registered digital cartographic overlays. These overlays are organized basically in a computer file system as an electronic map library for EEZ geological and geophysical data. After the marine data is analyzed and results published, the data is made available to the public on a systematic basis through the NOAA National Geophysical and National Oceanographic Data Centers.

These geological databases are created and maintained in numerous ways. The oil and gas data summaries are primarily provided to us by contractors. The oil and gas well data and associated production data in the U.S. is provided by Petroleum Information (PI) Corporation, a part of Dunn and Bradstreet. Subsets of these databases are then utilized in minis and micros for individual project studies. Likewise, for oil and gas data by fields and reservoirs, these data are provided by Nehring and Associates, a small firm in Colorado Springs, Colorado, and subsets are used on minis and micros for project studies.

The coal resources data, which is the basis of our coal correlative studies are provided in-house and through cooperative agreements with our coal-producing state geological survey(s). Subsets of these data are used on minis or micros as well. In addition, each state maintains its own coal data set on their own computer equipment which is linked to OEMG computers.

Geophysical data consists primarily of digitized logs of wells and seismic data collected on magnetic tape. Log and seismic data are not stored in a permanent on-line database due to the enormous amount of conventional storage required. However, current efforts are underway to look at unconventional storage media, such as VHS video tape and optical disk as storage media for this purpose. Large Digicon DISCO geophysical systems are installed in our Central and Western Region Offices for seismic stratigraphic interpretation studies. However, data entry, access, analysis, and evaluation of geophysical logs is limited by current technology. Paper logs can be digitized by machine, but interpretation capabilities are limited. CAD/CAM technology advances offer future opportunities for manipulation, analysis, and display.

Geochemical data resulting from analyses of rock samples are stored in the Rock Analysis Storage System (RASS). RASS is a quasi on-line system for data entry, validation, editing, storage, and retrieval of geochemical data by sample and by location. Compatibility with other related data sets is important but limited at the current time.

Current image-related data include tape archives of GLORIA data. GLORIA is a long-range sidescan sonar system developed at the United Kingdom's Institute of Oceanographic Sciences (IOS). Sidescan sonar was selected as the method to map our EEZ (about 3.4 million square nautical miles) because large areas can be mapped quickly. For example, the west coast EEZ (approximately 275,000 square nautical miles) was mapped from Canada to Mexico in 98 days in the summer of 1984 and is available in the Atlas of the Exclusive Economic Zone, Western Conterminous U.S. (1986). The atlas is composed of three sections which include the sonar-imaging mosaics of the EEZ seafloor along with generalized geologic interpretations and bathymetry, the seismic-reflection data collected during the surveys, and the data on bathymetry and residual magnetic anomalies throughout the survey area.

RELATED USGS SPATIAL DATABASES

The creation, maintenance, and distribution of digital cartographic data sets representing the contents of the topographic base map series is the responsibility of the Survey's National Mapping Division (NMD). Base categories of information are being digitized from its topographic maps and the data available from the National Digital Cartographic Data Base in two forms: digital line graphs (DLG) and digital elevation models (DEM). Digital line graphs are digital files consisting of planimetric (line map) information. Currently, the following categories of DLG's are being collected from 1:24,000-scale maps: the Public Land Survey System, boundaries, hydrography, transportation, and a limited amount of topographic relief. The 48 conterminous states have complete coverage of transportation and hydrography information as portrayed on the 1:100,000-scale map series. This 1:100,000-scale database, completed in cooperation with the U.S. Bureau of the Census, forms a comprehensive set of information for regional and national GIS analyses. Boundary, hydrography, and transportation features from the 1:2M scale sectional maps of the National Atlas of the United States of America are also available. Digital elevation models (a set of regularly spaced elevations) are available for about 20% of the 7-minute quadrangle series (with a 30-m horizontal spacing of the data) and for all of the 1:250,000 scale map series, with a 3-arc-second spacing of data points.

During the decade in which the Survey has been producing DLG data, the tasks for which the data are being used have become increasingly sophisticated. This has placed information demands on the data that were not planned for in its initial design. To respond to these requirements, USGS has begun the design of an enhanced version of the DLG, termed Digital Line Graph - Enhanced (DLG-E).

In simple terms, the DLG-E begins with the topological structure of the DLG and builds a cartographic feature layer upon the topology. The feature definition is open-ended, allowing users to define features of interest. Typically, these might be named features, such as the Potomac River. Cartographic entities and features will be described using an entity name/attribute value method of attribute coding. In addition, recommendations contained in the Spatial Data Transfer Specification regarding data quality information and formatting will be followed.

Other mapping agencies, including the U.S. Defense Mapping Agency, the French Institute Geographic National, the military mapping components of the NATO allies, and the mapping agencies of West Germany are using a feature based data model similar to the DLG-E model. This trend should be noted in the design of any future global databases.

PROGRESS IN DATABASE ADMINISTRATION FOR GLOBAL STUDIES

The collection and maintenance of the earth-science data-bases will be required for global data studies. A Data Base Administration (DBA) function to provide for a uniform database and for its maintenance will be essential. Modularity and flexibility in the database system are key concepts.

The basic approach is to provide a tool box of RDBMS tools that are interconnected to allow each project scientist to choose the best tool available for the task at hand. In some cases, the supercomputing tool for large database modeling will be best; in other cases, the microcomputer tool may be best for small database jobs. In other cases, the minicomputer RDBMS may be best. In each case, the user has an assortment of tools available for the appropriate job. However, these tools need to be interconnected in order to more easily access and integrate the databases.

Design and maintenance of databases is a substantial effort and one that must be planned. All pertinent data in given geological, geophysical, chemical, and cartographic fields must be input, updated, corrected, and modified as necessary in a timely fashion. Security of the database must be provided for as well, along with the integrity of the database.

Databases must be organized not only to allow efficient use of unique data sets, but also to allow distribution of these data over different physical locations. Project scientists in one location are more likely to have similar tools to use than scientists who are located in many different offices but may be looking at the same data sets. The DBA function must provide for the flexibility of using whatever tool is best adapted to the given task at hand with the resources available at that location.

Data standards are another DBA asset to integration of our data. Data standards which have been developed include the "Specifications for Representation of Geographic Point Locations for Information Interchange". This is described in USGS Circular 878-B (1983) and Federal Information Processing Standard (FIPS) Publication 70-1 (1986). Another data standard developed for hydrological data is the "Codes for Identification of Hydrologic Units in the U.S. and the Caribbean areas", USGS Circular 878-A (1982) and FIPS Publication 103 (1983). Additional data standards being developed currently include aquifer names and geologic unit codes, classification of wetlands and wildlife service, EPA parameter codes, codes for taxonomic identification of flora and fauna, land use and land cover codes, public land survey codes, and cartographic attribute /feature codes. All of these data standards will assist in data management and database administration by providing a standard method of reporting these data.

In a related area of activity, the Geological Survey has been delegated the lead role in implementing the Office of Management and Budget objective of fostering better coordination of all U.S. Federal digital cartography programs. In that role, the Geological Survey chairs the Federal Interagency Coordinating Committee on Digital Cartography. The Geological Survey also coordinates digital cartographic data programs and activities within the Department of the Interior by chairing the Interior

Digital Cartography Coordinating Committee. The Geological Survey continues to identify and respond to Federal digital cartography data requirements to provide a means for development of data standards, to serve as a forum for exchange of information on digital technology and methods, and to facilitate private sector use of the data.

The Federal Interagency Coordinating Committee on Digital Cartography and the Interior Digital Cartography Coordinating Committee are currently reviewing a draft digital cartographic data exchange standard. The proposed cartographic data transfer format standard is referred to as the Spatial Data Transfer Specification (SDTS), which will allow spatial data to be transferred from one system to another. SDTS was published in the Journal of ACSM (1988). During 1988 plans are to test SDTS and submit to the National Bureau of Standard (NBS) as a proposed FIPS initiative in 1989. This proposed standard will allow easier transfer of spatial data from one system to another.

PROBLEMS IN IMPLEMENTATION OF DATABASE TECHNOLOGIES

Current budgetary and personnel constraints in the Federal sector are significant factors in our database implementation plans. Efforts are more likely to succeed by utilizing existing staff and implementing from the "bottom up" within our existing computing staffs.

Current computer databases suffer from a lack of systematic methods for storage, retrieval, and dissemination. INGRES RDBMS will provide OEMG (only one office of 600 people in the Geologic Division) the tools for solving this problem in the future. However, in the meantime, correlation of our data, such as stratigraphic versus geochemical versus PI is still primarily limited to manual methods. Data exchange for purposes of working on similar aspects of geologic problems is difficult. Development of standards for definition, accuracy, and format of earth-science data will help, but progress in the development of these standards is slow. Multi-disciplinary studies, such as OEMG's sedimentary basin analysis program, suffer from the logistics of getting data from one system to another.

There is redundancy and overlap with duplication in much of our database analysis, storage, retrieval, and display. Due to the inability to transport programs from one vendor's system to another without major program conversion effort, many programs and data sets are duplicated.

Many of the existing problems outlined can be partially or wholly solved by a common operating system for all of our different systems and with the use of INGRES as a common RDBMS. However, many existing systems are totally dependent on current operating systems, and major conversion efforts would be required to go to one common operating system. Much research is still needed in database technologies to permit integration of systems, data sets, programs, and operation to allow studies to be conducted on a global-wide basis.

CONCLUSIONS AND RECOMMENDATIONS

This paper does not suggest ways in which USGS or other Earth observations can be stored and integrated for studies of global spatial processes. However, USGS efforts in database design and application of new technology in integrating our data sets for nationwide (small-scale) to local (large-scale) studies, will shed some light on the subject.

The USGS and the OEMG face a formidable task to integrate our data sets. We believe that using a RDBMS will be a major asset in that endeavor. I would recommend similar approaches where one has many different types of systems. Earth-science data standards are being developed in our operational programs, including the Spatial Data Transfer Specification (SDTS) and geographic point location standard. These will be of help by providing a standard method of reporting location data and a procedure for transfer of spatial data from one system to another.

Current GIS technologies and their application to Earth studies will assist us in understanding spatial processes. GIS research and development should be expanded and coordinated on an international basis. Expert systems allow us to capture the expertise of our scientific staff and develop techniques for analysis and understanding of Earth processes. Knowledge-based technologies should be applied on a broader basis for earth-science studies.

Access to supercomputing resources will provide the computational power to utilize large global databases. Supercomputer simulation can complement these studies. Supercomputers with large memory and special architectures can perform calculations much more rapidly and need to provide real time answers and images. Modeling of global changes as observed from analyses of these databases will be possible with these supercomputer resources. The computers will allow simulation of more complicated processes than conventional machines. The supercomputer tool will complete the spectrum of our tool box of computational resources and is one of the essential tools needed for future global monitoring of changes in and on the Earth.

Global-change studies provide an opportunity for international cooperation and collaboration. The barriers to such collaboration are problems that arise from the incompatibilities of our earth science observations, computer systems, and the difficulty sharing these data and systems. The degree to which these incompatibilities can be overcome will determine the degree to which we are able to apply our scientific expertise to global-change studies and the understanding of global spatial processes.

LITERATURE CITED

EEZ Scan 84 Scientific Staff, 1986. Atlas of the Exclusive Economic Zone, Western Conterminous United States. U.S. Geological Survey Miscellaneous Investigations Series Map I-1792.

Journal of American Congress on Surveying and Mapping (ACSM), 1988. The Proposed Standard for Digital Cartographic Data (ed. Richard E. Dahlberg). The American Cartographer, 15(1), 9-142.

National Bureau of Standards, 1983. Codes for the Identification of Hydrologic Units in the United States and the Caribbean Outlying Areas. FIPS Pub 103.

National Bureau of Standards, 1986. Specifications for Representation of Geographic Point Locations for Information Interchange. FIPS Pub 70-1.

U.S. Geological Survey, 1982. Codes for the Identification of Hydrologic Units in the United States and the Caribbean Outlying Areas. U.S. Geological Survey Circular 878-A, p. A-A115.

U.S. Geological Survey, 1983. Specifications for Representation of Geographic Point Locations for Information Interchange. U.S. Geological Survey Circular 878-B, p. B1-B24.

SOME VIEWS ON GEOREFERENCED DIGITAL DATABASES

Denny Kalensky

THE DEVELOPMENT OF A GEOGRAPHIC INFORMATION SYSTEM AT FAO

In 1983 an Interdepartmental Working Group on Land Use Planning was created by the Director-General to strengthen interdisciplinary co-ordination in the Organisation's field and Headquarters land use planning activities. This Group was <u>inter alia</u> to advise on creation of an integrated geographic resource database within FAO, for worldwide, regional and national land use planning. A subgroup was therefore created to:

- review and inventorise existing databases within FAO and identify the needs and feasibility for linkage of the existing systems;

- advise whether FAO should develop an integrated data system, what steps would be required to achieve such implementation and what were the implications.

The inventory of databases was carried out during 1984. It revealed that the 29 existing operational thematic databases and the ten others under development were largely unconnected. Twelve of them have information recorded at a more detailed level than the country (subcountry, smaller administrative units, polygon or point/station) of which ten cover either a Continent (region) or the world at large. Some of these databases relate to a single variable (soil, rainfall) and the others to a combination of variables (e.g. agro-ecological zone land resource, population potential).

The ten thematic databases covering a region or the world at large have the following names:

- Agro-ecological zone land resource
- Population potentials (potential land population supporting capacities at three levels of agricultural inputs)
- Irrigation potential

- Agro-climatological data
- Rainfall series for probability analysis
- Tsetse area (Africa)
- Africa desertification hazard map (with UNEP)
- Soil map of the world (with Unesco)
- Food consumption and nutrition (under development)
- World census of agriculture 1990 (under development

More recently two additional databases have been developed and are nearing completion, which are:

- Forest vegetation cover (tropical world)
- "Ecofloristic zone" map (tropical world).

Other georeferenced data on seasonal rainfall and yearly integrated vegetation indices will be available in the near future from a system being developed at FAO for acquisition and processing of METEOSAT and NOAA satellite data.

Linkage between all these databases and those to be developed in the future, whether of a physical or socio-economical nature and their combined use can greatly enhance FAO's capability to assist the community of its member countries. This assistance takes the form in particular of integrated surveys and outlook studies at national, subregional, regional and worldwide levels which FAO carries out at Headquarters, in compliance with its mandate as the intergovernmental organisation dealing with food, nutrition, agriculture, forestry and fisheries and related resources and products.

However, FAO also assists its member countries through its two thousand and five hundred field projects, mostly at national, subnational and local levels, which have a total budget of US $2 billion. Development of FAO's GIS capability and expertise in this field is required to assist individual countries in GIS applications to land use planning activities.

A feasibility study for the establishment of a GIS at Head-quarters identified some thirty products required by the various technical units for the period up to 1991 which could be obtained from an operational GIS. Examples of such products and their input layers are shown in Table 1.

GIS Products	Input Layers
Irrigable Soils Map	Integrated Terrain Unit Map (1:5M) Updated Soils Map (1:1M) Hydrologic Basins (1:5M) Mean Annual Rainfall (1:5M)
Aquifer Ranking Map	Integrated Terrain Unit Map (1:5M) Updated Soil Map (1:1M) Shoreline Map (1:5M) Administrative Units (1:5M) Hydrologic Basins (1:5M) Mean Annual Rainfall Map (1:5M)
Land Classification for Irrigation Potential Map	Integrated Terrain Unit Map (1:5M) Mean Annual Rainfall (1:5M) Irrigable Soils Map* (1:2M) Aquifer Ranking Map* (1:2M) Hydrologic Basins (1:5M) Shoreline Map (1:5M) Surface Hydrology Map (1:5M) Infrastructure Map (1:5M)
Population supporting Capacities Map and List	Agro-Ecological Zone Map (1:1M) Irrigable Soils Map* (1:5M) Integrated Terrain Unit Map (1:5M) Country Population data
Composite Degradation Hazard Map (1:1M)	Soil Constraint Map* (1:1M) Salinization Map* (1:1M) Water Action Map* (1:1M) Wind Action Map* (1:1M) Animal Pressure Map* (1:1M) Population Pressure Map* (1:1M) Shoreline Map (1:5M) Administrative Units Map (1:5M) Infrastructure Map (1:5M) Surface Hydrology Map (1:5M) Major Elevation Zones (1:5M)
Environmental Degra- dation Hazards Forest Degradation	Composite Degradation Hazard Map* (1:1M) Vegetation Map (1:5M) Administrative Units Map (1:5M)

Table 1: FAO product requirements.   * Interim products

The feasibility study concluded that there was sufficient need for manipulation of spatial data within FAO to justify the establishment of a GIS at FAO Headquarters.

A VAX 11-750 minicomputer available at FAO Headquarters was reserved for GIS applications. It is being used in the current preparatory phase for evaluation of GIS software by benchmark testing and for other on-going GIS work by the main user units. One vector and one raster-based GIS software (ARC/INFO and ERDAS) are being used during this phase. The final GIS hardware-software configuration will be selected after completion of this preparatory phase at the end of this year and FAO will then enter into the implementation phase proper.

FAO'S PERCEPTION OF SOME TECHNICAL ISSUES RELATED TO DIGITAL DATABASES AND GIS

The comments which follow on some of the technical and scientific issues proposed for discussion during the meeting reflect FAO's viewpoint and priorities as a user and developer of global and regional digital databases (as well as national ones in co-operation with member countries).

Some of these issues need to be considered in view of the expected future developments in computer technology. Such developments, in the past already introduced the terms "cashless banking" and "paperless office". Someday we may also speak about "paperless cartography". Encyclopaedias and dictionaries are already sold on optical disks. If we consider how we use maps, we may realise that atlases may also follow suit soon.

Often we need to look at maps to see the spatial relationship of objects. Sometimes we use them to calculate distances or areas. In yet other applications, such as navigation, we may need the maps to identify location and to chart the future course. We may agree that in many such instances we may not actually need a hard copy of the map we are using. It may be easier for a computer to calculate distances or areas or carry out navigation from an electronically stored map. A "soft copy" displayed on a colour monitor may be sufficient for most purposes. In fact electronic displays have several advantages over printed copies. A large amount of effort goes into making the maps pleasing or less confusing to the human eye. With the soft copies, this problem is easier to solve. Users can eliminate the features they do not need on the screen, they can modify shapes or colours of the symbols, zoom on an area or even make some features blink.

Issues related to integration for global information systems

The first major FAO effort in development of global databases was the preparation of a World Soil Map at 1:5M scale. This work involved manual integration of many soil maps which were available only at different projections, scales and legends.

The base map chosen for the soil map was made in two different projections, namely Miller Oblate Stereographic Projection and Bipolar Conic Conformal Projection for the Eastern and Western hemispheres respectively. The selection of the base map was done quite carefully after long investigations in the early 'sixties. At a time when GIS was just starting, little attention was paid to the unavailability of analytical conversion methods for its two projections. The selection of these projections proved to be rather unfortunate.

It is difficult to estimate the amount of work that went into the preparation of the soil map. Even a conservative estimate would be over one hundred and fifty man-years. The amount of manual labour that was required for conversion of scales and projections and for planimetering can be contrasted with the capabilities provided by GIS to-day.

FAO has recently initiated work on updating of the Soil Map of the World in co-operation with other International and national institutions. A trial area covering the Nile Basin at 1:1 million scale has been correlated using a revised map legend and the Operational Navigation Charts as the base map.

Another major digital database product is an integrated terrain unit map for Africa at 1:5M scale. This map was prepared for FAO under a contract for mitigation of the "silver polygons" problem often encountered in overlay operations. It includes seven layers of maps with a total of approximately 40,000 polygons with nineteen attributes each. Forty-five man-months of specialist time were needed to complete it manually.

311

Some issues related to costs including copyright and data interchange formats

The cost of reproducing a map from a GIS database is much lower than a colour reproduction on paper, re-printing paper maps, particularly if revision is involved. The most expensive part of a digitised map is the cost of digitising. But in most cases even this is cheaper than preparing a map for colour printing. As digitised maps are used more widely, the cost of digitising can be spread to many users and eventually a digitised map on an optical disk may cost less than the same database on paper.

Two actions are important for reducing the cost of digital databases; they are the establishment of:

a) copyrights: copyrights will encourage companies to invest in digitising maps and developing databases because they can recover their expenses from the users;

b) standards for data interchange formats: FAO, as an international organisation with one hundred and fifty-eight member countries, cannot over-emphasise the importance of this aspect.

Interchange standards do not have to be identical with the internal data structures used by the GIS software. However, each software should at least have a routine for converting to and from one specific format for interchanging the data with other GIS software. It may be necessary to have several such standards, e.g. raster and vector formats at least. These standards should be applicable to PCs and main frames, optical disks, tapes and floppies. Endorsing a particular optical disk standard is especially important at present, because they have a potential for widespread application in GIS.

In establishment of raster formats we should co-operate with institutions that supply satellite imagery. At least the optical disk formats of raster GIS and remote sensing data should be compatible.

Interchange standards should also include a note on data quality, origin of the data, how and when the map was prepared and digitised and all the other relevant information which may be needed by the user.

Current prices of GIS software will not be an impediment to widespread use of GIS. Once the digitised databases become available on optical disks at prices comparable to the price of a printed atlas, prices of at least the PC versions of GIS software will also come down dramatically, as it has already occurred for other database management systems.

Some issues related to capabilities of GIS software

Most GIS software packages need to be improved in many aspects before they can be used more widely. Particularly needed are more user-friendliness and better help routines. The level of training and computer expertise needed for using currently available GIS is much too high.

GIS software should be much easier to learn and use. Help routines should be expanded to give information not only on available tools but also on what tools should be used and in which order to achieve a particular result. Development of software based on expert system techniques will also be useful in this regard. Error diagnostics should also be improved. When something goes wrong, the user should be given sufficient information to correct the situation. The user should be informed at every intermediate stage about what has been done so far. The software should take every opportunity to instruct the user about its functions. Advanced users should be able to turn off the instruction routines. Needless to say, good documentation, tutorial and demonstration routines are also very important in this respect.

There is considerable room for improvement also in some other aspects of GIS software. The difficulties that particularly stand out are slowness and unreliability of vector software in overlay operations. Better algorithms for vectorising scanner output data are also needed; current algorithms do not produce clean vector data and require too much editing. At present most GIS operations require too much human intervention: application of artificial intelligence techniques to GIS may reduce it in the future.

Issues related to data structures and topological coding

More research is needed also in the areas of data stuctures, degree of topological coding and performance characteristics of spatial data processing algorithms. Data structures, coding schemes, algorithms and programming techniques which would make parallel processing of vector data possible would be particularly helpful. Optical disks, cheaper memory and array processors can make raster formats much more advantageous than they are to-day.

It may even be feasible to store and maintain two copies of all the databases, one in vector and another in raster formats. Development of some fast hybrid algorithms may then permit the simultaneous use of both types of data. Also it may be possible to develop some algorithms which can provide approximate quick look results by taking advantage of such a dual database. Such algorithms would be particularly useful as a guide to non-experts and in preparation of large operations.

Issues related to quality of data

Besides improvements in the software, we also need some improvements in quality of data. Digital databases have to comply with some special requirements so that the results we obtain in some complex operations can be meaningful.

The formation of sliver polygons in many natural resource applications are often due to representation of continuous variation patterns by sharp lines on the original thematic maps. One way to solve this problem is manual integration of the layers on the paper maps before digitising. Another solution might be inclusion of some information on the reliability of classes on the thematic maps or confidence widths of boundaries. An indication of the confidence levels of classes of confidence widths of boundaries might be too impractical on paper maps but it would not be so in a computer database. Some algorithms based on the theory of fuzzy sets can use this extra information for elimination of the slivers more accurately. In thematic maps made from remotely sensed data, such confidence level information is only already available as a by-product of the classification process.

CONCLUSION

FAO intends to continue digitising and integrating its global and regional georeferenced databases for their more efficient utilisation, and to support its member countries in this field at national and subnational levels. It considers it important to resolve some of the main issues to be discussed during the meeting, such as that of data interchange standards; and it looks forward with interest to the conclusions and recommendations of the meeting.

314

APPLICATIONS OF GEOGRAPHICAL INFORMATION SYSTEMS WITHIN THE UNITED NATIONS ENVIRONMENT PROGRAMME

D. Wayne Mooneyhan

ABSTRACT

The Global Environment Monitoring System, a major element of the United Nations Environment Programme (UNEP) has been developing data collection networks for environmental data since it was founded in 1974. These data plus historical data stored in data banks around the world plus information developed from todays satellite systems provide an immeasurable quantity of information about our globe. Since these data are collected by many organizations for different purposes and stored in various formats, it is difficult for the average scientist or resource manager to locate and use these data effectively. The Global Resource Information Database (GRID) was established for the purpose of bringing these disparate datasets to a common geographic base and to provide georeferenced integrated environmental datasets to scientists and planners both inside and outside of UNEP. Additionally, GRID provides training in the technology of geographic information systems to scientists and managers from developing countries, such that an increasing number of countries are capable of using the growing information base in the GRID for environmental assessment and development planning.

BACKGROUND

The need for a geographic information system (GIS) with the capability of storing and manipulating global datasets was recognized by the scientists and managers of the GEMS (Global Environment Monitoring System) of UNEP as early as 1981 when consultant experts were employed to study the GEMS requirements and to determine if existing systems could provide the needed capability. The results of the study made by Messrs. Stein Bie and Jurgen Lamp are recorded in a report to GEMS entitled "Criteria, Hardware and Software for a Global Land and Soil Monitoring System", November 1981.

As a follow-up to the study, GEMS convened a group of experts in London, 31 May-3 June 1983, to study the Bie/Lamp report and other sources and recommended to GEMS appropriate options for consideration. The results of the meeting of the Group of Experts are documented in a report entitled "Report on an Ad Hoc Expert Group Meeting to Review of Hardware and Software Criteria for a Global Resource Information Database", June 1983.

Following these reports, GEMS scientists again through a consultant conducted a review of most of the major United Nations databases to determine which of them were appropriate for use in a geographic information system. The report from that study entitled "Global database study for Global Environment Monitoring System of the UNEP", November 1983, also recommended a hardware/software system to support the long term requirements for handling the reviewed databases as well as an interim system to support a pilot phase to determine the feasibility of implementing a GIS within UNEP.

In September 1984 the Executive Director of UNEP reviewed the capabilities of the proposed system and approved the implementation of the pilot system for a period starting in April 1985 through 31 December 1987. In May 1985, a demonstration version of the pilot system was temporarily installed at UNEP headquarters during the meeting of the UNEP Governing Council to demonstrate to the delegates the utility of a GIS for UNEP purposes. Since GRID was designed as a distributed global system, it was decided that the pilot phase would consist of a central processing facility located in Geneva, Switzerland, and an African node located at UNEP headquarters in Nairobi, Kenya. The central processing facility's first computer was made operational in September 1985 and the Nairobi facility became operational approximately 3 months later. All of the equipment and software with minor exceptions were contributed by U.S. organizations and the principle core of professional staff were seconded to UNEP from NASA. Facilities and institutional operations cost were provided by the Canton of Geneva and 10 fellowships for developing countries trainees are provided each year by the Swiss Development Cooperation. Other organizations which are presently providing professional staff are the countries of Norway, Finland, Switzerland, Denmark and the Economic Commission of Europe. The UNEP fund provides for general service and administrative cost and for some equipment, maintenance, and communications cost.

THE PILOT PROJECT

Starting in April 1985 and ending in December 1987, the Pilot Project was given four objectives:

(1) to develop geographic information system (GIS) methodologies and procedures for constructing, manipulating and making available to users global environmental data sets for the purpose of conducting environmental analyses and assessments.

(2) to demonstrate that GIS technology as applied within GRID is an effective tool which combines global and national data sets for resource management and environmental planning applications at the national level.

(3) to establish the framework for co-operation and data exchange within international and intergovernmental organizations which deal with environment-related matters, such as FAO, WHO, WMO, ICSU, ILCA, IUCN, etc.

(4) to provide training opportunities in GIS and data management technologies employed by GRID to the scientists and resource managers from participating developing countries.

Against objective number (1), much progress has been made during approximately 30 months since the first computer was brought on line. One GIS/IP software package has been modified to handle data at a global scale, 22 mathematic map projection transformation software algorithms have been written to transform from 22 different projections into longitude/latitude. Twelve data parameters for the entire world which represent more than 300 global datasets have been accumulated and many of them have been georeferenced and archived. In addition, numerous data parameters for the continent of Africa, the area of special emphasis during the pilot phase, were also entered into the database. A partial list of datasets held in GRID is presented in Annex 2 (at end of paper).

One regional and one continental study have been initiated using the African database. The regional study made in conjunction with CISFAM (Consolidated Information System for Famine Management in Africa) is to develop methods to provide optimum information for prevention of famine related diseases. The continental study is a joint study with the World Wildlife Fund and the ELSA Wild Animal Appeal to determine the environmental and socio-economic factors that constrain the number and distribution of elephants in Africa.

317

In support of objective number (2), numerous case studies are in progress or have been completed with national governments for the purpose of demonstrating that GIS technology applied within GRID is a valuable technical tool at the national level. The problems addressed in these studies were defined by the participating country scientists and resource managers and the scientific and management assessments were the conclusions of the participants. GRID provided the GIS and image processing, assisted in some cases with training in ground truth acquisition and produced the models and final output products. National case studies to date are as follows:

(1) China. Land use planning for resettlement of populations affected by the proposed Three gorges dam. (In progress - early stages).

(2) Costa Rica. Siting of both on shore and near shore aquaculture facilities to accomodate optimum environmental and economic models in the Gulf of Nicoya. A joint study with FAO Fisheries Division and the Costa Rican Fisheries Department. (Completed).

(3) Indonesia. Analysis of carrying capacity of lands of Western Java. (In progress - late stages).

(4) Kenya. Development of a country-wide natural resource database to support numerous studies, such as: fuelwood plantation siting, critical habitat mapping for selected wildlife, etc. The participating Kenyan agency is in the process of implementing a modern GIS. (In progress - middle stages).

(5) Panama. Development of a country-wide natural resource database to support environmental and resource management studies including potential impacts of the three "new canal" alternatives. An operational GIS for Panama is a part of the joint plan. (In progress - middle stages).

(6) Peru. Development of land use potentials in southern province of Chumbivilcas. The participating Peruvian agency has a small operational GIS. (In progress - late stages).

(7) Thailand. Analysis of 10 years of deforestation trends in Chiang Mai Province of northern Thailand and associated environmental hazards including a soil loss study of Mae Klang watershed. (Completed).

(8) Uganda. A nation-wide natural resource database has been constructed to support an analysis of the current distribution of forest and wetlands including a retrospective analysis of area specific change over the past 10 years. (Completed).

(9) Saudi Arabia. A study to map the marine mammal shallow water habitats of the Arabian Gulf jointly with IUCN and the host country has been completed and reported. A second study to identify sites for two national reserves (one coastal and one interior mountains) is nearing completion.

(10) Several projects are in the discussion stages.

Objective number (3) to establish a co-operation and data exchange with other agencies involved in environment related matters has progressed rapidly. It can be noted (see appendix I) that data are being received from many organizations both international and national (i.e. FAO, WMO, WHO, IUCN, NASA, NOAA, etc.). The list of cooperating agencies continues to grow as data needs for GRID develops. Training of developing country scientists and resource managers (objective 4) ha s been very successful with 20 candidates completing training courses in Switzerland in 1986/87/88. The training programme is funded by the Swiss Development Cooperation and conducted in part by the Federal Institute of Technology at Lausanne with GIS training at the GRID-Processor facility in Geneva. Two approaches to training were evaluated in 1986/87. The first was an intensive 90 day course in GIS technology only. The second was a 180 day course which consisted of 60 days of refresher course work in the environmental sciences and a brief course in data management, followed by 120 days of intensive GIS training, in which the trainees in their practice sessions worked on projects from their own country. The second approach proved to be the most effective and is now being used consistently. To date, personnel from China, Costa Rica, Ghana, Indonesia, Kenya, Peru, Philippines, Sudan, Thailand, Western Samoa, Argentina, Madagascar, Uruguay, Panama, Senegal, Uganda, Nigeria and Brazil have received GIS training at GRID.

THE SYSTEM

The hardware and software systems currently utilized by GRID have for the most part been donated by their vendors or developers. Each of the two existing centers has three separate hardware/software systems. The Geneva center has a Perkin Elmer 3241 computer with an ELAS software sub-system (raster based) that was developed and donated by NASA. The second system is a Prime 750 computer with an ARC/INFO software sub-system (vector based) that were donated by Prime Computer Co., ESRI, and HENCO respectively. The third system is an IBM PC-AT computer with an ERDAS software package (raster based) and is used exclusively for training purposes. The Nairobi center has essentially the same equipment and software. Archival of data is on magnetic tape and disc at the present, however, it is planned in 1988 to move to high volume optical disc for long term archival.

During the final months of the pilot project GRID convened a group of GIS/data systems experts to review the entire scope of GRID operations and recommend an approach to hardware/software systems for GRID during the follow-on phases. The outcome of that systems study (GRID series no. 12) along with the budget constraints will determine which systems will be used by GRID in the long term. Several hardware/software options are being considered and the final determination will be made during 1988. Two small computers (micro Vax III) have been procured as an interim step to the long term future system.

THE FUTURE

In January 1988 a meeting of the "GRID Scientific and Technical Management Advisory Committee" was convened to review the results of the GRID Pilot Project and to advise GEMS with regard to follow-on activities of the GRID project. (The Committee participants are listed in Annex 1). The full report of the committee is contained in a report published in January 1988 (GRID Series 15). Perhaps the best view of the future of GRID is the following exerpt from that report:

"3. Overall conclusions - Pilot Phase.

The Expert Group finds that the objectives set for the Pilot Phase have been fulfilled. In particular we are impressed by the technological progress made.

The dedication of highly skilled UNEP staff, the generosity of donors and the cooperative spirit of many national and international organizations have convinced us that the Pilot Phase has laid good foundations for an implementation phase.

Consequently this expert group recommends that a GRID implementation phase be carried out during 1988 and 1989.

Drawing on experience, both positive and negative, listed above together with general knowledge, the Expert Group offers its advice on the Implementation Phase.

4. Implementation Phase - general strategy.

4.1. A more mature user community.

During the 2 1/2 years of the Pilot Phase there has been a growing world awareness of environmental problems at a global scale.

Recent public attention to the Antarctic "ozone hole" is one example.

The dying lakes and trees of Northern Europe and parts of North America have demonstrated the likely need for understanding the interrelationships between atmospheric, hydrological, pedological and biological variables, and with it comes a suspicion that socio-economic and technical variables play a dominant role.

Industrial nations are not the only ones to experience phenomena of vast areal extents. The drought and famine in the Sahel during 1984 - 1986 brought home to many the relationship between a host of natural and anthropogenic variables and the economic development across a whole continent.

The report of the World Commission on Environment and Development submitted in 1987, illustrates the foresight of UNEP's GRID. There is no longer a question as to whether harmonized and integrated data on a global scale have a use. There is worldwide political acceptance of the need for monitoring of environmental phenomena on a geographical basis, although the political will and ability to put such monitoring into force has yet to be proven.

Many countries in the industrialized world experience a new "green wave" among people. Also in the developing countries there is a growing concern for the balance of nature and development, and donor countries and agencies more frequently insist that environmental considerations of proposed projects be taken into account.

Now that the World Commission has pointed to many of the environmental problems and challenges at global and national levels, there is a clear need to provide global and national data that may help finding solutions.

The Pilot Phase has demonstrated GRID's potential to contribute to a more sensible utilization of natural resources and more rational environmental planning decisions.

The Expert Group sees the following objectives for the proposed Implementation Phase 1988 - 1989:

- Objective 1: the establishment of improved and updated global, regional and (for some countries) national datasets of known quality within GRID.
- Objective 2: the establishment of computer-based systems that can give improved access to and adequately handle the above data at those geographical levels.
- Objective 3: the establishment of regional GRID nodes for the handling and analysis of relevant data, and the encouragement for the formation of national and special subject nodes compatible with GRID strategy.
- Objective 4: the training of sufficient staff, particularly from developing countries, to achieve the above.
- Objective 5: Closer contacts with the international scientific, development and conservation communities to ensure improved use of GRID data.

4.2.   Objective 1 (Improved datasets).

The Expert Group recommends:

4.2.1. Close liaison with Specialized UN Agencies and Programs.

Many such agencies, and notably FAO, UNESCO, WHO and WMO, as well as UNDP and the UN itself, possess environmental data not yet within GRID, at global, regional and national level.

4.2.2. Close liaison with the international scientific community.

The constructive cooperation with ICSU, and with International Geosphere-Biosphere Programme and associated national academies of sciences and other cooperating institutions in particular is a potentially most valuable source of quality data. In addition this scientific community should be commissioned to work on problems of data compatibility; particularly on problems of data aggregation and disaggregation from national to regional to

global scale and vice versa. IGBP should be requested to provide a Senior Scientific Adviser in residence to support the liaison between the scientific community and GRID.
Since GRID relates data to location, whenever possible data sets should be able to be geo-referenced, and such referencing should be a prerequisite for UNEP financial support.

4.2.3. Close liaison with non-governmental institutions.

A number of potentially valuable databases can be found within a wide variety of academic, non-governmental and private-sector organizations at the national level, and such institutions as the IUCN at the international level. Relationships should be explored with these institutions in order to take advantage of their data sets which may be of value to GRID users.

4.2.4. Data transfer.

Development must be considered for cost-effective standard-ized methods of data transfer, from outside agencies to GRID, and from GRID to regional national nodes and external users. We expect that this will entail use of a variety of media, including optical disc technology and evaluation of available high-speed data networks. The strategy for data transfer aims at encouraging data transfer and not imposing undue constraints on established routines.

4.3.   Objective 2 (GIS-systems).

4.3.1. The Expert Group agrees with Ad hoc Expert Workshop of September 1987 (GRID Information Series No. 12) in their recommendations for the acquisition of new computer hard-ware, and the retention of present software packages, provided they can be made compatible with the new hardware. We feel that the new hardware technology represents a significant technical advancement on the previous gener-ation of hardware currently residing in GRID facilities.

4.3.2. We also recommend that GRID concurrently monitor new and relevant releases of hardware and software both from the commercial and public domains, particularly with a view to assembling low-cost systems for national nodes and for educational and training purposes. GRID may consider drawing up specifications for such low-cost systems in order to encourage potential vendors.

4.4. Objective 3 (Regional and national nodes).

4.4.1. The Expert Group agrees with the notion implicit in the Final Report Pilot Phase (GRID Information Series No. 14) on the establishment of new regional centres or nodes. We feel that these nodes be placed where present infra-structure, particularly in respect to data collection and systems operation, may maximize chances of successful operation. In addition to existing nodes in Nairobi and Geneva, the Expert Group would welcome the establishment of two new regional nodes during the Implementation Phase: one in South-East Asia (probably Bangkok) and one in South America. During the Implementation Phase GRID should explore the feasibility of future regional nodes in West Asia, and with special-function nodes in developed countries, e.g. in North America.

4.4.2. The Expert Group recommends that GRID develop specifications and recommendations for the equipment and staffing of national nodes, and encourage their estab-lishment. Recommendations on how to develop datasets useful both at national, regional and global scale are essential. In addition these national nodes should be encouraged to have facilities for assessment applications in support of resource management and planning. UNEP should endeavour to persuade international aid agencies and bilateral donors to consider the strengthening or estab-lishment of national institutions capable of exploiting data from GRID for better national inventories of resources and modelling of the sort than can contribute to sustainable development along lines suggested in the WCED Reports.

4.5. Objective 4 (Training).

4.5.1. The Expert Group recommends the establishment of a suggested syllabus for training of GRID regional and national node personnel, as well as centrally placed users. In addition to expansion of teaching facilities connected to the Geneva GRID node, close cooperation with UNITAR on the use of other world-wide centres of learning should be considered.

4.5.2. In addition to syllabus GRID may consider the provi-sion of suitable computer-aided instructional material, preferably in forms and on machines that can later serve as production tools in a regional or national centre or with an end user.

4.5.3. The Expert Group recommends that GRID and UNITAR cooperate closely to establish suitable selection procedures for candidates for GRID training. The Senior Scientific Adviser (see 4.2.2.) may be considered a useful consultant during the selection of candidates for training.

4.6.   Objective 5 (Cooperation development agencies).

4.6.1. The line with the argument forwarded under 4.4.2 (above) the Expert Group regards it of paramount importance that a much closer relationship be established between GRID and centrally placed development agencies. Both for scientific and economic reasons close cooperation with the World Bank and the Regional Development Banks is desirable and may improve the direct utility of GRID data. At the same time large data sets collected by development agencies as part of their own projects may be available in a harmonized form to a larger user community. This is particularly true of UNDP given its primary role of strengthening national capabilities in developing countries.

4.6.2. A similar argument applies to bilateral aid agencies.

5.   Conclusions - Implementation Phase.

The Expert Group:

5.1. recommends that the Implementation Phase be initiated immediately.

5.2. recommends that GRID establish close working links with both the global scientific and international development aid communities.

5.3. is deeply concerned that the budgetary provisions available for the execution of the ambitions of the Implementation Phase are not adequate. Additional funding, in cash, kind and services should be vigorously sought for both core GRID funding, as well as in support of GRID application and demonstration activities. We expect that a doubling of the provisions made would be required for a satisfactory completion of the Implementation Phase.

5.4. recommends that an Advisory Group be constituted to support GRID development in the fields of science, technology and financing. In this group the representation of developing countries, the international development community and IGBP is most important.

5.5. recommends that an evaluation of the implementation period be completed during the last quarter of 1989".

SUMMARY

The Pilot phase of GRID has been successfully completed and the Implementation phase has been approved by the UNEP Governing Council and the Executive Director. The Advisory Committee has made specific recommendations that have been accepted by UNEP/GEMS. These recommendations will be implemented as funding and manpower become available from donor countries and organizations and from the UNEP fund. The plan to expand GRID to a distributed global system has been approved and definite plans have been made to open a Regional GRID node in Southeast Asia in July 1988. The center will be located at the UNEP Regional Office in Bangkok. Tentative plans have also been made to open a node in Latin America by late 1989.

Upgrade of the system hardware is being considered and an additional equipment for Geneva and Nairobi has been purchased for the interim period. Plans to place a data catalogue on the networks are being developed for implementation by the end of 1988.

Additional global data sets are being identified and will be acquired for consolidation into the database. The efforts to obtain addition useful datasets will increase in the implementation phase and continue indefinitely to support global analysis by scientists both inside and outside of UNEP. Datasets will be provided upon request to all organizations conducting legitimate environmental research and resource management applications. Assistance in identification of additional important environmental data is being provided by a scientific consultant under contract to NASA and NSF(US).

Application work will continue at the global regional and national levels. A joint GEMS/FAO project is underway to develop remote sensing methodology to maximize the use of satellite data to map and monitor deforestation on a global scale by the end of 1990. Existing global datasets such as soils, topography and climate play an important role in the classification scheme of the forest project. Regional and national applications will also continue. A UNEP regional study is underway to determine the effects of predicted sea level rise on five major river deltas in the Mediterranean area. This study is a joint effort among GEMS, Regional

Seas and several national laboratories. Approximately 8 to 10 national case studies are in progress at any one time. The number of national case studies should start to decrease in a few years as more and more developing countries obtain their own GIS systems.

The ultimate success of GRID which depends upon many things such as funding, vitality of staff, quality and quantity of datasets and responsiveness, will be judged by the usefulness of the results of the applications using GRID datasets. Some of the applications are inside UNEP, however many applications are and will be by other organizations.

Annex 1: GRID Scientific and Technical Management Advisory Committee, Nairobi, Jan 1988: List of Participants

Dr. Stein W. Bie	Norwegian Computing Centre
Ms. Nassrine de-Rham Azimi	UNITAR European Office
Dr. Ian Crain	Environment Canada
Mr. Jack Dangermond	ESRI (apologies)
Prof. A. Donath	Univ. of Geneva (apologies)
Prof. J. Estes	Univ. of California, Santa Barbara
Dr. Jurgen Lamp	Inst. of Soil Science and Plant Nutrition, Kiel, FRG
Prof. A. Musy	Institut de Genie Rural, Lausanne
Dr. S.I. Rassool	NASA
Mr. B. Spiering	NASA
Mr. Peter S. Thacher	World Resources Institute
Dr. Shelby Tilford	NASA
Mr. Jim Weber	Universities Space Research Association, Columbia, Maryland
Ms. Christina Boelcke	}
Ms. Anne Burrill	}
Dr. H. Croze	}
Dr. M.D. Gwynne	} UNEP-GRID
Mr. Mitchell Loeb	}
Mr. W. Mooneyhan	}
Mr. Otto Simonett	}
Mr. Morten Sorensen	}

Annex 2: Status of preliminary GRID Global Datasets as of 1 February, 1988.
(All datasets are held at GRID-Processor, Geneva).

Parameter	Cover	Source	Georef	Proj'n	Avail	D.Q
BOUNDARIES (Land-water, political)	Global	World Database II (WDBII) - US State Dep't	Y	Long-Lat	Y	A-3
ELEVATION (10 min. grid)	Global	National Geophysical Data US-NOAA	Y	Long-Lat	Y	A-3
SOILS	Global	FAO/UNESCO 1.5m soils map	Y	Long-Lat	Y	A-3
VEGETATION	Global	GISS }	Y	Long-Lat	Y	A-3
CULTIVATION INTENSITY	Global	GISS } (Elaine } Mathews)	Y	Long-Lat	Y	
ALBEDO- 4 SEASONS	Global	GISS }	Y	Long-Lat	Y	
VEG'N INDEX (Weekly 4.82-4.85)	Global	NOAA	N	Polar Stereogr.	Y**	B-1
PRECIPITATION ANOMALIES (Monthly 1985 on)	Global	Climate Anal. Centre US-NOAA/ WMO (Dig. by GRID)	Y	Long-Lat	Y	A-2
TEMPERATURE ANOMALIES	Global	. . . " . . .	Y	Long-Lat	Y	A-2
SURFACE TEMPERATURE	Global	NASA-JPL/GSFC from HIRS2 & MSU	Y	Long-Lat	N***	B-1
OZONE DIST'N	Global	NASA, TOMS	N	-	N***	B-1
VEGETATION	Africa	DMA 1.2m Topo Maps (Dig. by ESRI for UNEP/FAO)	Y	Long-Lat	Y	A-3
	Africa	White's UNESCO/ AETFAT map (Dig. by GRID)	Y	Long-Lat	Y	A-2
	Africa	FAO/Toulouse	in progress			

Annex 1 cont'd.

VEG'N INDEX (Seasonal '82)	Africa	NASA/GSFC (from AVHRR 4 km data)	N	Mercator	Y		B-1
WATERSHEDS	Africa	FAO Data 1.5m (Dig. by ESRI for UNEP/FAO)	Y	Miller Ob. Stereo.	Y		A-3
RAINFALL (Mean Annual)	Africa	. . . " . . .	Y	Long-Lat	Y		A-3
NO. WET DAYS (Mean Annual)	Africa	. . . " . . .	Y	Long-Lat	Y		A-3
WINDSPEED (Mean Annual)	Africa	. . . " . . .	Y	Long-Lat	Y		A-3
PROTECTED AREAS	Africa	IUCN/CMC (Centre pts. and areal extent)	Y	Long-Lat	Y		A-3
BIO-GEOGR. PROVINCE	Africa	IUCN Paper 18 (by Udvardy)	Y	Long-Lat	Y		
SPECIES	Africa	IUCN/CMC (Centre pts.of 20 endangered species and animals)	Y	Long-Lat	Y		A-3

D.Q - Dataset Qualifiers; see Interim Data Release Policy.
** - Data are held as received from NOAA and will not be geo-referenced into long-lat. as standard archive practice unless there is a specific request.
*** - Awaiting modified datasets from NASA.

A GLOBAL DATABASE ON THE STATUS OF
BIOLOGICAL DIVERSITY: THE I.U.C.N. PERSPECTIVE

Robin A. Pellew and Jeremy D. Harrison

SUMMARY

As the foremost international conservation agency, IUCN is concerned with the global status and distribution of the world's remaining biological diversity. Its data on plants and animals, critical sites, natural ecosystems and protected areas must be geographically-referenced if that information is to have any practical application. IUCN is, therefore, interested in the development of digitized cartographic systems which can be accepted as global standards to which IUCN can contribute its data relating to conservation, and which can then be used for the manipulation and analysis of that data. IUCN is also interested in the development of standards and protocols for transfer of data between databases, and in the establishment of regional and national conservation databases as sources of high resolution data. IUCN also works closely with UNEP, and the work of the IUCN Conservation Monitoring Centre is a contribution to their Global Environment Monitoring System.

IUCN'S ACTIVITIES

IUCN, the International Union for Conservation of Nature and Natural Resources, is the international coordinating organisation for conservation. It is a membership organisation with some 62 governments, 125 government agencies and 400 international and national NGO members, spread across a total of 117 countries. Its mission is to promote the conservation of the world's biological resources through programmes for their sustainable development as set out in its World Conservation Strategy (IUCN, 1980). IUCN is all too aware that its operations will be of lasting value only if they are firmly rooted in reliable quantitative information drawn from the analysis of scientific data. In recognition of the need for a central clearing-house of data on the status of threatened species, rates of species extinctions, and the monitoring of critical ecosystems, IUCN brought several separate monitoring projects together in 1982 to form the IUCN Conservation Monitoring Centre (CMC).

CMC has now developed into the leading repository for information on the status of the biological diversity of the world. Based at the University of Cambridge, but with its botanical operations at the Royal Botanic Gardens at Kew, CMC has now grown to employ some 30 professional scientific staff. It maintains global databases on:

- the status and distribution of threatened plant and animal species - there are now records for some 47,000 plant taxa (with an additional 22,000 records for 5,000 threatened plant taxa in cultivation) and 18,000 animal taxa;

- critical sites of conservation concern, particularly covering tropical forests, wetlands and coral reefs - there are some 9,500 text files each with a comprehensive bibliography;

- the location and extent of the world's protected areas, including brief data on the species and habitats they contain, and the effectiveness of management - data on some 11,500 protected areas with descriptions and bibliography are now held;

- the utilisation and trade in wildlife species throughout the world and its impact upon wild populations - data on some 700,000 trade transactions are now held, together with an expanding bibliographic database on wildlife utilization.

These global overview data can be accessed by country, region or continent, and in some cases by biogeographical province, protected area, habitat or species. The databases are regularly published, as finance permits, as species Red Data Books, Protected Areas Directories, critical sites reviews, country biodiversity profiles, and so on. CMC provides an information service to support the programmes of IUCN and other conservation organisations, but increasingly its services are being sought by aid and development agencies and by multi-nationals involved in the natural resources sector. A general description of CMC is provided by Harrison et al (1987), and of the databases by Mackinder (1984).

A Global Database on the Status of Biological Diversity

IUCN'S NEED FOR GLOBAL DIGITIZED DATA

The data that CMC holds on the status and distribution of
the world's biological diversity must be presented in a
form easily comprehensible to land-use managers to assist
policy decisions relating to the sustainable use of natural
resources. Such data must be accurate, integrated with
other data sets, and readily accessible to both internal
and external, remote users.

To be of practical value, the data must be geographically
referenced to identify what is where (in terms of species
or habitat distribution) and what is happening where (in
terms of threats to biodiversity or the effectiveness of
protected area management), and to draw appropriate
conclusions. However, as well as ensuring a basis for the
internal geographical management of its own data, CMC must
also be in a position to integrate its data with other
natural resource data sets developed by other
organizations.

CMC therefore requires an appropriate standard set of
digitized base-maps which can be interfaced with its own
data. We need to be able to handle data at levels of
resolution varying from from global (1:1,000,000), through
country-wide (1:250,000) to local area (1:100,000), and in
various projections. We need to be able to easily relate
our information to the usual topographic and political
features, such as coastlines, international and major
administrative boundaries, major cities, towns and
communication lines.

On top of this we need to ensure that our data sets can be
compared and integrated with a range of data sets derived
by, and managed by, other agencies. Such data sets would
include climate parameters, soils, topography, watersheds,
land use, and so on. Overlay of our data with these other
data sets would facilitate the analysis of the information
we have, and help us to address more complex questions
relating to the effective conservation of biodiversity.
For example, the overlay of our data set on protected areas
with information on natural vegetation and land use would
allow us to make more effective reviews of the adequacy of
existing protected areas networks. Much of this work would
be carried out in collaboration with other organizations
and programmes, such as the UNEP Global Environment
Monitoring System (Gwynne, 1982) and its Global Resource
Inventory Database (Mooneyhan, 1988).

A Global Database on the Status of Biological Diversity

STATUS OF IUCN'S DATABASE DEVELOPMENT

CMC is about to undertake a major restructuring of its databases, as part of a move to a more powerful and sophisticated computer system, with improved database management and program development tools. This will allow us to build in a greater integration between the data we manage, thus increasing the flexibility of our operations and outputs.

An essential structural element in this integration must be the integral use of a proper geographic framework as the base-line for both internal management of information and comparison of our data with other geographically referenced data sets. To date, we have relied on the use of latitude and longitude co-ordinates, supplemented by area or country presence or absence data, but this clearly is too crude to meet the more detailed information needs of many of our current users. We are now exploring the use of Geographic Information Systems, but before we invest our scarce financial resources in purchasing any GIS or cartographic system, we must be confident that the facilities and the cartographic data sets available will meet our needs, whilst enabling us to relate to other databases.

SOME PROBLEMS AND ISSUES

Data-related problems

With a focus primarily upon developing countries, CMC faces inevitable problems of varying data quality and patchy data availability. Although rigorous attempts are made to verify the input, especially when drawn from unpublished sources, through the expertise of the IUCN's Commissions, the users of CMC's outputs must appreciate the practical limitations of data availability and the problems involved in standardizing disparate and fragmented data sources. Cartographic inconsistencies, particularly in the coverage of remote parts of developing countries, where reference features may be lacking, can generate further problems.

Resolution

A global overview of biological resources is important to provide a proper perspective of the status and trends of threatened species and ecosystems, and to monitor the biological impact of global change. However, much conservation action occurs at the national or local level, and there is a clear need to develop the capacity for information management at that level. A distributed network of databases at the national or regional level can accommodate data at a higher level of resolution than a centralized global overview.

IUCN is now discussing with several developing countries in Africa and Asia plans for the establishment of national conservation databases, using data CMC already holds as part of the start-up resource. As well as being a focus for information at the country level, thus contributing to improved local resource management, these databases will in time form a significant input to our own database providing higher resolution information.

However, developing a distributed network system generates its own problems of standardization and comparability, and, for example, some developing countries may not have reliable maps at scales less than 1:1,000,000 available.

Data standards and protocols

Because of the variety of users and the wide range of user needs, it is unrealistic to expect all databases to use a standard data management system. However, this is less important than the acceptance of common definitions and terminologies for data fields and for data transfer formats. The current lack of an internationally accepted protocol for nomenclatures, terminologies and classification systems places restrictions on the electronic transfer of data between databases. We now need to establish an international forum to co-ordinate the exchange of data between databases through the establishment and acceptance of protocols to promote standardization. But as has been experienced by CORINE within the European Community (Wyatt et al, 1988), even where a protocol has been agreed, enforcing it is another matter.

IUCN has made some progress in addressing the problem of standardization through the production of the International Transfer Format for Botanic Garden Plant Records (IUCN, 1987). This document describes a set of standards for exchanging computerized data on the plants growing in botanic gardens throughout the world, this information being used to co-ordinate the cultivation of threatened species with a view towards re-introduction into the wild. Work in collaboration with other database agencies is now progressing on other data transfer formats and on standards

334

for data content and structure, but there is still a long way to go before this work is complete.

Species distribution

While data on the distribution of protected areas or of land use can be mapped reasonably accurately, mapping of the distribution of a taxon is problematic because of the imprecise nature of the data. One of the few studies of the distribution of a single species using GIS techniques is the study of the African elephant by Burrill and Douglas-Hamilton (1987), and despite the years of research on that species, and the wealth of data, accurate assessment of populations in different parts of the continent was deficient. Where this was difficult for the elephant, the problems are likely to be magnified many times for other, less studied species.

Ground truthing

Rapidly increasing volumes of data from remote sensing will become available in the near future, particularly from NASA's Earth Observing System and such global projects as the International Geosphere-Biosphere Programme. Although techniques are becoming more sophisticated for relating these data to biological features on the ground, there will be major problems of ground truthing. IUCN, through its various networks, regional offices, field operations and thematic programmes, is in a strong position to contribute to ground truth surveys. This will also be an important role for the national conservation information centres, as and when they are established.

Also, through its work with the Unesco-MAB Biosphere Reserve programme, CMC should be in a position to relate information arising from the proposed Geosphere-Biosphere Observatories (Dyer et al, 1980) to similar areas, and therefore to help in the development and application of that programme.

Financial and administrative limitations

Like most database agencies in the non-governmental sector, CMC suffers from the high costs of update and maintenance of information within the database, and funding is the single most serious limitation to our work. There is a universal tendency for administrators to regard databases as potential assets, which can be exploited to provide a marketable information service and thus earn their keep.

Whilst this may in part be true, a database is also a financial liability, as data are dynamic and must be continually updated. This is particularly so where data on status and management activity form the core of the database.

Our belief is that a global database of the kind that we manage requires at least 50% of its revenue as unrestricted income which can be used for review, update and improvement, quite apart from replacement of obsolete equipment. This is probably true whatever the origin of the information, be it from original sources or from a range of national databases. At present we have difficulty keeping pace with the information that is coming in, let alone having time for the full development of systematic processes for update and review.

Sponsors and administrators often hold unrealistic expectations of the time involved for a database to show material returns on the invested capital, and this can lead to conflict between incompatible political needs for immediate results and the longer-term needs for a rational structured approach to data management.

Release of information

It is IUCN's belief that information should be released into the public domain as rapidly as possible with the minimum copyright restrictions. There is an increasing tendency amongst database administrators to withhold commercially marketable data to recover front-end costs and indeed to share these costs with commercial organizations who will impose copyright restrictions. IUCN does not sell its data which are often readily available through its publications; it does, however, market an information service based upon the analysis and interpretation of its data.

However it is important to realise that information that is incomplete can be a liability, and that time must be allowed to ensure accuracy before information can be released. This is particularly so when modern methods allow quick production of very professional looking outputs. For example, the production of good quality coloured maps using GIS can give a spurious sense of credibility to unreliable data which may encourage political decision-makers and end-users to ignore the accuracy warnings.

CONCLUSION

IUCN is itself both a user and a generator of global data sets. As we develop our new database capabilities, we will need digitized base-maps to which we can relate our own data. To facilitate data exchange and integration, we also need to ensure that our base-maps conform to accepted standards, although we look to other more directly involved agencies to provide the lead. However we also need to develop further our capacity to collect and manage information, and to provide useful products to our data users. Part of this can be achieved through the establishment of a distributed network system of national databases, although the primary reason for the establishment of such databases is to promote effective conservation within the countries concerned.

Finally, we emphasise the necessity of collaboration in the development of global databases. In the context of the development of global digital map databases, IUCN is willing to contribute, but as a data user its expertise may be too far down-stream. As regards conservation databases, IUCN sees its role as that of a catalyst within the conservation community promoting collaboration and the exchange of information between agencies. However, we cannot operate in isolation from other global database efforts in the natural resource sector, and our work must be integrated with the activities of UNEP-GEMS, FAO, IUGS and other agencies. This will necessitate the acceptance of agreed protocols and standards to facilitate data exchange, analysis, and application.

REFERENCES

Burrill, A. and Douglas Hamilton, I., 1987. African Elephant Database Project: Final Report. GRID Case Study Series No. 2. UNEP, Nairobi.

Dyer, M.I., di Castri, F. and Hansen, A.J., 1988. 'Geosphere-Biosphere Observatories - their definition and design for studying global change'. Biology International Special Issue 16.

Gwynne, M.D., 1982. 'The global environment monitoring system (GEMS) of UNEP'. Environmental Conservation, 9, 35-42.

Harrison, J., Karpowicz, Z. and Leon, C., 1987. 'Monitoring environmental conservation: towards an integrated global overview'. Proceedings of the International Symposium on Integrated Global Monitoring of the State of the Biosphere. Tashkent, USSR, 14-19 October 1985. World Meteorological Organization Technical Document No. 151, Vol. III, 95-105

IUCN, 1980. The World Conservation Strategy. Copublished by IUCN, WWF and UNEP. Available from IUCN, Gland, Switzerland.

IUCN, 1987. The International Transfer Format for Botanic Garden Plant Records. Plant Taxonomic Database Standards No. 1. Published for the IUCN Botanic Gardens Conservation Secretariat by the Hunt Institute for Botanical Documentation, Carnegie Mellon University, Pittsburg.

Mackinder, D.C., 1984. 'The Database of the IUCN Conservation Monitoring Centre'. In: Databases in Systematics, ed. R. Allkin and F.A. Bisby. Systematics Association Special Volume No. 26, pp. 91-102. Academic Press, London.

Mooneyhan, D.W., 1988. 'Applications of Geographic Information Systems within the United Nations Environment Programme'. This volume.

Wyatt, B.K., Briggs, D.J. and Mounsey, H.M., 1988. 'CORINE: An information system on the state of the environment in the European Community'. This volume.

THE SCIENTIFIC COMMITTEE ON PROBLEMS
OF THE ENVIRONMENT AND GLOBAL DATABASES

Paul G. Risser

INTRODUCTION

The Scientific Committee on Problems of the Environment
(SCOPE) is a committee of the International Council of
Scientific Unions (ICSU). The purposes of SCOPE include
the following:

- To advance knowledge of the influence of man on his
  environment, as well as the effects of these environmental changes upon man, his health and his welfare - with
  particular attention to those influences and effects
  which are either global or shared in common by several
  nations.

- To serve as a non-governmental, interdisciplinary and
  international council of scientists and as a source of
  advice for the benefit of governments and intergovernmental and non-governmental bodies with respect to
  environmental problems.

In the conventional mode of operation, SCOPE does not
conduct primary research, except occasional studies which
involve modelling (White, 1987). Most SCOPE projects
entail a series of workshops, usually held in various
countries, on topics which are:

- considered to be emerging topical areas which would
  profit from an evaluation of potentially fruitful future
  directions, or
- characterised by significant previous research and would
  benefit from synthesis of these ideas.

At any one time, SCOPE manages a number of topics which are
in stages ranging from initial planning of workshops to
completed manuscripts for the SCOPE series published by
John Wiley and Sons or in other publications. Example
topics of current projects include the following:

- biogeochemical cycles, carbon, phosphorous and sulphur cycles
- atmospheric acidification in tropical countries
- ecology of biological invasions
- genetically-engineered organisms
- biogenic trace gases
- organic matter budgets
- coastal embayments and river deltas
- groundwater contamination.

There are four other current SCOPE activities of particular interest to the Global Database Planning Project, and these will be briefly described in the following sections. The first two projects are underway; the latter two are in the advanced planning stage.

ECOTONES

Ecotones are described as transitional areas of the bio-sphere, for example, the transitional area between a forest and grassland or between a forest and a stream. The general definition can be stated as follows (Holland, 1988):

- An ecotone is a zone of transition between adjacent ecological systems, having a set of characteristics uniquely defined by space and time scales and by the strength of the interactions between adjacent ecological systems.

Considerable information about ecotones suggests that these systems may play significant ecological roles as important habitats for certain species, sources of and refuges for agricultural pests and their predators, locations of high species and genetic diversity, and controls on the flow of water, nutrients and other materials across the landscape. Also, because of their transitional nature, ecotones may be sensitive indicators to changes in the global environment.

Despite these presumed important characteristics, the data and information about ecotones has not been summarized. Therefore, SCOPE has begun a project on ecotones which will summarise the existing data, synthesize the general prin-ciples and describe ways in which this information can be employed in the management of landscapes with ecotones. Because of the breadth of the topic, special attention will be paid to the role of ecotones in supporting high biodi-versity, their function in controlling the flow of water,

341

nutrients and other materials, ways of classifying ecotones, and procedures for incorporating the characteristics
of ecotones in the management of landscapes.

INTERNATIONAL GEOSPHERE BIOSPHERE PROGRAM

Because the similarity of the SCOPE purposes and the
expectations of the International Geosphere Biosphere
Program, there is considerable collaboration of both
programs and among individual scientists. The current
status of development of the program has involved the
establishment of an international ICSU Special Committee
which has provided the first program guidelines. A set of
four panels has been established:

- Terrestrial biosphere-atmosphere chemistry interactions
- Marine-biosphere interactions
- Biospheric aspects of the hydrological cycle
- Effects of climate change on terrestrial ecosystems

In addition, the Special Committee has established initial
working groups to assess the current and anticipated
research capabilities in four areas:

- Global geosphere-biosphere modelling
- Data and information systems
- Techniques for extracting environmental data from the
  past
- Geobiosphere observatories

National committees are developing research programs which
will be discussed in an international forum in the Fall of
1988, leading to a research program in the 1990's, focusing
on global issues in the time scales of decades to
centuries.

The United States has established a Committee on Global
Change under the auspices of the National Research Council
of the National Academy of Sciences. This Committee has
begun to identify important topics for research programs to
be recommended to the Special Committee as candidates for
initial research projects. In reaching these recommendations, the U.S. Global Change Committee recognised several
important themes:

- Documentation of global change will be a major component
  of any research program.

- Investigations should focus on ecosystems likely to be sensitive to changes in the global environment.
- Understanding the environmental history of ecosystems is necessary for analysis of current and future conditions.
- In addition to long-term trends, it will be important to understand periodic and episodic effects.

The selection of initial ideas placed a priority on topics which:

- were global in nature;
- would be likely to lead rapidly to an understanding of the phenomenon;
- were important to the well-being of society;
- transcended traditional disciplinary boundaries and would not be conducted via existing research programs;
- and which were amenable to research within the time span of a few to ten years.

Although the following topics will undergo further deliberation, the initial discussion focused on four general topics:

(a) developing global models of the hydrological responses of terrestrial ecosystems to changes in climate, land-use, and other stress factors, and the feedbacks of these systems on the climate system
(b) evaluation of nutrients across the landscape
(c) understanding the effects of climate change on ocean biogeochemical cycles and their feedback to the climate, and
(d) reconstruction of the environmental history of the earth, particularly atmospheric composition and climate.

As a part of the International Geosphere Biosphere Program, a number of geo-biosphere observatories will be established. Again, the planning for these observatories is at a very preliminary stage. The IGBP Working Group has made the preliminary recommendation that this network be hierarchical in nature, and consist of three levels:

Level I - International Geosphere Biosphere Research and Training Centers

Level II - Existing Sites Already Established for Long-Term Research

343

Level III - Existing Relatively Specialized Monitoring and
        Field Stations

The Level I stations would be newly established, funded by
multi-national consortia, and would perhaps number
approximately 10 and be distributed as one or two per
continent and major ocean. These stations would represent
the essence of the IGBP, contributing to vertically and
horizontally organised interdisciplinary experimental
research programs and detailed observations. At the second
level, there might be about 100 sites designated, but these
would consist largely of existing research locations where
experiments or observations were already being conducted.
Funding would be provided through the IGBP effort.
Finally, the Level III stations would consist of existing
networks, frequently measuring one or a few parameters.
These sites would be monitoring rather than experimental
sites, and funding would be from various sources. In all
cases, efforts would be made to increase the quality of
exiting networks, and to coordinate data sharing among
investigators associated with these stations. Thus the
discussions of this meeting are particularly important in
the planning of data bases to be associated with these geo-
biosphere observatories.

LONG-TERM ECOLOGICAL RESEARCH: A GLOBAL PERSPECTIVE

Though there are a few notable exceptions, relatively few
comprehensive research programs exist throughout the world
that focus on long-term ecological phenomena. The arguments for long-term studies usually recognise that certain
processes, e.g. succession or natural frequency distribution of climate regimes or disturbances such as fire, are
long-term processes and must be studied under that temporal
framework (Strayer, 1986). In fact, the literature is
replete with examples of data trends in which short-term
interpretations yield significantly different results from
longer term analyses. However, long-term studies present
certain challenges, for example, new technologies may
render the measurements trivial or uninteresting, the
reason for the study may be successfully addressed by new
and different research approaches, and the continued
expense and management of these studies is quite consequen-
tial. On the other hand, there are circumstances where
there appear to be no feasible alternatives to these long-
term studies.

344

SCOPE is in the planning stages of a project to address long-term ecological studies in the international context. The purposes of this project are to:

- articulate a rationale for deciding the proper conditions and circumstances for undertaking long-term ecological research
- identify the most important ecological questions which are amenable to this approach, especially in the context of global change
- explore the desirability and feasibility of international coordination of long-term ecological research networks.

A workshop will be held this Fall in Europe and the results will be published and available to the scientific community.

APPLICATION OF SCIENTIFIC INFORMATION FOR SUSTAINABLE DEVELOPMENT

There has been a continuing focus on the effects of economic development on the environment, and on the ability of the earth's natural resources to sustain development. It is the responsibility of the research community to provide the scientific information necessary for carrying out policies conducive to sustainable development. Experience with environmental impact assessment indicates that effective planning requires systematic and early integration of environmental considerations. For this information to be utilised, it is necessary not only to synthesize the scientific understanding, but to present the information in a form that can readily be understood by planners and policy makers at both levels of national planning agencies and international development agencies. Thus, SCOPE is planning a project with the following three integrated parts:

- Determination of the available scientific data and information that is critical for incorporating environmental considerations into strategic-level development planning, both at the national and international levels.

- Evaluation of the current and potential use of existing technologies to provide and communicate relevant information.

- Consideration of ways to increase the influence of the scientific information in the development planning process.

Of particular importance to the Global Database Planning Project, is the incorporation of remote sensing information and geographic information systems.

SUMMARY

SCOPE is in the process of two projects and planning two additional projects which are of relevance to the Global Database Planning Project. The ecotones project and the International Geosphere Biosphere Project will provide both information to and a rationale for planning and implementing global databases. The long-term ecological studies and the sustainable development projects, when implemented, will provide further applications for global databases.

REFERENCES

Holland, M. M., 1988. 'Technical consultations on ecotones', Biology International, forthcoming.

Strayer, D., 1986. 'An essay on long-term ecological research'. Bulletin of the Ecological Society of America, 67, 271-274.

White, G.F., 1987. 'SCOPE: The first sixteen years'. Environmental Conservation, 14, 7-13.

IOC OCEAN MAPPING ACTIVITIES

Victor Sedov

BACKGROUND

The need for exploration and exploitation of the oceans increases every year. It requires the preparation of bathymetric charts representing the sea bottom in as much detail as possible. Ocean mapping has made considerable progress in recent years and has become one of the major IOC activities.

However, for compilation of bathymetric charts knowledge of the measured depth alone is not enough. Knowledge of geomorphology, geology and sedimentology is also essential and the participation of the IOC scientific community is therefore extremely important. On the other hand, the production of bathymetric charts can also be a stimulus to the research of many marine scientists, because the topography of the ocean bottom strongly influences physical, chemical and biological processes, especially in the near bottom layers.

The great majority of existing bathymetric charts are compiled with data from merchant vessels. The uncertainties in the determination of a ship's position limit the accuracy of the isobaths. The IOC co-ordinates international efforts to collect available data, to undertake additional investigations of some regions, and to compile and print bathymetric charts for distribution throughout the scientific community.

All bathymetric charts compiled under the aegis of the IOC are prepared to a common standard for the cartographic specification and legends. All of them are designed to meet the following requirements:

(i)   Simple, easy to read, clear

(ii)   Provision of correct and comprehensive information on the bottom topography

(iii)   Provision of the most detailed and accurate value
        available for the depth at any point on the sheet.

In recent years, many national and international organisations have taken on the task of compiling charts for
various ocean regions.   In some cases, this has been done
principally to facilitate the exploitation of particular
ocean resources.   The IOC aim is to ensure a planned
approach to the long-term mapping of the world ocean
bottom, not only to meet current needs, but in the perspective of the long-term development of the ocean sciences and
services.

In general for any given ocean region, a bathymetric chart
is first compiled which serves as a base chart, and then
geological/geophysical charts (overlay sheets) are
prepared.   The same base chart can also be used for the
compilation of charts of the distribution and circulation
of water masses and of living or non-living resources.

The IOC has been active in ocean mapping projects over a
long period.   In 1972 the compilation of a geological
/geophysical atlas of the Indian Ocean was begun on the
basis of data collected during the International Indian
Ocean Expedition.   In the same year the IOC and the
International Hydrographic Organisation (IHO) agreed to co-
sponsor the production of a new chart series, the Fifth
Edition of the General Bathymetric Chart of the Oceans
(GEBCO).   The compilation of the Fifth edition in 1982 has
resulted in 19 charts depicting the bathymetry and
morphology of the worlds oceans, for the first time taking
advantage of the development of new concepts of global
tectonics and of modern navigational systems.   In 1973
following Resolution VIII-II of the IOC Assembly, a special
group of experts was set up to prepare a large scale
bathymetric base chart of the Mediterranean Sea.   With the
co-operation of IHO, national hydrographic services and
individual scientists the First Edition of the International Bathymetric Chart of the Mediterranean was
published in the USSR in 1982.

The IOC has now set up an effective structure of subsidiary
groups for the management of Ocean mapping activities.   The
activities of the various groups are described in the
remaining sections of this paper.

THE IOC CONSULTATIVE GROUP ON OCEAN MAPPING (CGOM)

At its Seventeenth Session in January-February 1984 the IOC
Executive Council established the Consultative Group on
Ocean Mapping (CGOM) wishing to have within the structure
of the IOC an appropriate advisory body, formed of highly-
qualified scientists in the field of ocean mapping and
related activities, to act as an overall technical
mechanism linking together the diverse ocean mapping
projects sponsored or co-sponsored by the Commission.

The Group is composed of the Chairmen of the supervisory
groups of the mapping projects already existing within the
IOC and it is expected to be enlarged soon by the presence
of the Chairmen of other groups, mainly devoted to regional
bathymetric problems. The Group, which is currently
chaired by Mr D.P.D. Scott, who has been concerned with
ocean mapping over a long period and is a former Secretary
of IOC, meets annually to discuss current activities and
reports to the biennial IOC Assembly.

GENERAL BATHYMETRIC CHART OF THE OCEANS (GEBCO)

The main task in recent years has been digitisation of the
GEBCO (5th edition) contours. As reported at the Sixth
Meeting of the GEBCO Officers (14-15 April 1988) the five
Circum-Antarctic sheets (5.13, 5.14, 5.15, 5.16 and 5.18)
have been processed by BGI. The quality of the output was
extremely high (less than 0.01% error rate). The BGI has
completed preliminary digitisation of sheets 5.01 and 5.08.
The recommended priorities for further digitisation are:
sheets 5.04, 5.17, 5.05 and 5.09. A new member of the
GEBCO Sub-Committee on Digital Bathymetry, A. Popov from
the USSR, Head, Department of Navigation and Oceanography
has offered to collaborate in this task. One of the
Circum-Antarctica sheets or sheet 5.02 would be appropriate
for this exercise.

Work on the International Gazetteer of Undersea Feature
Names has been finished and the GEBCO Officers recommended
the circulation of a draft of this document to member
countries of IHO. A draft of the new GEBCO Regulations was
also discussed and was accepted in principle.

The new (Sixth) edition of GEBCO will be printed in 1995,
after the digitisation of all sheets and the preparation of
electronic charts containing the same information as the
updated GEBCO paper sheets.

At the Sixth Meeting of GEBCO Officers the possibility of the preparation of a terrain model of the world ocean bottom and the possible creation of an IHO Data Centre for Digital Bathymetry were also discussed.

GEOLOGICAL/GEOPHYSICIAL ATLASES OF THE ATLANTIC AND PACIFIC OCEANS (GAPA)

The second IOC, Global Ocean Mapping project: Geological and Geophysical Atlases of the Pacific and Atlantic Oceans is progressing well. In addition to the 1977 Geological /Geophysical Atlas of the Indian Ocean, other Atlases planned will cover almost all the World Ocean with a series of bathymetric, geological and geophysical charts. It is expected that the Atlantic volume will be published in late 1988 and the Pacific volume two years later.

INTERNATIONAL BATHYMETRIC CHART OF THE MEDITERRANEAN (IBCM)

IBCM is developing as one of the most successful regional ocean mapping projects. Using the bathymetric chart, printed in 1982, as a base, five geological/geophysical chart series (each of ten sheets) are being compiled. The first of them, the Gravity Anomalies series, will be printed in late 1988, and after that one series will be printed each year up to 1992.

INTERNATIONAL BATHYMETRIC CHART OF THE CARIBBEAN SEA AND PART OF THE PACIFIC OCEAN OFF CENTRAL AMERICA (IBCA)

The first session of EB-IBCCA (Aguascalientes, Mexico, 29 September - 2 October 1986) prepared the assembly diagram for the sheets of the chart and agreed on national responsibilities for compiling plotting sheets.

The next session of the Editorial Board and a Workshop on data sources and map compilation of the IBCCA are scheduled for this year.

INTERNATIONAL BATHYMETRIC CHART OF THE CENTRAL EASTERN ATLANTIC (IBCEA)

The Fourteenth IOC Assembly agreed to establish an Editorial Board for IBCEA and the constitution of the Board is now in progress.

INTERNATIONAL BATHYMETRIC CHART OF THE WESTERN INDIAN OCEAN
(IBCWIO)

The IOC Executive Council at its Twenty-first Session,
established the Editorial Board for IBCWIO and appointed
Dr. W. Bettac (FRG) as Chief Editor of this chart. This
Board is also in course of constitution.

OTHER POSSIBLE REGIONAL OCEAN MAPPING PROJECTS

The compilation of a Bathymetric chart of the Red Sea and
Gulf of Aden was proposed by the Institute of Oceanographic
Sciences, Wormley, UK. However, up to now, this project
has been frozen because the source of funding has not been
determined.

The proposal for an IOC International Bathymetric Chart of
the Central Indian Ocean will be discussed during the
foregoing session of IOCINDIO-1.

Willingness to compile bathymetric charts was expressed
also for the Southern Ocean and WESTPAC during meetings of
the relevant IOC Regional Committees.

CONCLUSION

The preparation of regional bathymetric charts at a scale
of not less than 1:1M will eventually lead to full coverage
of the worlds oceans. The preparation of electronic charts
and the development of an IHO Data Center for Digital
Bathymetry will be a step towards the preparation of a
Digital terrain model of the ocean bottom. Overall, these
activities will make a significant contribution to the
exploration of the worlds oceans.

THE DIGITAL GEOGRAPHIC DATABASE
ACTIVITIES AND PLANS OF MILITARY SURVEY

Brian J. Tew

INTRODUCTION

A number of papers have been presented by Military Survey during the last three years in both National and International forums. Collectively they chronicle Military Survey's developing philosophy and plans to establish a digital Geographic Database designed to satisfy the escalating demands from digital data users, as well as supporting the continuing requirement for conventional maps and charts. The most relevant of these papers are listed in the reference section.

THE CURRENT SITUATION

There is little to be gained from presenting here a detailed repetition of the content of these papers. In summary attention has hitherto been focussed in our automation effort on two areas. The Production of Automated Charts Europe (PACE) was introduced to provide current air information and economy of 1:500,000 and 1:1,000,000 scale map and chart production. Digital Terrain Elevation Data (DTED) and Digital Feature Analysis Data (DFAD) allow generation of continuous radar scenes in the Digital Landmass Simulator (DLMS), though this data has subsequently been used for much wider applications.

Digital Geographic Information is increasingly required by many users to support navigation and guidance, command control and communications, training simulators and finally efficient map production. The pressing needs of some systems have inevitably led to user initiatives developing their own variants, both within UK and internationally. Proliferation in this respect results in an inability to support all needs. Hence it has been necessary for our organisation to play a central role within MOD UK, and to cooperate closely within NATO, in order to establish universally accepted digital data standards. A further ongoing activity is the definition of a range of standard digital products, each identified for a generic group of users.

DEVELOPMENT PROJECT

The CREST 7 project, originally launched as a Data Structures Study in 1985, has latterly broadened its remit to include recommendations for introducing an operational Defence Geographic Database (DGDB). The study determined that a full topological structure containing centre line data and a high level of feature attribution was essential. Integrity is to be maintained by a Source ID data, whilst a Toponymic Database and a Geo Cell Management System are proposed. The Database System will employ a Multi Product Operation procedure whereby a range of products covering a common area will be derived from a single database population. A transformation process extracts data from the Multi Product DGDB to an accepted 'product generation specification'. Several such standards are envisaged to cater for the entire range of products and users. On receipt the individual user will have to convert data to the form demanded by his system. CREST 7 has progressed to a stage of completing the Final Study Report by end June 1988. Management will shortly thereafter address the size of the facility in order to provide an operation database within a given timeframe. Procurement is expected to permit partial installation at the beginning of the financial year 1989/90.

The system is to be developed over the next two years and will take account of existing auto carto and other relevant equipment. It will also examine procedures for incorporating existing digital data into the DGDB.

GLOBAL DATABASE PLANNING

The large majority of requirements we have to meet are concentrated on a medium scale related database with some specific large scale needs identified for local areas. The need for a small scale global database is of relatively low priority. Our experience however would lead us to conclude that it will be essential at the very outset to define clearly the objectives of such a database. Having done so, then two issues warrant priority consideration. Firstly whether it is to be a global database that is required as opposed to a databank. Secondly there must be a common referencing system.

SOME PLANNING ISSUES

Database v. Databank

A database as being introduced by CREST 7 suggests an integrated set of data with a minimum of redundancy consistent with fast performance, a common data dictionary for all data items stored, and a powerful data structure capable of being exploited by a standardised spatially extended query language. A fundamental component of this database would be a comprehensive management system. Centralised and distributed architectures would need investigation, and such a major project would need to be initiated by drafting terms of reference for a Feasibility Study. A databank is a much simpler concept, with a repository for all the datasets created. The facility would indicate the datasets available, and furnish copies for each user on demand.

Global Referencing System

It is assumed that this would be geographics based on WGS 84, whilst a common backdrop, such as the current proposal for the 1:1m ONC dataset would be desirable.

Common Data Coding

All datasets should code the same item (i.e. attributes and permissible values) in the same way, or coding translation tables will be necessary where this is not possible. This would be enforced by a data dictionary in a database and by exchange standards in a databank, both mechanisms being made capable of providing for change and expansion.

Associated Software Tools

Exploitation of the data collected will be facilitated through the common development of a set of software tools related to the four locational primitives: pixel, point, line and area. Considerable duplication of effort will otherwise occur.

RELEVANT MILITARY SURVEY EXPERIENCE

Experience in the creation and use of global databanks is mainly through involvement with the DLMS group and with the Digital Geographic Information Working Group (DGIWG). Both are groups of co-operating nations with common defensive policies who have agreed to capture and exchange digital data for a common purpose(s).

The DLMS group

Two main products, Digital Feature Analysis Data (DFAD) and Digital Terrain Elevation Data(DTED), are produced and exchanged by this group. DFAD is vector data with specified features and attributes captured, while DTED is a regular array of elevations at a specified interval. Both products are captured to a detailed specification and produced in a common standardised format. There is a centralised databank called the Cartographic Data Base (CDB) to which each nation sends its data. The data is validated for content and format on input to the CDB. Each nation produced indices, over its area of responsibility, showing current capture, proposed capture and data entered into the CDB. The CDB circulates, twice yearly, a consolidated index of its holdings, and distributes data on request.

The DGIWG

This multinational forum originally proposed to create a common database but concluded, because of the inherent complexity, that independent national databases exchanging data utilising a common exchange standard (i.e. interface) was the only practical solution. To ensure that each individual database will be compatible with the eventual exchange standard, the group has discussed and resolved common and individual problems prior to the implementation of the national databases.

The exchange standard, as well as designating a preferred reference system (WGS 84), defines the three major areas following:

- The data structure to be accommodated (e.g. topological, raster etc.).

- The feature and attribute coding catalogue (FACC).

- The exchange media and format.

The problem of defining quality, accuracy, currency etc. is complex and difficult to attempt. For this reason the DGIWG adopted the findings of the Moellering Committee

Geographic Database Activities and Plans of Military Survey

(Report #7 of the US National Committee for Digital Cartographic Standards) as the basis for this aspect of the standard.

REFERENCES

Harvey, M., 1987. 'Meeting the future defence Requirement for Digital Geographic Data'. Paper No. 10, NAV 87, London.

Lankester, J.S., 1987. 'Database developments within Military Survey'. Paper No. 12, NAV 87, London.

Kennedy-Smith, C.N., 1986. 'Data quality - a management philosophy'. Proceedings, AutoCarto London, ed. M. Blakemore, Vol. 1, 381-390.

Thompson, C.M., 1985. 'The development of a Geographic Database for Military Survey'. Presented at Survey and Mapping 85, University of Reading.

Thompson, C.M., 1986. 'Managing the transition to supporting the production of digital geographic products in military survey'. Proceedings, AutoCarto London, ed. M. Blakemore, Vol. 2, 226-236.

THE GLOBAL SYSTEM, OBSERVING AND MONITORING CHANGE, DATA PROBLEMS, DATA MANAGEMENT AND DATABASES

S. Unninayar

THE ISSUE

We are faced today with the following scenarios: an increasing world population, high technology and indust- rialization, deforestation and land-use changes, exponen- tially growing concentrations of radiatively active green house gases (GHGs) such as O3, CO2, CO, chlorofluorocarbon compounds, halons and oxides of nitrogen, and increasing emissions of toxic pollutants. Of particular concern is the effect all this "uncontrolled" activity is going to have on global climate, food production capability and environmental integrity. Compounding the problem is the lack of understanding of natural climate system variability even without anthropogenic forcing. These are the basic issues. The question is whether we have or can develop the means to tackle the problem. The issue of global change must also be considered in the context of rather ponderous social and economic systems world-wide, typically respon- sive only to immediate crises and requiring very long lead times (approximately 30-50 years) to institute corrective or adaptive measures even if warned of potentially adverse future scenarios. Inevitably, improvements are required along established lines such as (a) enhanced global observ- ing, data collection, data exchange and monitoring systems, (b) well-coordinated diagnostics and analysis procedures to flag key problems as they arise and feed information to decision makers for action, (c) more research into predic- tion models of the global system. There is a corresponding need for well organized, reliable global databases.

THE GLOBAL SYSTEM AND TIME SCALES OF CHANGE

A major part of the "global system" can be said to comprise the physical climate system consisting of the atmosphere, hydrosphere (oceans and other elements of the hydrological cycle such as lakes, rivers, subterranean waters), cryo- sphere (the ice fields of Greenland and the Antarctic, other continental glaciers, snow fields and sea ice), the

357

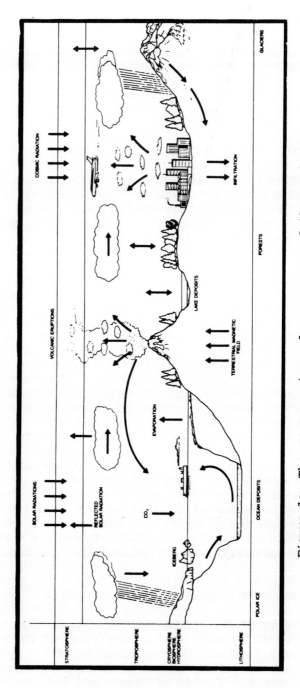

<u>Figure 1</u>: The components and processes of the climate system whose behaviour ultimately defines climate and the environment we live in (from Frasseto, 1985).

lithosphere (continents and their orography, ocean bottoms etc.), and the biosphere (vegetation cover, continental fauna, and the flora and fauna of the oceans) (ICSU, 1987). Figure 1 illustrates, in schematic form, the various component subsystems of the global climate system. The system is in a continual state of flux or change with parts of the system leading and others lagging in time. The highly non linear interactions between the subsystems tend to occur on many time and space scales. Therefore, the subsystems of the climate system are not always in equilibrium with each other, and not even necessarily in internal equilibrium. Due to the complexity and interactive nature of the global climate system, it has been convenient to select a combination of its components and define this set as the "Internal" system, considering the remaining components as the external system (Peixoto and Oort, 1984). The atmosphere is the fastest changing component of the climate system and also the most responsive.

In the past, the atmosphere alone was regarded as the climate system. However, the strong coupling between the atmosphere and oceans has forced the recognition that both subsystems must be considered as a more complete internal system. Climate variability during the recent history of the planet demonstrates that the cryosphere played a significant role and hence the cryosphere needs to be included in the "internal" climate system. This leads us to the present notion of the climate system wherein the atmosphere, hydrosphere (especially ocean) and the cryosphere are defined as the internal physical climate system and the lithosphere and biosphere as external components. The definition is somewhat ad-hoc, and forced by our present mathematical capabilities to model the global system within the constraints of existing computer power.

The above definition is, however, consistent with the distinction made between the "physical" aspects of the global system governed by dynamic or thermodynamic and empirical mathematical equations, and biogeochemical processes involving the biosphere and the lithosphere. The physical global system is popularly referred to as the global climate system primarily due to (a) the lack of a better term and (b) the manner in which scientific research is currently organized and carried out. To this simplified definition of the global system must be added anthropogenic forcing and other influences due to changes in solar output and orbital fluctuations. Furthermore, when studying or modelling the physical processes which link any two components of the global system, elements of other components of the system are inextricably involved. For example atmosphere - hydrosphere coupling must include processes involving moisture recycling through vegetation (evapo-transpiration). During the last few years signicant advances have been made in developing generalized biosphere models (Sellers, 1987; Dickson, 1984) which will substan-tially improve atmosphere land-surface / vegetation inter-action in global models.

In reality, the global system is totally interactive, even though certain processes of very long time-scale (e.g. over 1000 years) may be considered, for simplicity, unchanging or constant when dealing with fluctuations and issues of much shorter time scale. Some hypothesize that the "total" global system represents an entity which optimizes itself (Lovelock, 1987). Irrespective of whether this is accurate or not, what is not clear is whether the "optimal" state is the best for human life - a frightening thought to the global ego. Of particular interest to scientists and governments alike are the characteristics of the global system at any given point in time as defined by, for example, mean state, variability and the frequency of occurrence of extreme events, and whether these charac-teristics are changing or likely to change.

To render the mathematical treatment of the global system tractable, the above mentioned features of the global system are taken advantage of. For example, for forecast-ing weather (time scale: few days) the ocean surface temperatures may be regarded as constant over "weather" time scales. On seasonal and inter-annual time-scales, fluctuations in the upper layers of the ocean need to be taken into account - thus coupled models need to include the thermodynamics of the upper ocean circulation and interactions at the atmosphere - ocean interface. On longer time scale (e.g. 10 years to 100 years) the entire ocean circulation must be modelled in any prediction scheme. Using similar arguments, orbital variation may be assumed to be constant, on the 10 to 100 year time scale but not so on the 1000 year time-scale. For a full comprehension of the carbon cycle and atmospheric CO_2, the carbonate - silicate geochemical cycle (500,000 year) is involved, where atmospheric CO_2 dissolves in rainwater forming carb-onic acid (H_2CO_3) which erodes surface rock releasing calcium and bi-carbonate ions into the ground water flowing into the ocean (Kasting and Pollack 1988). In the oceans, CO_2 is trapped as shells of $CaCO_3$ by plankton and other organisms, eventually depositing as ocean sediment. Sedimentary layers of the earth get drawn into the interior

of the earth at subduction zones where, at high temperatures, CaCO3 reacts with silica (quartz) reforming silicate
rocks and releasing gaseous CO2. Outgassing into the
atmosphere occurs at midoceanic ridges and through volcanic
erruption near the margins of tectonic plates. Various
processes in this cycle involve feed-back which have been
hypothesized to have held the global system within a
certain range of livable temperatures (see Figure 2).

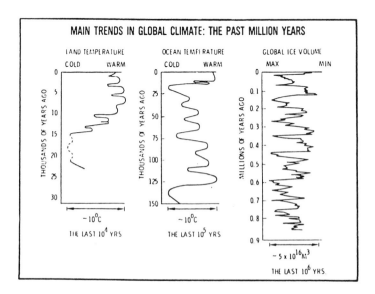

Figure 2: The main trends in global land temperature for
the last 23,000 years, in global ocean temperatures for the last 150,000 years, and in global
ice volume for the last 850,000 years (from
Bergman, 1983).

Interaction between the components of the global system
generally lead to a quasi-equilibrium "climate" on time
scales of 10 to 20 years. Beyond this it becomes necessary
to factor in influences due to changes in the radiation
balance (and the effect of GHGs), the biosphere
(deforestation, land-use, etc.), the geosphere (solid
earth, crustal movement, volcanic eruptions), and solar
fluctuations. Figure 3 summarizes the characteristic time
scales over which possible causes of climatic change take
place. A more detailed description of the fluctuations of

the global system on time-scales from weeks to millions of years, is contained in Unninayar (1986).

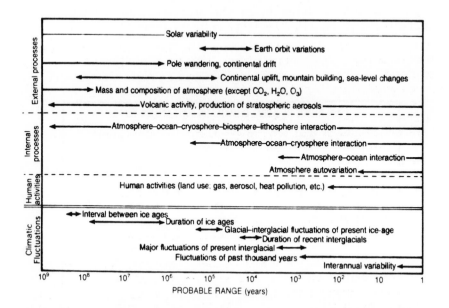

Figure 3: The characteristic time scales over which possible causes of climatic change take place (from Bergman, 1981).

Human activity has been traditionally regarded as external to the dynamics of the global system and something which merely responds to boundary conditions set by nature. Over the last 50 years, however, this scenario has been rapidly changing. We must now consider the anthropogenic factor as one of the mechanisms which can bring about rather rapid change, change which could normally have been induced perhaps only by large, relatively catastrophic events on a geological time scale. Increasing emissions of CO2 will alter the radiation budget, global temperatures, cloud and precipitation distribution, and effects will be felt on many space and time scales.

Clearly, the inter-annual to decadal (and up to 50-100 years) is of particular interest for global change which may result from anthropogenic alteration. We need to know what policy actions should be taken over the next 5 years to ensure that human and other life forms continue in some rationally acceptable manner. If nothing else, it should be ensured that global databases are readily available for research, and for guiding policy decisions.

REQUIREMENTS FOR OBSERVING AND MONITORING THE GLOBAL SYSTEM

Until the last 20-50 years, monitoring anything on a global scale was practically impossible due to a lack of observing technology, telecommunications and the ability effectively to handle large quantities of data. Science generally concentrated on specialization and disciplinary research on processes, to begin building simple models of how things worked in nature. Weather forecasting, commercial and defense aviation and shipping, provided the initial impetus for global observations, simply due to the fact that the atmosphere swirls around the globe rather rapidly (within a span of a few weeks to a few months) and forecasting weather at any one point required a knowledge of what the atmosphere was doing at locations far removed. Waves in the atmosphere propagate faster, and to make a 5-day forecast, global data is absolutely essential.

Clearly any global observing system must comprise both surface-based and space-based instrumented platforms. Satellite remote sensed data need to be calibrated using surface measurements and ideally should be operationally calibrated at a representative selection of surface target sites. The advantage of satellite technology is that it is truly global and can measure certain parameters which cannot be monitored easily or at all, otherwise. Fairly high resolution surface-based, direct measurements are required for process studies. A comprehensive description of the potential of remote sensing for the study of global change is contained in Rasool (1987).

The following need to be monitored in a systematic manner (adapted and updated from Unninayar, 1986; WMO/ICSU, 1975):
- Atmospheric structure: Wind, temperature, moisture, pressure, stream function and velocity potential at several levels and time series information of indices of atmospheric structure and circulation state;
- Ocean: Sea surface temperature (SST) and time series of SST indices which are indicators of major climate system events (e.g. El-Nino/Southern Oscillation), temperature and salinity at different depths, sea-level, near-surface currents, deep ocean circulation, ocean biomass /plankton;

363

- Cryosphere: Snow cover, sea ice, sea ice boundaries, sea ice thickness, elevation of continental ice sheets and glaciers, ice sheet boundaries, ice sheet thickness, movement of ice sheets and glaciers;
- Land surface, the hydrological cycle and vegetation: Precipitation, evaporation, evapotranspiration, water run-off/streamflow, water storage (snow, lake, etc.), soil temperature, soil moisture, vegetation cover (including type and state), soil type and soil nutrients, erosion, mineralization;
- Radiation budget: Radiation budget components at the surface and the top of the atmosphere (albedo, emission), equator to pole gradients, solar constant, solar UV flux;
- Atmospheric composition: Concentration and distribution of CO_2, CO, chlorofluorocarbons, ozone, halons, oxides of nitrogen, stratospheric/tropospheric aerosols and turbidity, chemical exchange between the atmosphere and the ocean, biosphere and lithosphere;
- Geosphere: Land surface and ocean bottom elevation changes, solid earth rotation, earth mantle-core interaction, tectonic plate movement, volcanism, geomagnetic fluctuations;
- Solar: Solar fluctuations (sunspots, flares, etc.), solar constant.
- Impact parameters: A variety of social and economic response parameters which either are proxy parameters of physical variables of the global system, or parameters which transform physical variables into applications information - e.g. food production or crop-yield indices, surface and ground water availability, energy production/consumption, population stress and movement, disease outbreak and health, economic indices.

DATA QUALITY, SPACE/TIME RESOLUTION, AND DATA MANAGEMENT PROBLEMS

It could be safely assumed that there will always be problems with data quality, the accuracy and space/time resolution of measurements by observing systems, and with data management procedures. However, first, the problem in question has to be defined and second, it should be recognized that the problems will differ with the type of application or use the data are required for.

The ideal observing system yielding data at the space/time resolution and accuracy required by research is rarely, if ever, achieved, particularly on a global basis. Most of the time, the researcher uses data from operational observing systems (e.g. surface and upper air meteorological/climate stations, meteorological satellites) deployed for a different purpose. Global observing systems are very expensive to operate and maintain, and any one research initiative can rarely afford to set up for a long period of time, such systems. It has been the practice, during global observing experiments such as the ICSU/WMO Global Weather Experiment (GWE), to enhance operational observing systems for a limited length of time e.g. 3 months to one year. During these selected observing periods a multitude of new and specialized measurements have been made with instrumented research aircraft, dropwindsondes and research ships. When possible operational or stand-by satellites have also been moved to new locations to better suit the research objectives of the programme.

Even if an "ideal" observing system is achievable, there could be other significant deficiencies arising from our limited knowledge of the global system and what we are attempting to investigate. There has been more than a latent tendency to specify requirements for data (type, resolution, accuracy) on the basis of whatever models are in use at the time, i.e. on the basis of model grid-size, initialization and verification parameters required, and some ad-hoc multiple of the model integration time step. Obviously, this could lead to faulty experiment design, since perfection has yet to be achieved in the art of modelling.

The conventionally used observational frequency is more a matter of convenience than science. There is some basis for using daily data, but the diurnal cycle is immediately ignored in the process. Monthly data are often thought to be sufficient for climate studies, but there is no physical basis for a 30 to 31 day period based on the ad-hoc division of the calender year. Besides, the 30-day or monthly arithmetic mean is probably the worst way to filter a data time series if indeed the purpose is to remove high frequency fluctuations. Ten day data are commonly used in agrometeorological applications, though this assumes that the distribution of the variable in question is either uniform over the 10-day period or otherwise known. Rather serious errors can result in the use of 10-day data if these assumptions are not met (e.g. in semi-arid zones). Weekly (7-day) data have no particular scientific basis either, except perhaps that 7 days is a quarter of the lunar cycle.

The accuracy of measured variables does not always correspond to the accuracy required of derived quantities. For example, for air-sea momentum exchange studies, the accuracy with which wind components are measured, even if marginally acceptable for wind, yield errors in momentum calculations which are larger than the accuracy requirements for the momentum flux terms. Precipitation data are required at an accuracy of 10 W/m2 based on thermodynamic considerations of atmospheric processes, which translates to approximately 50-75 surface stations over a 5 degree longitude/latitude grid (WMO, 1986). However, global databases typically contain only between 1 to 10 stations per 5 degrees grid box. Complicating matters further, to estimate latent and sensible heat fluxes at the atmosphere - land surface interface, besides precipitation, soil moisture and evaporation / evapotranspiration are required with the same accuracy as precipitation, namely 10 W/m2. Measurements of these variables are not exchanged globally, even if available. Thus, the global databases used for research can be quite deficient and we should be wondering about the results of some research inadvertently using inappropriate databases.

Other problems arise from the data assimilation models used to produce the grid-fields which are used by most research studies. Data assimilation models contain a variety of assumptions and approximations, and inject model physics into data fields through first guess fields. Models are used in order to either fill data sparse areas and/or filter the data so that it does not produce an overwhelming shock to the model during the initialization stage. Divergence/convergence fields, vertical motion and thereby precipitable water and precipitation, all very significant variables for atmospheric motion, have been known to change rather dramatically when the data assimilation schemes were changed and improved during, for example, the re-analyses of global data from GWE (1979) at ECMWF and GFDL. Though there is no clear alternative approach in sight, one has to ask the question whether we are studying what we already know (i.e. the physics programmed into the model) and could these studies lead to "new discoveries"? Even worse, research using some datasets could lead to erroneous conclusions and suspect improvements to model physics.

Signal to noise ratio is of great significance when designing and using observing systems. For operational purposes, in the mid-latitudes for example, where the day to day temperature could fluctuate as much as 20 degrees to 40 degrees, a measurement error of 5 degrees C may be tolerable. Thus, the data are still useful and can yield information since the signal is large. This same station's data time series would pose major problems if it is being used to detect climate change of the order of 1 degree C in 50 years. Furthermore, extraneous influences cause local changes of the same (if not more) order of magnitude in the measured variable - e.g. change in location and exposure of a station; change in the environment such as shading; urban effects; changes in instrumentation, observing personnel and calibration; change in computational procedures. Time continuity and data homogeneity are issues which need special attention.

Signal to noise ratio problems (in a spatial sense) also arise in the application of satellite spectral data for the derivation of land surface characteristics. For example, the vegetation indices derived from the visible and near-infrared channels 1 (055-0.68 microns) and 2 (0.73-1.1 microns) of NOAA's Advanced Very High Resolution Radiometer (AVHRR) data have a spatial resolution of approximately 1 to 4 km at the satellite nadir point. Thus, the sensor detects a spatially averaged signal reflecting at best the photosynthetic capacity of an unknown mix of vegetation or plant varieties. Unknown because various combinations of vegetation types could lead to the same satellite derived vegetation index. Thus, attempting to obtain sub-grid scale classification information could either be very difficult or impossible unless it is inferred from ground truth verification data and the distribution is assumed to remain stable with time. Namely, the signal is buried in the noise or ambient field. The only instance when a sub-grid scale feature can be unambiguously detected is if the spectral signal from the feature in question saturates the pixel (e.g. oil flares).

With the advanced technology used today such as satellite and radar observing systems, two factors affect the homogeneity of data time series, namely, changes and improvements in the sensors used and changes in the algorithms used to transform spectral radiance signals to the physical variables which are required. To maintain continuity in the observing programme, it is necessary to repeatedly (and operationally) carry out data intercomparisons, sensor and algorithm calibrations. With remote sensed data, continuous monitoring is also necessary of the factors influencing the transmission and reception of the electromagnetic waves and the media the signal travels through. To detect problems, "ground truth" comparison must be made mandatory at a suitable number of target sites around the world and at a selection of latitude zones reflecting the macro-diversity of climatic and biospheric regions.

A peculiar type of camouflaged error could also exist in certain types of digital data fields. For example when digitizing geographical boundaries from maps, the resolution of the final dataset will be determined by the accuracy with which the original measurements were made either by surface surveys, aerial photography or remote sensing. The use of very high resolution laser-raster scanners to digitize data from maps does not mean that the original map was drawn with the same resolution. The resolution of aerial photographs and remote sensed data also depend on how well the image is navigated and georeferenced. Further, it is possible that relative accuracy is high but absolute accuracy may not be as good - this is typical of satellite derived measurements such as sea surface temperature also.

Data management is an often neglected aspect of global observing programmes. There are various obscure reasons for this. The problem is partly due to the traditional dominance of real-time or near - real-time operational requirements. Thus, data are collected, used immediately for whatever purpose they were collected, and dispatched for archiving. This archive usually constitutes an infrequently visited burial yard. In many countries there are 10 to 100 years of manuscripts and log books, lying in piles in some back room with little protection from moisture, dust, fungi and pests. Modern technology can resolve the problems of archiving manuscripts by transfer-ring the data to non-perishable media such as microfiche. But modern technology may also introduce new problems. For example, with the high bit-rate of advanced sensors, data volume is high, resulting in crypts of magnetic tapes which nobody has the resources to check, re-copy (to prevent catastrophic read-error rates due to the deterioration of the media or magnetic leakage), or re-process. World-wide computerization and the use of laser optical disk (random access) archive devices will go a long way in solving the archive problem.

No matter which data archive management procedure is used there are very simple criteria that must meet, namely: (a) data security - i.e. the data once archived should not be susceptible to loss for any reason. There are many means by which data can and should be protected from the obvious (protection against change due to fire, moisture, water, dust etc.) to the sublime (re-copying of tapes every 3-5 years, changing the physical media every 10 years, checking for epitaxial crystal growth every 25 to 50 years on optical disks etc.); (b) The data should be "instantly" retrievable. The latter point is critical. It is pointless if nobody knows what the archive contains, where it is, and how to get it out. Thus data dictionaries, directories, catalogues, inventories and database management systems (DBMS) are required. The principles apply irrespective of whether the procedures being implemented are manual or computerized.

The electronic hardware and software technologies available today are capable of handling data management in a comprehensive and efficient manner. Substantial advances have been made in recent years particularly in computer processor speeds, archive/retrieval software and storage media. Initially, DBMS's should be used to enable the system to keep track of data, and data retrieval programmes written to permit user access by externally specified key words. Eventually, Expert Assistance and Artificial Intelligence systems should be used to intercept data requests, locate the data and copy the data for distribution. Such systems should also generate messages regarding data security. Despite advances in technology, many data centres, even in developed countries, significantly lag behind what technology can currently provide. This is partly because of the heavy investments made some years ago on hardware which is now obsolete, but still in operation. Upgrading equipment and procedures cost money, and upgrades to data management is usually put in the back-burner category to be implemented when possible. In times of budgetary constraints, this component of science is the first to get cut because it lacks glamour. This scenario could change if data centres expand their scope and generate end products that are perceived by governments as directly (i.e. without any further processing) useful for social and economic planning and development.

TYPES OF DATASETS REQUIRED TO MONITOR AND STUDY THE GLOBAL SYSTEM

Information from a monitoring system should include spatial fields of variables at discrete intervals of time (sampling frequency) and time-series of indices constructed from measured or estimated parameters. With the explosion of data volume from automatic sampling by high resolution sensors, it has become critical that the raw data be properly managed if it is to have meaning to decision makers. Generally, decision-makers need digested, graphical information, not basic data.

To make monitoring and diagnoses tractable, the global system should perhaps be divided into a discrete set of components and zones and monitored through indices of a set of parameters derived for each index zone using all available observational data. For most purposes, a weekly to monthly time scale would suffice, with the exception of data required for process studies and certain applications. Several classes of data or datasets are needed for global system research, diagnostic studies, model development, initialization and verification, and applications to support sustainable economic development. For detailed process studies it is customary, through dedicated experiments, to collect and prepare datasets comprising high resolution and often specialized data measurements of a range of parameters not routinely observed such as turbulent fluxes from instrumented research aircraft - these specialized data are not the subject of this paper. Basically, there is a need for three classes of datasets:

(a) Global Reference datasets: Spatial data fields representing either "normal or long-term average" conditions (e.g. climatic parameters) or classifications (e.g. soils, vegetation) or statistics (e.g population and population density distribution, energy production/consumption distributions). No dataset or data field, irrespective of whether the described field in question is the "normal" or not, can permanently, and forever represent any characteristic feature of the global system. This is simply because the global system is continuously changing. For practical purposes, a specific time period may be selected to derive "normal" values. For example, WMO uses 30 years for global reference purposes. The climate "normal" could and will change, perhaps not in 10 years, but quite possibly in the 20 to 50 year time scale. Consequently all "time-averaged" datasets need to be updated, at least every 10 years in order to (a) detect change in the mean state and (b) represent what is perceived as typical values. The spatial and temporal sampling resolution and quality of existing datasets are highly variable as also the form in which they are available;

(b) Global Monitoring dataset (Synoptic): In addition to updating normal or reference data fields, an action tantamount to monitoring the relative mean state of the global system, it is also important to monitor global system fluctuations and variability. Thus, a variety of datasets and databases need to be prepared which can be applied towards studying global change on several different time scales. The data should periodically sample global system variables at discrete intervals of time. Both snap shots of global spatial distribution and time series of data at individual geographical points or zones will be required. The key word is "change", i.e. data to keep track of "change" rather than to define the "mean state".

For simplicity datasets with a sampling frequency substantially less than the averaging time period used to derive the reference fields may be called "monitoring" datasets and are likely to be in the form of global spatially analyzed data fields averaged over weeks to months (e.g. 1 month or 3 months) or a couple of years (e.g. 5 years). Social, economic and "impact" data should be included for the proper monitoring of the global system. The actual averaging time should ideally depend on the rate of change of the global system variable in question, but realistically it may be determined (de facto) by whatever measuring or sampling frequency is in use. datasets comprising two and/or three dimensional fields of global system variables at specific time intervals represent, in fact, a time series of snap-shots of the global system - commonly referred to as synoptic fields. Examples are fields of temperature, precipitation, wind, pressure, snow/ice cover etc. These datasets are, however, not commonly referred to as time-series datasets which primarily are in the form of a set of scalar variables at a single point. Hence, the third class of data is described in the following section.

(c) Global Monitoring datasets (Time Series): As the name implies, these datasets would contain time series of either (a) the absolute values of global system variables at a selection of points distributed over the global surface, or (b) time series of indices of key global system elements, variables, processes or interactions. An index could be in the form of a derived or computed quantity such as evapotranspiration, surface heat flux or angular momentum using observed data at the same selection of grid points as in (a) or spatially averaged values of parameters over "an index area or zone" or a count such as the sun spot number. Examples of "index zones" are the central and eastern Pacific Ocean areas used to derive the Sea Surface Temperature (SST), Outgoing Long Wave Radiation (OLR), and wind indices to monitor the El-Nino/Southern Oscillation phenomenon. Other examples are the zonal wind index, vegetation index (satellite derived), the blocking index, hemispheric and global surface temperature indices etc. The number of indices of the global system currently available are indeed very few, partly due to the lack of observing stations (spatial density) and/or time continuity, and/or sufficient research and analyses into how "Key" zones are to be defined.

The development of a comprehensive matrix of global system indices is considered crucial for improvement in monitoring, diagnostics, and our understanding of the physics of the system. It should also enable keeping track of fluctuations of the global system in a systematic manner, and in particular, the identification of "key" parameters to capture the global behaviour or state of the system. Of importance is the need to extract the information signal in data fields in a form easy for the human brain to assimilate. It is not sufficient to only be able to measure 50 variables at 20,000 or more grid-points at 40 vertical levels around the globe. In the future three dimensional graphics could provide considerably more insight into global circulation physics than the currently used two dimensional display formats.

GLOBAL DATABASES

A cross-disciplinary mix of databases is required by the scientific community to carry out fundamental research on the global system, and by technologists concentrating on data application towards social and economic planning and development. For the databases to be usable, they need to be available in a uniform, geo-referenced, inter-comparable format. This task should be undertaken by either existing or planned global data centres with a specific mandate to (a) re-process the data from individual discipline oriented data centres, and (b) provide data and product distribution services.

Examples of the types of spatial and time-series databases likely to be required for global system studies are:

(A) GEOGRAPHIC/DEMOGRAPHIC (GLOBAL) (EXAMPLES)

(1) Political boundaries
(2) Natural boundaries
(3) Elevation
(4) Soils
(5) Vegetation classification/distribution
(6) Agroclimatic zones (classification)
(7) Land use (classification including agricultural practice, cultivation intensity
(8) Deforestation areas and rates
(9) Desertification
(10) Soil nutrient base
(11) Erosion (top-soil) and rates
(12) Ground water availability
(13) Water consumption rate
(14) Energy production rates - global distribution by type (e.g. fossil fuel, hydro, nuclear, wood-burning etc.)
(15) Energy consumption rates
(16) SOx, NOx, CO2, Ch4, O3 production rates, sources and sinks
(17) Areas prone to various airborne and water borne diseases
(18) Areas prone to the occurrence of plant and animal diseases
(19) Population (totals and density distribution)
(20) Biomass amount, concentration and production rates (land surface areas)
(21) Ocean-biomass/plankton amount, concentration and production rates
(22) Glacier areal extent, movement

Time Resolution: As available, 5-10 year updates. In areas of rapid change e.g. desert margin zones, tropical forests (deforestation) more frequent updates (e.g. 1 year) would be necessary. Space Resolution: Variable, depending an application (100m to 100km). Possible Sources: FAO, ICSU-WDCs, UNESCO, IOC, WRI, UNEP, National Geological Survey Depts, etc.

(B) GEOPHYSICAL (SPATIAL GRID FIELDS) (EXAMPLES)

(1) Surface Air Temperature (land surface and ocean)
(2) Sea Surface Temperature
(3) Precipitation (land and ocean areas)

(4) Evaporation and Evapotranspiration, soil moisture /temperature
(5) Cloudiness and diabatic heating
(6) Surface wind (speed and direction)
(7) Upper air (Troposphere) 200 mb, 300 mb, 500 mb, 850 mb, 1000 mb - stream function, velocity potential, geo-potential height, wind vectors (divergent and non-divergent components), moisture, temperature; Stratosphere (temperature, wind)
(8) Sea level pressure
(9) Sea-level
(10) Thermocline depth
(11) Near surface ocean circulation
(12) Albedo (surface and planetary)
(13) Solar radiation absorbed, long-wave radiation, radiation balance
(14) Sensible heat flux, heat balance
(15) CO2 concentration/distribution
(16) O3, SOx, NOx, CH4 etc. concentrations/distributions
(17) Aerosol concentration, atmospheric turbidity, optical depth
(18) Snow cover
(19) Sea-ice
(20) Deep ocean circulation

Time Resolution: daily, monthly, seasonal and annual as appropriate. For example, monthly fields for precipitation (daily data are required for site specific or regional application); 10 years for deep ocean circulation from observations using tracers and model output. Long-term (30 years) means would provide reference states or normals. Monitoring datasets of the same variable would typically consist of deviation from normals or normalized anomalies. Update frequency for reference datasets: 5-10 years or running annual updates as in the case of CO2 and GHG concentrations. Some data fields are currently not directly measured globally (e.g. ocean circulation). In such cases data fields derived from spot measurements, if available, and model output may be used as an interim measure. Space Resolution: 50 km to 250 km. Possible Sources: WMO-WMC/CAC, Washington D.C., (and others), NCAR, NOAA/NESDIS for 1,2,3,4,8,12,13,18,19; NASA for 5,12,13, 14,15; NOAA/GMCC for 16,17; IOC/IODE, NOAA/NODC for 9, 10; NOAA/NWS/CAC, NOAA/GFDC, NCAR for 11,20; IOC/IGOSS-SOC (Hawaii) for 9.

(C) GEOPHYSICAL TIME SERIES datasetS (EXAMPLES)

(1) ENSO Pacific indices:
   - SST1, SST2, SST3, SOI
   - Darwin SLP, Tahiti SLP
   - West. Pac. SST max. longitude (position)
(2) Atlantic SST, Surface Pressure, Wind (target zones), NAO index
(3) SST(NH) - SST(SH) index (Trop. ITCZ)
(4) Upper ocean heat content (Pacific)
(5) Precipitation indices (CAC/NMC):
   Sahel - Lamb index;
   SE Africa - index; Eastern Central Africa
   Indian Monsoon;
   Brazil; S. America;
   Australia; Southeast Asia.
(6) Zonal T index for different latitude zones
(7) Sea level - target areas in Pacific
   e.g. Western, Central, Eastern - monthly
   Regional T indices (index zones):
   Western Canada; Eastern Canada; Western Europe;
   West-USA; Central; Eastern USA; Centra Asia; etc.
(8) SH & NH blocking index
(9) Tropical E-W Overturning circulation index (from velocity potential field) - not yet available, but needed
(10) N-S Hadley Circulation Index (regional and zonal average)
(11) Zonal wind index; set stream position
(12) Arctic, Antarctic Sea-ice
(13) Snow cover
(14) CO_2, CH_4, O_3, etc. (Single station and composite)
(15) River run-off - major rivers
(16) Lake level
(17) LOD/Earth Rotation Spd & Atm. Angular Momentum
(18) QBO (Balboa wind) index
(19) Sun-spot number (index)
(20) N. Vegetation index (inter-annual aggregated over target areas e.g. Sahel
(21) Kuroshio, Gulf stream flow volume estimates (research data)
(22) Geomagnetic
(23) Paleoclimatic:
   - Precipitation from tree rings (target sites)
   - CO_2, O_2-isotope etc. from glacial cores
   - Temperature (Antarctic cores)
   - Global T

Time Resolution: daily, monthly, seasonal and annual (as available). Space Resolution: variable - zero (single point data) to approximately 20 degrees to 20 degrees polygons to global, depending on the definition of index zones and the parameter or index in question. Possible Sources: WMC/CAC, Washington for 1,2,3,5,8,9,10,11,12,13, 18; MGO-Leningrad for 6; WMC-Melbourne for 8; WMC/CAC, ICSU/WDC-Glaciology for 12,13; UNESCO for 15,16; ICSU/WDC -Solar/Terr., Boulder, Zurich for 19,22; NASA, NOAA/NESDIS for 20 23; ICSU WDCS, National Centre for 23.

(D)   SOCIAL, ECONOMIC AND OTHER DATA (EXAMPLES)

   (1) GNP - Global distribution
   (2) Human population distributions by language (major), religion, anthropological/ethnic sub-divisions
   (3) Wild-life distribution; endangered species
   (4) Plant gene-pool distribution; endangered varieties
   (5) Event related impact data; e.g. El-Nino and food shortages, import/export statistics
   (6) Fossil Fuels - reserves, consumption rates
   (7) Minerals - reserves, distribution extraction rates
   (8) Human health and disease; growth and decay of epidemic distributions
   (9) Demand/supply and import/export
   (10) Social and economic stress indices (?)

Time Resolution: Variable and as available, but in the range 5-10 years for reference data, annual for indices, and 1 to 3 monthly for event related impact data. Space Resolution: Variable. Possible Sources: UN, IUCN, FAO, UNESCO, WHO , WRI, National Census Bureaux, Ministries of Planning etc.

REFERENCES

Bergman, K.H., A.Hecht, and S.H.Schneider, 1981. 'Climate Models'. Physics Today, October 1981, 44-51.

Bergman, K.H., 1983. 'Climate Change'. Intern. J Environmental Studies, 20, 91-101.

Dickinson, R.E., 1984. 'Modelling Evapotranspiration for three dimensional Global Climate Models' in Climate Processes and Climate Sensitivity, ed. J.E. Hansen and T. Takahashi. Geophysical Monograph 29, AGU.

Frassetto, R., 1985. 'L'Oceanografia Verso Il Duemila'. Scienza & Technica, Annuario della Est, 60-88.

ICSU, 1987. Report of the Final Meeting of the ICSU Special Committee on the IGBP.

Kasting, J.F., O.B. Toom and J.B. Pollack, 1988. 'How Climate Evolved on the Terrestrial Planets'. Scientific American, February 1988.

Lovelock, J.E., 1987. Geophysiology: A New Look at Earth Science, in The Geophysiology of Amazonia - Vegetation and Climate Interactions, pp. 11-23. John Wiley and Sons.

Peixo'to, J.P. and A.H. Oort, 1984. 'Physics of Climate'. Reviews of Modern Physics, 56(3), 365-429.

Rasool, S.I., 1987. 'Understanding the Global Change: An opportunity to Seize'. EOS, 24 November 1987, 1609-1611.

Rasool, S.I., 1987. 'Potential of Remote Sensing for the study of Global Change'. Advances in Space Research, 7(1), 97.

Sellers, P.J., 1987. Modelling Effects of Vegetation on Climate, in The Geophysiology of Amazonia - Vegetation and Climate Interactions, pp. 297-339. John Wiley and Sons.

UNEP, 1985. Global Resource Information Database (GRID). UNEP/GEMS Publication, 16. pp.

Unninayar, S., 1986. 'Climate System Monitoring'. The Science of the Total Environment, 56, 55-65. Elsevier Science Publishers.

WMO, 1986. Review of Requirements for Area-Averaged Precipitation Data, Surface-Based and Space-Based Estimation Techniques, Space and Time Sampling, Accuracy and Error; Data Exchange.

WMO/ICSU, 1975. The Physical Basis of Climate and Climate Modelling. Global Atmospheric Research Programme (GARP) Publication No. 16, 265 pp.

CORINE: AN INFORMATION SYSTEM ON THE STATE OF THE ENVIRONMENT IN THE EUROPEAN COMMUNITY

Barry Wyatt, David Briggs and Helen Mounsey

ABSTRACT

CORINE (Co-Ordinated INformation on the Environment in the European Community) is an experimental programme of the Commission of the European Communities which aims to harmonize the collection of information and data on the state of the environment in the European Community and to develop an integrated Geographic Information System (GIS) as an aid to environmental policy formulation and implementation. This paper summarises the progress that has been achieved and identifies some of the problems involved, including particularly the practical limitations of data availability and the difficulty of harmonizing data derived from a variety of sources covering many inter-related thematic areas.

BACKGROUND

CORINE (Co-Ordinated INformation on the Environment in the European Community) is an experimental programme of the Commission of the European Communities, authorized by Decision of the Council of Ministers (Council Decision, 1985) and managed by DGXI, the Directorate-General for the Environment, Consumer Protection and Nuclear Safety.

The purposes of this programme are twofold. Firstly, it is intended as the means to develop a methodology for the collection, storage and analysis of data describing the state of the environment throughout the Member States of the Community. Secondly, it is designed so as to produce results which are of immediate practical utility in the Commission's task of responding to specific environmental problems. (It will become apparent that these dual objectives are not entirely compatible, within the constraints of an experimental programme of limited duration and funding).

378

While the system is not strictly global in coverage, its parish encompasses much of the continent of Europe - a region of considerable geographic diversity and an area where there is a profusion of data and data sources. In consequence, the challenges which CORINE presents are comparable with the problems of planning for many global systems.

OBJECTIVES

Information on environmental states and trends in the European Community is needed for many reasons, for example:

- as an aid to the formulation of Community policies for environmental protection;

- to help the Commission to monitor the effects of its policies;

- to allow the Commission to assess possible impacts on the environment of Community policies in other sectors (e.g. agriculture, regional development);

- as a source of environmental information and statistics for the European Parliament, for governments in the Member States and for the general public.

The detailed objectives of the CORINE programme and the design strategy that has been adopted for its implementation have been described previously (e.g. Commission of the European Communities 1983, Rhind et al 1986, Wiggins et al 1986, Hartley and Higgins 1987, Briggs and Martin 1988).

Briefly, the long-term goal is to develop a framework for collecting, handling, interpreting and disseminating environmental information to meet the needs of environmental management in a consistent fashion across the whole of the European Community.

In the first instance, collaborative programmes for the collection of data on a wide range of environmental attributes have been initiated with governmental and non-governmental agencies in each Community Member State. The purpose of these programmes is to agree specifications for data descriptions and formats that are generally acceptable and capable of adoption as standards within the European Community and, by wider international agreement, elsewhere.

Of central importance to the CORINE programme is the compilation of a spatially-referenced database, recording these attributes and covering the territories of all 12 countries of the European Community. Bearing in mind the need to demonstrate operational capability at an early stage, the database is being developed in a modular fashion, concentrating on selected thematic areas. However, it is recognised that, to achieve the eventual goal of a comprehensive Community information system, the architecture must be capable of accommodating data models which describe the complete range of user interests and should be capable of recording or generating appropriate linkages between various thematic datasets. In this way, the system may be extended in the future to include new data in a way that remains compatible with the existing database.

There are several pre-requisites for the establishment of this integrated environmental database. These include

i)   the provision of standards for recording environmental data,
ii)   the development of modelling procedures to assist interpretation and to provide predictive capabilities, and
iii) the acquisition of hardware and software to enable the data to be stored and manipulated efficiently.

Each of these design tasks has potential applications outside the CORINE programme. Standardization of environmental data will facilitate the dissemination of information and statistics on environment and natural resources throughout the European Community and many of these standards are being adopted by international agencies with interests outside Europe. The systems and data processing methods that are being developed for European applications are also helpful for agencies in the Member States when setting up national environmental databases.

EXPERIMENTAL PROGRAMME

The present programme is an experimental study. Its immediate objective is to investigate the feasibility of:

- acquisition of suitable data covering the whole of the European Community;

- establishment of a computerized environmental database, making use of Geographical Information System (GIS) techniques;

- development of the means of improving the availability and consistency of data which already exist at national or international levels.

SCOPE

The duration of the programme is four years (from 1985 to 1989), and the budget is relatively modest; therefore work has been concentrated in a limited number of priority areas, chosen because of their perceived importance in relation to policy issues at the European Community level.

These are:

- Biotopes (ecological sites) of major importance to the Community for nature conservation;

- acid deposition, especially in relation to information on atmospheric emissions and the potential damage to biotopes and the soil;

- resources and problems of the Mediterranean region, including land use, land quality, soil erosion, water quality, water resources, problems of coastal regions and seismic risks.

It is intended that these pilot studies will be test-beds for drawing up specifications for hardware, software and data standards in the longer-term, but will also furnish information of immediate utility within the chosen priority areas.

DATA

These themes are extremely broad in scope. Within each thematic area can be visualised many specific problems and applications, each of which must assess or model a different set of environmental conditions or processes. The data needed to support these analytical activities are correspondingly diverse.

For example, in order to develop models of the vulnerability of land to soil erosion, data are needed on soil conditions, climate, topography and land use. Each of these, in turn, is characterised by a number of independent measured variables.

Similarly, the task of protection and enhancement of Community ecological resources demands the systematic assessment of their present status and future trends. This requires that, for those examples which are of Community importance, information is recorded on their distribution and detailed characteristics, including their location, their extent, the nature of biological species and habitats represented, their vulnerability to damage, pressures form human activities, their ownership and their protection status.

In order to provide information of relevance to the three themes which comprise the experimental programme, it will be necessary to gather data on at least 200 individual environmental variables. Some indication of the scope of the database is indicated in Table 1. The current state of the database is summarized in Whimbrel Consultants Ltd (1988).

Two fundamental principles are that the system should exploit existing data resources as far as possible and that, where possible, data should be suitable for multiple uses. These decisions (dictated by the expense and difficulty of initiating Europe-wide programmes of environmental data acquisition) have a number of important consequences, mainly resulting from the shortcomings of existing datasets.

It is inevitable that data which are, in general, collected by national agencies for national purposes will exhibit differences which reflect the differing perceived priorities. Data from different countries and regions may be recorded in different units, perhaps using different measurement methods. They may be presented at different spatial and temporal scales and non-quantitative information may use different classifications which may be difficult to reconcile.

Therefore major concerns of the programme have been

i)   where possible, to introduce a degree of harmonization
      into these diverse datasets;
ii)   to develop models and procedures for data
      interpretation which are tolerant of the limitations
      in the data;

Table 1: The Scope of the CORINE Information System: examples of datasets included.

SUBJECT AREA	THEME/ITEM	1:1m.	1:3m.
Topography	Coastline	x	x
	Water pattern	x	(x)
	Slope gradient	(x)	
	Settlements	(x)	
Geographical glossary		(x)	(x)
Administrative regions	National boundaries	x	x
	Regional boundaries		x
	Social statistics		x
	incl. Population, Agriculture, Employment, Production, Transport, Wastes, etc.		
Climate	Station data (20 variables)	x	x
Land resources	Soil type	x	
	Land quality (Southern EC only)	(x)	
	Soil erosion risk (Southern EC only)	(x)	
	Land cover (Portugal only)	x	
Coastal erosion	Coastal erosion risk	(x)	
Seismic risks	Earthquakes	(x)	(x)
Nature/Wildlife	Biotopes	x	x
	Designated areas	(x)	(x)
	Vegetation zones		(x)
Air	Atmospheric emissions		(x)
	Air quality		(x)
Water resources	Stream discharge (France, Spain and Portugal only)	x	(x)
	Water quality (18 parameters)		(x)
Pollution sources	Power stations	(x)	(x)
	Oil platforms	(x)	(x)
	Refineries	(x)	(x)
	Major industries	(x)	(x)

Note: x - dataset already held in the CORINE database
      (x) - dataset in process of collection

iii) to develop methods for handling spatially-referenced data which are sufficiently flexible to permit the use of material in various forms (e.g. raster (grid) datasets, point-line-polygon data), at different scales and geographical projections.

CARTOGRAPHIC BASE DATA

A requirement that is common to many of these topics is the need for a digital cartographic base map. At its simplest, this is needed so that the output can be presented in graphical form as maps. Other applications envisage more sophisticated use of the cartographic database, including spatial overlay and quantitative estimation of areal and linear features.

DATA SOURCES

Given the diversity of the data requirements, it is not surprising that the sources of these data are correspondingly diverse. As indicated earlier, CORINE is designed as a secondary data source, and the guiding principle has been to make use of existing data sources wherever possible.

Therefore wherever data sources covering the whole (or large proportions of) the Community exist, these have been used. Examples of this include:

- a map of soils in the European Community at a scale of 1:1M, compiled by the European Commission;

- a digital map of the coastal outline and surface water pattern, compiled by the Institut fur Angewandte Geodaesie;

- a map of administrative units in the Community, compiled by the Commission's Statistics Office and digitized at Sheffield University from maps provided by the Commission;

- digital maps of physical geographic features covering the northern half of Europe and compiled by the Mapping and Charting Establishment of the UK Ministry of Defence for air navigation purposes (the PACE Project - Production of Automated Charts for Europe);

384

- OECD data on atmospheric emissions of sulphur oxides and nitrogen oxides.

When Community-wide data sources do not exist, national sources have been consulted. For example, National Meteorological Offices have provided climatic data, and National Nature Conservation Agencies supplied details of sites of biological importance.

Information on land cover underpins many of the topics which CORINE is intended to serve. It is planned to stimulate the compilation of a digital land cover map of the Community derived from remotely-sensed imagery, using a single unified land classification system.

As noted earlier, the CORINE programme is a framework for bringing together and harmonizing existing data: neither the expertise nor the resources are available for extensive primary data acquisition. However, for some applications, data do not exist in a suitable form to be used directly. In such exceptional circumstances, it has been necessary to undertake some re-processing of the primary data. For example, a map of mean slope is being compiled for southern Europe on a 1km grid to assist in assessing soil erosion hazards.

Where data exist in digital form, they have been incorporated directly into the database. It has invariably been necessary to invest considerable effort to the problems of inter-conversion between different physical and logical data formats, and for harmonizing different units of measurement, classifications, and different cartographic conventions. A particular problem has been the need to reconcile boundaries which are common to two or more digital maps.

Where the data exist only in paper form, it has been necessary to digitize the maps (or to key tabular data). For obvious reasons, this activity has been kept to a minimum.

TIMELINESS AND UPDATING POLICY

Since CORINE has only been in operation for 2 years, and since efforts have been concentrated initially on the acquisition of data and the compilation of a consistent database, the problem of updating has not yet been put to the practical test.

Clearly, after the present experimental phase, procedures must be implemented to ensure that the data are timely and accurate. Consideration has been given to this in the planning and design of CORINE. The requirement for currency and the consequent frequency with which the database needs to be updated is, to a large extent, data dependent. For example, the nature of soils changes only slowly, and revision of the soil map should not be needed in the foreseeable future. Most of the climatic data recorded in CORINE consists of 30-year means; these too are comparatively stable and revision at a frequency of the order of ten years should be adequate.

On the other hand, human geographical features change rather more rapidly, and some elements of the cartographic base (e.g. roads, urban boundaries) will require more rapid revision. Land cover generally is liable to change and the effects of this change can have major impacts on environmental quality (e.g. landscape value, habitat quality). The ability to monitor change in land cover patterns is therefore an important requirement for CORINE, and one that it will be difficult and expensive to achieve, even with the use of remote sensing.

Some of the themes covered by CORINE are particularly susceptible to change - both natural fluctuations and trends induced by changes in environmental conditions. For example, biological populations can change suddenly and dramatically and it is important that decisions on the ecological value of Community sites are taken on the basis of recent information. Updates to the Biotopes database are likely to be needed at a frequency of at least 3 - 5 years.

However carefully the database is compiled, it is probable that it will contain errors and inaccuracies and that these will become apparent through validation checks or in normal use. Irrespective of the need to maintain currency, it is important to ensure that such errors are corrected rapidly after their detection.

Data revision can be just as resource-intensive as the compilation of the original data. It cannot, and should not be the function of CORINE (or of any similar global or international system) to attempt to undertake extensive revision of primary data. Instead, CORINE will depend upon existing programmes of data revision in the regional or national sources where the data originate. For example, revisions to map sheets will be incorporated into the database as and when they are published.

ACCURACY, PRECISION AND SCALE

Ideally, questions of accuracy and precision should be determined by the uses to which the data are to be put. Unfortunately, given CORINE's dependence upon existing primary data sources, accuracy is largely pre-determined, and varies both between and within thematic overlays.

Of particular relevance in this context is the question of spatial scale. In view of the variety of potential applications for CORINE, an early objective was to design a database that was largely independent of scale. However, there are difficulties in achieving this objective. Generalization of mapped data from large to small scales is fraught with problems. Conversely, attempts to superimpose small-scale and large-scale overlays will at best give meaningless results and at worst, will give rise to wholly erroneous conclusions.

Yet some compromise is necessary, given the diversity of scales at which environmental data are recorded across the Community. In the short term, two parallel databases are being compiled. The main system is building the larger database, at a notional scale of 1:1M. A more generalized system is also being compiled at a scale of 1:3M, which will include those features which are at present recorded only at the smaller scale.

DATA VOLUMES

It is possible to estimate data volumes only approximately, since this is so dependent upon methods used for data storage (e.g. the extent to which data compaction techniques are used).

At a scale of 1:1M, the territories of the European Community are covered by seven standard map sheets. The variables listed in Table 1 correspond to about 10 - 12 thematic overlays, so the complete 1:1M database is equivalent to about 70 - 80 map sheets.

In terms of digital data storage, the 1:1M database presently occupies 200 Mbyte and is expected to grow to about 500 Mbyte by the completion of the present programme in 1989. The 1:3M database presently occupies 12 Mbyte and is projected to expand to approximately 25 Mbyte by 1989.

STRUCTURE OF DIGITAL REPRESENTATION

Data have been acquired by CORINE in both vector and in raster form.

Some datasets record variables associated with a point location. For example, Biotopes are at present located with reference to the centroids of the areas described (though it is intended eventually to record the actual boundaries of the larger sites in digital form). Climatic data are at present associated with the location of the meteorological stations from which they originate; the intention here is for automatic generation of rainfall and temperature contours.

Most of the mapped data are recorded as points, lines and polygons as vectors. A minority of datasets (e.g. slopes, atmospheric emissions) were compiled in raster form, but provision is being made for inter-conversion from raster to vector format, so that it will be possible to select the format which is most appropriate for any given application.

To improve efficiency of access, the 1:1M database is structured as tiles, each of which corresponds to an area 2-deg in longitude by 1-deg in latitude. This tiling is transparent to the user. There has been no need to structure the 1:3M dataset in this way.

USERS AND USER NEEDS

The development of a computer system to handle the large volumes of data resulting from the CORINE programme is an important element of the work. The purpose of a GIS is to provide a means of storing, processing and displaying geographically-referenced data according to the needs of its users. Since the nature of the data varies considerably - in geographic scale, resolution, projection, format, whether they relate to point, line or polygon features, etc. - an operational GIS must be capable of receiving and handling great quantities of a wide range of data types, of converting them to a standard format for analysis and of outputting the results in almost any number of ways to satisfy the demands of the user. This requires sophisticated and powerful computer facilities, while the design of a GIS demands an understanding not only of the hardware and software tools used, but also of the characteristics of the data and of the needs, aspirations and limitations of the potential users.

In the case of CORINE, the principal users are the staff of the Commission of the European Communities (initially the Environment Directorate, but increasingly staff from other Directorates of the Commission, including particularly the Agriculture Directorate and the Statistics Office). Other potential users include national governments and other international agencies (e.g. the Council of Europe, FAO etc), but it has not been possible to consider in detail the needs of these secondary users.

Detailed data requirements in relation to each of the thematic applications mentioned above have been specified by Project Teams - groups of advisers with experience in the relevant scientific disciplines. In addition, a number of user studies have been commissioned with the intention of drawing up specifications for the computer system (Rhind 1981, Hanke et al 1985). The Commission will shortly publish the results of an internal study, with the purpose of drawing up technical specifications for a computer system capable of servicing the operational requirements of the CORINE programme.

HARDWARE AND SOFTWARE

In the meanwhile, given that specification of user requirements remains incomplete and that no single system is yet available which is capable of satisfying all the applications envisaged, it was decided to establish an interim system. This interim system is intended to provide both the processing facilities needed during the experimental stage and the experience necessary to help define the specifications for a final system.

In fact, several computer systems have been used during the experimental programme. The main 1:1M database has been established using Arc/Info software, running on a DEC VAX-11/750 at Birkbeck College, University of London. In addition, a much smaller work station has been installed in the CORINE offices in Brussels, using a Siemens machine running SICAD. The SICAD system supports the 1:3M database. A pilot database recording land cover in one Member State (Portugal) was developed from remotely-sensed imagery, using an International Imaging Systems IIS Model-75 image processor, and a small raster database has been established for experimental purposes, recording a number of relevant thematic overlays at a scale of 1:100,000.

THE CORINE DATA TRANSFER FORMAT

Consistency is important not only in the collection of data but also in their transfer and exchange. Given the diversity of its data sources and the number and geographic dispersal of its potential users, this is of particular concern for the CORINE programme. Ultimately, the problem needs to be tackled at a wider international level. In the meanwhile, data transfer specifications have been devised which are used for all data exchange into and out of the CORINE system (Hayes-Hall 1988). It is hoped that these standards will provide a framework for the design of systems for wider international use in the future.

LAND COVER INFORMATION

During the course of the CORINE project, innovative procedures for the extraction of information on land cover, based on machine-assisted photo-interpretation of satellite imagery, have been developed (CORINE 1987). A standard land-cover classification, suitable for the range of vegetation and cover types encountered throughout the Community, has been developed and tested. Land-cover maps are generated as thematic overlays on photographic prints of false-colour composite images. Digital image-processing techniques are used to enhance the imagery in order to resolve any ambiguities in interpretation. Finally, the thematic map is vector digitized and entered into the CORINE database.

ACCESS CONDITIONS

Conditions under which the database may be accessed are still under review. In general, data which are held in CORINE in a processed form (for example, maps of land quality derived from a combination of soil, hydrological and climatic data) are considered to be freely available; the raw data would be accessible only by agreement with the original source.

Users in national agencies and sources which have contributed to data held in CORINE are encouraged to access the system, since it is through use of the data that problems can best be identified and solved. Other users may be allowed access by agreement.

However, it must be recognised that CORINE is presently (and will remain for the foreseeable future) under development. The database contains known errors and inconsistencies. All information provided from CORINE carries a statement which disclaims responsibility for the consequences of using the data. This disclaimer will remain until the process of quality checking and verification is complete.

PROBLEMS AND ISSUES

The CORINE programme has encountered a number of technical and scientific problems, mainly arising from a failure to appreciate, at the time the themes were selected, the practical limitations of data availability and the difficulty of harmonizing those data which do exist at national or Community level. At the very least, future users of the CORINE system must be made aware of these limitations if the data are not to be misused and misinterpreted.

To take just one example, information on the levels of atmospheric emissions of sulphur oxides is required in order to assess their potential environmental effects on a Community scale. Data recording these emissions directly are not generally available. CORINE has chosen to use information which records the level of industrial activity in the various industrial sectors as an indicator of levels of emissions. Unless users are fully aware of the history of these data, there is a risk that they could be mis-interpreted; for example, it would be all too easy for the naive user to take these maps of 'emissions' and to derive convincing, but spurious correlations between atmospheric pollution and the incidence of a particular industry.

Therefore, great emphasis is placed in the CORINE programme on the importance of full and accurate documentation of data. A technical handbook has been published, describing the provenance, completeness and characteristics of each dataset in the interim database (Whimbrel Consultants Ltd., 1988), and a computerised register of data sources is in preparation.

The problems of achieving cartographic consistency between different databases have been legion, and their solution has required the investment of many hours of laborious manual editing. A particularly common unforseen difficulty has been the absence of basic information about the coordinate reference system, and sometimes the projection used for published maps. As a result, the task of overlaying datasets which at first sight appeared straightforward, was often extremely time-consuming.

The lack of Community-wide data to common standards was a common problem and was particularly acute in the case of basic cartographic data. The PACE dataset provides a useful digital record of many important geographical features at an appropriate scale (1:500,000), but covers only the northern half of the Community. There is no corresponding dataset for the Mediterranean region. Therefore a less detailed map of coastal outlines and the surface water pattern compiled by IFAG was used as a topographic base. (Even the IFAG database did not cover Greece, so that the Greek coastline and rivers had to be separately digitized).

Standardization of data formats has also provided interesting problems and examples of human perversity. In addition to the standards for data exchange mentioned earlier, each of the main thematic activities necessitated the specification of standards for recording the various data. It rapidly became clear that the specification and documentation of such standards is one thing; achieving adherence to those standards is quite another matter! In practice, when the problems of data acquisition were acute (as they were in most cases), it was usually easier to make ad hoc arrangements to read and interpret the data than to attempt to enforce the standards. Consequently, most groups associated with the CORINE programme rapidly became adept at writing 'one-off' programmes to read foreign datasets.

Beside these rather fundamental difficulties, the shortcomings of particular GIS systems paled into insignificance. There have been few instances where it has not been possible to generate a products requested by a user because of the limitations of a computer system. There have been many such instances where the quality of the data available have prevented a useful response, or have introduced considerable delay.

One feature of the computing arrangements is worthy of note, since it could be relevant to the implementation of other international systems. This concerns the location of the GIS separately from its users (in London, rather than in Brussels).

Although Arc/Info is an interactive system, it is not amenable to interactive use across slow and unreliable telecommunications lines, particularly given the volumes of data associated with the CORINE files. Therefore it was impractical for users to acquire 'hands-on' experience with Arc/Info or with the database. To overcome this particular concern, it was decided to locate a second system (Siemens /SICAD) in the Commission building in Brussels. This also provided the opportunity for informal evaluation of a second GIS in an operational context and ensured a faster response to the production of cartographic output in response to user enquiries and for promotional and publicity purposes, while allowing the main Arc/Info system at Birkbeck College to concentrate on the task of building the database.

CONCLUSIONS

Even at this early stage in the CORINE programme, it is possible to identify a number of positive achievements.

Most notable of these has been its success in evolving standards for recording environmental data. This has been achieved in several sectors and in some cases extends beyond the European Commission and now includes other national and international agencies. The success of this element in the programme is not entirely coincidental, since explicit efforts have been made to build upon and to harmonise with existing practices and standards, wherever possible.

The programme has already demonstrated the feasibility and utility of an integrated Community Environmental Information System. The CORINE database is already extensive (see Table 1) and is in regular use, not only by the Environment Directorate-General, but by other Directorates of the Commission and by other collaborating national and international agencies.

Finally, CORINE has provided a stimulus for similar integrative activities at the national level, and is providing a template for national environmental information systems in several Member States of the European Community.

However, the lessons to be learned from the CORINE programme go further than the technical issues: they include more general and far-reaching considerations which should be taken into account in any continuation of the programme or in similar extensive international exercises.

Foremost among these is that an information system - whether relating to the environment or any other policy area - must be reasonably complete and coherent if it is to be effective. Information systems can only be justified if they allow users to perform a wide range of analyses on the database, according to their own needs, thus minimizing the need for ad hoc data collection.

But this is only feasible if:

- the information in the system is logically and geographically consistent;

- the information relates to themes that are themselves logically related;

- the system is fully operational.

The experience with CORINE suggests that a short-term experimental programme, based around a collection of loosely-related themes, is not the most effective framework for building an effective information system.

In future, more thought needs to be given to building such systems from the bottom up. This would entail concentration in the initial stages on the design of the system and the compilation of basic data, rather than on the provision of aggregated information on policy themes. The disadvantage of this approach, of course, is that politically attractive results do not emerge so quickly.

The fact that the CORINE programme is answering a perceived political need gives it clear advantages and provides a strong orientation for the work. However great its immediate shortcomings, the eventual practical benefits as a policy tool are apparent. Nevertheless, to optimize its value, it is essential that the technical implications should not be overlooked or ignored in the ambition to meet political needs and demands. It is also of crucial importance to find the means by which political goals can be translated into clear technical specifications.

In conclusion, the CORINE programme has emphasized the need for harmony between political objectives and financial commitment on the one hand, and technical reality and scientific rigour on the other. This harmony is, perhaps, one of the most elusive goals of public policy making.

ACKNOWLEDGEMENTS

The authors are consultants to the Commission of the European Communities, with the responsibility for advising on the design and the development of CORINE. They are grateful to the Commission for permission to publish this material. This paper records the views of its authors, and does not necessarily represent the opinion or policy of the European Commission.

REFERENCES

Briggs, D.J. and Martin, D., 1988. CORINE: an environmental information system for the European Community. European Environmental Review, 2(1), 29-34.

CORINE, 1987. Land Cover. Etude de faisabilit. Commission of the European Communities. Brussels.

Commission of the European Communities, 1983. Communication of the Commission to the Council concerning a methodological approach to an information system on the state of the environment and natural resources in the Community (1984-87). Commission of the European Communities, COM(83) 528, Brussels.

Council Decision of 27 June, 1985 on the adoption of the Commission Work Programme concerning an experimental project for gathering, coordinating and ensuring the consistency of information on the state of the environment and natural resources in the Community (85/338/EEC). Official Journal of the European Communities L 176/14, 6 July 1985, p.4.

Hanke, H., Ophoff, W. and Wyatt, B.K., 1985. Study of user needs for a computer system for an information system on the state of the European environment. Commission of the European Communities, Brussels.

Hartley, R.P. and Higgins, M.J., 1987. 'Developing a GIS for the European Community within the CORINE programme'. Proceedings of the SORSA Symposium. Durham, May 1987.

Hayes-Hall, E., 1988. CORINE data transfer specifications. Version 4.0. London: Birkbeck College, Department of Geography.

Rhind, D.W., 1981. Computer processing and mapping requirements of the 'Ecological Mapping' Community Project. Commission of the European Communities, XI/443/81, Brussels.

Rhind, D.W., Wyatt, B.K., Briggs, D.J. and Wiggins, J.C., 1986. 'The creation of an environmental information system for the European Community'. Nachrichten aus dem Karten und Vermessungswesen, Series II, 44, 147.

Whimbrel Consultants Ltd., 1988. The CORINE interim database. Version 1.0. May 1988. Brussels: Whimbrel Consultants Ltd.

Wiggins, J.C., Hartley, R.P., Higgins, M.J. and Whittaker, R.J., 1987. 'Computing aspects of a large geographic information system for the European Community'. International Journal of Geographic Information Systems, 1(1), 77-87.

SUMMARY OF THE RESULTS OF THE TYLNEY HALL MEETING

Michael F. Goodchild

This text was presented by the author at the Royal Society, Friday May 13th 1988.

CAVEATS

My task is to summarize the discussion which took place at the First Meeting of the Global Database Planning Project at Tylney Hall, and to present the findings of the meeting. I would like to begin, however, with a few caveats and apologies.

The individuals who participated in the Tylney Hall meeting came from a variety of disciplines and backgrounds, each with its own terminology and assumptions. Over the course of the meeting some convergence occurred: acronyms were explained and new ones defined. I would like to report the results of the meeting in the broadest possible context, but inevitably there will be terms which are well understood by the participants but may be entirely lost on some of the audience here today. I would also like to be able to lay the groundwork on which many of the results are based, but that is simply not possible in the time available.

THEMES OF THE MEETING

The Global Database Planning Project began with several objectives, and it is clear from the discussions which have taken place over the past week that the project will continue to develop along several distinct but mutually supportive directions. First, the project is concerned with the problems of constructing and maintaining databases at global scales. During the course of the week the point was made repeatedly that this objective lies in the area of applied science or engineering; that it is concerned with the application of existing knowledge about the handling of spatial data to the particular problems of the globe. This knowledge includes the results of research on the digital representation of spatial data, including methods of structuring such data and the algorithms which must operate on it. In addition the construction of global databases must be sensitive to, and informed by, research on the nature of spatial data itself, including models of measurement error and time dependence.

Second, it is clear that any comprehensive effort to design and build databases at global scales will be multidisciplinary in character, requiring effective communication between the disciplines which accumulate knowledge about the handling of spatial data, including computer science, statistics and geography, and those which model global processes, such as oceanography and meteorology. Spatial data handling is an enabling technology with potential benefits for a range of scientific disciplines. Its effective exploitation raises fundamental issues of science policy - how does one bring the relevant disciplines together and ensure effective awareness of their respective needs and skills? Is this best done through the work of international, multidisciplinary scientific organizations such as ICSU, or is it possible to rely on traditional methods of communication through the scientific literature? Or is this a case requiring the introduction of international scientific standards, by analogy to the SI system or latitude and longitude?

The third theme of the meeting revolved around the need for basic research and development. Many of the principles on which good global database planning must rest are not yet adequately researched. We lack a full understanding of the statistics of uncertain spatial data, and good methods of subdividing the area of the globe into discrete elements suitable for a wide range of modeling. These and other questions will require multidisciplinary cooperation between the earth sciences, computer science, spatial statistics and geography.

The mixed themes of the conference have inevitably produced a mixed bag of results. Some of the proposals which I describe below are items for action in the short term. Others are proposals for longer term research, and some are fundamentally elusive. The six which follow have been ordered from the most immediate and pressing, for which we have already developed detailed courses of action, to the most speculative but nevertheless of great significance in the long term.

Legal and copyright issues

Some sources of global data, such as NASA, provide complete coverage of the globe from a single measurement system. Other data must be assembled from national or regional organizations under a wide range of conditions of availability. This is particularly true of social data, which will be of increasing importance in studying man's effects on the global environment and the effects of global environmental change on human existence. Issues of accessibility, copyright and legal responsibility will be of increasing importance, and there is a pressing need to clarify the current situation in many of these areas. This is particularly so in the light of increasing involvement of the private sector in global database construction.

We therefore propose the immediate establishment of a working group to assemble information on issues of accessibility and copyright, to report within the next six to twelve months. Its mandate will be to assemble relevant and useful information on the legal issues surrounding the use of data from multinational sources, and to recommend actions which might be taken to improve access.

Directory of global datasets

The second item for short-term action is the establishment of a working group to prepare a directory of existing datasets suitable for inclusion in global databases. The IGBP and parallel efforts to promote a program of research into human response to global change have created the need for a new level of integration of data about the globe. Data must come from sources as disparate as remote sensing platforms and published cartography, and methods must be developed for integrating such data into comprehensive models. We might consider global spatial data as arrayed along a continuum, from the most stable and general-purpose at one extreme to the most transitory and special-purpose at the other. The former is typified by cartographic data; although a major change occurred in the outline of the Antarctic continent in the past year, such changes are thankfully uncommon. The transitory extreme might be typified by data collected at sample points for the purposes of a single project. In between the two extremes lie sources such as Landsat, transitory but of use in many applications.

Although there have been highly successful efforts to establish global databases in the past, efforts such as the World Data Center program seem largely concerned with relatively small windows of this continuum. The new interest in global science requires the unprecedented integration of all of these sources, and creates new imperatives for access and compatibility. A directory which spanned the continuum would be immensely useful to workers in the various disciplines of global science. We see this working group as reporting within twelve months.

Quality standards and interchange formats

Quality control is a major issue in spatial data handling, particularly when disparate sources are involved. Many of the models being built for global science are highly nonlinear, so that small errors can propagate uncontrollably. The Butterfly Effect, the notion that because of the nonlinearities of the global atmosphere it is possible for the beating of a butterfly's wings in Beijing to affect the weather over the UK, has profound implications for a cartographic discipline which is unused to expressing its accuracies in objective terms.

We see an immediate need to establish quality standards and interchange formats for global data. A working group will be formed, to report within six to twelve months, to extend and integrate the work already carried out at the national level in several countries, and to adapt it to the specific needs of global science. In the longer term we propose that a group be established with the objective of promoting and monitoring the adoption of these standards. We also see the need for basic research on the propagation of errors originating in spatial data through the models of global systems currently being built.

Global databases and the needs of global science

This is the first of our longer-term proposals. There was lengthy discussion during the meeting of the ways in which research in spatial data handling might influence and inform efforts at global modelling, and our first three proposals are aimed at addressing the needs of the latter in a direct fashion. In the longer term we see the need to promote and summarize research on improvements in spatial data handling technology which are driven directly by the needs of global science. We see several areas in which this technology needs substantial improvement, and in which new methods and results are needed. In addition this work

400

needs to be brought together and published in an accessible form, in a major publication.

In the area of data structures, it is clear that emerging views on the nature of global systems requires analysis over a wide range of scales and levels of resolution. Current systems for spatial data handling lack the means to represent objects at multiple levels of resolution, or to handle generalization in a comprehensive manner.

Global science will require attention to the accessibility of spatial data. The ability to visualize data will be important, and will require the development of new methods of display which deal with time dependence and uncertainty. There is a need for extensions of the concept of exploratory data analysis to the spatial domain. Much of the current technology for spatial data handling is based on a two-dimensional, static view of data which is appropriate for stable coastlines but not for modelling ocean systems. We need to develop workstations and systems which will allow scientists to work with time-dependent global data in appropriately designed environments and exploit the full advantages of spatial data handling technology.

Long-term scenarios

Current efforts to build global databases are based on existing levels of sophistication in hardware, software and communication networks. We see the need for an extended discussion of possible future scenarios in each of these areas, in order that planning for global databases can be as fully informed as possible. What communication networks can we expect to be in place in thirty years, and how can these be anticipated in decisions we make today for data collection? What will be the likely developments in hardware speeds and storage capacities? Will improved communication networks make it more effective to distribute or centralize global database construction?

Clearly we cannot anticipate future developments. But we can consider the implications of possible future developments for current actions, and work to remove some of the inevitable uncertainty. The lead times for spatial data collection are very long so that decisions which are made today will affect the availability of global data for decades to come. We propose a working group with a relatively long-term mandate to assemble and develop future scenarios for global databases and their implications for actions in the short term.

Mechanisms for continued coordination

Our final proposal concerns the need for continued coordination of global database planning activities. We plan to continue to work through organizations such as IGU and ICSU, and to build on earlier efforts to coordinate databases at national, international and global scales. Meetings such as the one now concluding must act to bring together expertise in the numerous areas which impact global database construction and use, and to build on previous experience. In the immediate future we will be presenting the results of this meeting to the IGBP in Moscow in August.

CONCLUSION

We feel that a great deal has been accomplished in the past week at Tylney Hall. The proposed working groups will be put in place in the next two months, and the proceedings of the meeting will be available in August, hopefully prior to the Moscow meeting. This brief summary has been a very rapid overview of the meeting but I hope I have given you an adequate understanding of its major results.

RETROSPECT

J.T. Coppock

The forty nine people who gathered at Tylney Hall for the first meeting of the Global Database Planning Project of the International Geographical Union came from a variety of backgrounds and brought a wide range of experience. Categorising them is complicated by the fact that many wore more than two hats, both as an employee of a governmental organisation or academic institution and as a represent- ative of an international body. By affiliation, and counting people with multiple affiliations more than once, the largest proportion, just over a third, came from governmental organisations, with a quarter each from academia and international agencies. Not surprisingly, given the dominant role in relation to databases played by national and international bodies, only five were in the private sector. By country of residence, two fifths of those attending came from North America and two fifths from Europe (with the United Kingdom providing the largest contingent), but there were also three representatives each from the Soviet Union and two from the People's Republic of China. On a rough estimate, just over half of those attending were geographers.

The number of participants could, of course, have been very much larger. Not all relevant international agencies or scientific bodies were represented, nor were the space agencies of Europe, India, Japan and the Soviet Union; it would also have been useful to have had a member from each of the Working Group on Data and Information Systems of the International Geosphere-Biosphere Programme Committee, the Planning Committee on Global Change of the International Social Science Council and, in view of the importance of liaison at international level and the possible lessons from national experience, the Interagency Working Group on Data Management for Global Change of the US Government. But fifty was probably the maximum number who could have participated effectively in a meeting of this kind, and the group was sufficiently varied to ensure effective and informed discussion.

403

STATUS, DESIGN AND PROBLEMS OF GLOBAL DATABASES

The first day and a half were devoted to a review of the status, design and problems of existing and planned global databases, the presentations on which form the bulk of this volume. In reality, although all those who presented papers had something interesting and relevant to say on these topics, they were not all correctly described under that heading, since some were not concerned with global databases, but had focused their attention on a single country or part of a country, or on a larger region, as with the CORINE project, and others were primarily involved with national databases and had varying degrees of interest in global systems. Of the four international agencies, three of them under the United Nations' umbrella, the Food and Agricultural Organisation (FAO) was a line agency which needed global data to fulfil its operational functions and already held numerous datasets for that purpose, the Global Resource Information Database (GRID) was a pilot system until December 1987 and met on demand the requests it received for data from a large number of databases which it had obtained from other sources, the World Meteorological Organisation (WMO) collected no data and served primarily as a coordinating body for national meteorological agencies, and the International Union for the Conservation of Nature and Natural Resources (IUCN), a non-governmental body that was nonetheless the principal inter-national agency for conservation, was investigating the re-structuring of the four principal databases it held and their possible incorporation into a geographical information system (GIS).

The international scientific bodies were similarly varied, most being essentially coordinating bodies that depend heavily on actions by other bodies and/or individuals. Some such as the Commission on the World Digital Database for Environmental Science (WDDES), the International Oceanographic Commission and the International Society of Soil Science are concerned with the production of a single global product in digital form and are at various stages of development towards that end. Others such as the International Geographical Union's (IGU) Commission on Global Monitoring and Forecasting, the International Council of Scientific Unions' (ICSU) Scientific Committee on Problems of the Environment, and its Committee on Data for Science and Technology's Programme of Remote Sensing in Earth Science, are investigating various topics that bear upon the creation of global databases. The most relevant to the work of this meeting and to the Project as a whole are the World Data Centres (WDCs) operating under the aegis of ICSU; for these have the principal function of receiving, holding and transmitting to users a wide variety of scientific data, some of it global, supplied by others.

Perhaps the most interesting among the national agencies from the perspective of global databases are the National Aeronautics and Space Administration (NASA) and the National Oceanographic and Atmospheric Administration (NOAA) which have responsibility for many of the non-military satellites launched from the United States, since these have generated a large proportion of the global databases that are available. Although these are national agencies with national responsibilities, they have international functions, and plan to play a major part in collecting data required for the International Geosphere-Biosphere Programme (IGBP), along with the European Space Agency and others. Not only are these two agencies much larger in terms of resources than most other bodies involved in the collection and use of global data, but they highlight many of the problems of relating the provision of data to users needs for data and, at least prospectively, conflicts between scientific, operational and commercial considerations. Their activities also foreshadow the awesome prospect of exponential growth in the volume of global data and the potential problems that poses for receiving, archiving and manipulation of such data. No doubt the other national space agencies have similar contributions to make, although apart from a brief reference to the System Probatoire de l'Observation de la Terre (SPOT), their potential was not discussed.

Another major category of generators of global databases was one that played only a subdued part in these discussions, namely military organisations, although the Defence Mapping Agency was represented, and B. Tew presented a paper on work in the British Military Survey. Laymen can only speculate on what military organisations hold by way of global data that would be of value to scientists, although the existence of military satellites is well known. Military mapping agencies are also heavily involved in the development of digital mapping and geographical information systems, and have interfaced with non-military (including scientific) bodies for the release of material which does not imperil military security. In the context of the discussions at this meeting, the Defence Mapping Agency has already stated its intention of producing a world digital topographical map at a scale of 1:1M by 1990 and there are also indications that it may subsequently produce a global map at 1:250,000. Because of such activities and the much larger resources commanded by these agencies, D.W. Rhind argued for greater collaboration between military map makers and the scientific community.

Despite the variety of these contributions, a number of points of wider interest did emerge. The question of motivation for establishing global databases was raised directly in two of the papers, those by S.A. Evteev and S.B. Rostotsky, and by S. Unninayer, and also in discussion. It should not be assumed as axiomatic that global databases are necessary simply because they exist. Data are costly to collect, to store and to maintain (even if the cost is somewhat hidden in large organisations), and it is essential that the potential users of data and their needs be identified before steps are taken to create such databases. For some, a global view is unnecessary; soil scientists for example, see little value in a world soil map at a scale of 1:5M (but may make use of one at 1:1M). For others, a global database serves primarily as a source of data for individual countries or regions. Some global databases clearly arise in response to a specified need for global monitoring or forecasting, as with meteorological data; others are a response to a perception of a more general need as with the global database assembled by GRID, rather than pressure from a clearly defined clientele of users. The World Data Centres, in contrast, arose for a specific scientific purpose, related to the International Geophysical Year, but have since developed and expanded their role. A distinction could usefully be made between those databases that are created because the data are there (even if collected for some other purposes), and those where an unmet need leads to the collection or assembly of data not previously available (or unavailable in that form). Whatever the origins, there is certainly enough evidence to suggest that the nature and needs of prospective users do not receive sufficient attention before decisions to create databases are made. The kind of market research undertaken in respect of WDDES appears to be the exception that proves the rule.

The question of needs overlaps that of the characteristics of the data required, particularly their up-to-dateness, resolution and degree of generalisation. D.P. Bickmore highlighted this question of data quality in his remarks about the need for substantial editorial work on the 1:1M Operational Navigational Charts (ONC) once these have been digitised and before they are entered into the database. The CORINE project demonstrated how questions of timescale

and resources made it necessary to use data of variable
quality collected by others and even, on occasion, to use
surrogate data because no satisfactory data on the required
topic were available; topics for investigation were also
chosen for political reasons despite the fact that good
data were lacking. The need for updating and the cost of
maintaining an archive up-to-date also received attention;
but in the main, there was surprisingly little discussion
in these accounts of data quality and of the need for
proper documentation. Speakers seemed more concerned with
the admittedly important questions of volumes of data and
the integration of disparate sources.

Relatively little attention was paid in these discussions
to the source of data, apart from those derived from
sensors or satellites. Three presentations from the
Commission on WDDES, from the Intergovernmental
Oceanographic Commission and from the International Society
for Soil Science were specifically concerned with projects
to create new digital databases at scales of 1:1M, by
digitising an existing source of data, the ONC and the
General Bathymetric Chart of the Oceans, respectively, or
by creating a new database from maps of larger scales where
available and from other sources. A.V. Drozdov and his
collaborators were unusual in stressing the large
quantities of data that had been collected by field
observations over many years and the contributions that
these might make to IGBP. He also stressed the importance
of field stations as a source both of data and of ground
truth for the interpretation of satellite imagery, a role
also envisaged for IUCN's field operations around the
world. Clearly the collection of data in the field will
have to play a major part in securing satisfactory data on
conditions on the land surface of the planet, where
problems of interpretation of satellite imagery are more
acute than in the atmosphere and in the oceans.

Another part of the hidden agenda was cost. Figures were
given for the capital and on-going costs of holding data in
the NASA Ocean Data System, but these are only a small part
of the total costs of acquiring, processing, archiving and
distributing these data. One indication that did emerge of
the cost of obtaining global data was the 150 man-years
required to produce the FAO/UNESCO Soil Map of the World,
but in general the availability of data was taken as read
and not regarded as part of the cost of developing the
system. Not surprisingly, it was a non-governmental
organisation, IUCN, that made specific reference to its
cost, in its expectation that 50% of the revenue from sales

407

of data would be devoted to updating and improving the system. Similarly, D.P. Bickmore's Commission on WDDES, a scientific initiative of the International Cartographic Association, has had to await a commercial sponser before it could go ahead - a development with implications for the likely cost of datasets to users. In contrast, much of the cost of running the WDCs is borne by national governments and data have usually been supplied free to users or at a minimum charge to cover the cost of handling. The GRID system, too, has largely been funded by gifts of equipment and data and by secondments of staff from national agencies, and has similarly pursued a policy of providing data to users without charge. Such policies may change in a climate that increasingly sees information as a marketable resource, and as commercial interests in global data grow. The commercial value of data is already seen as a constraint on the development of global databases and the USSR has identified the commercial value of data as an obstacle to the exchange of data with those countries with market economies.

Cost is only one factor affecting access to data, which will also be determined by official policies and by administrative arrangements. The policy adopted by the WDCs, which should serve as a model for all, is that they will accept no constraint on access to the data they hold and no data that implies such constraint. The Centres freely exchange data across international boundaries and between countries with such different philosophies and attitudes to data as the Soviet Union and the United States. Moreover, since the role of the Centres is to hold data for the benefit of the scientific community, such access is facilitated, enquiries and visits are welcome, and data dictionaries and guides provided. The National Space Science Data Center in Washington is similarly a source of information and data for scientists. Line agencies, on the other hand, necessarily adopt a less open door, since their prime function in holding databases is the more efficient fulfilment of their functions, in such circumstances, they may have an interest in distributed systems that are easy to use by staff but are less readily accessible to those outside the agency. There are also arguments for and against concentration of data in a few and its dispersal in many centres. GRID, for example, proposes to extend the number of centres where data and processing facilities will be available, whereas the trend in WDCs has been towards a few large, comprehensive centres. The advent of more powerful workstations and the development of networks are both likely to be major influences on such decisions.

Many technical questions were raised in the presentations, but, with so many papers, the time available for discussion was limited, and most of the points were discussed in the following session on the Principles and Problems of the Design, Implementation and Utilisation of Global Databases, and in the subsequent working groups, which concentrated primarily on technical issues. This session was, however, proceded by a presentation by John Woods, a member of the ICSU Special Committee for IGBP, in which he outlined thinking on the implementation of the programme, as he saw it, with a focus on the chemistry of the atmosphere, with particular reference to sources and sinks of chemicals in the oceans and on the land. In many ways, it was unfortunate that this meeting preceeded that of the Special Committee in October when the plan for IGBP would be discussed, for subsequent discussions at Tylney Hall revealed that there were differences of emphasis among the national committees of IGBP which would no doubt be resolved at the meeting in Stockholm. There was also an underlying discussion, never fully resolved, on how far IGBP included reference to Man and his modifications of the environment and whether, if not, these questions wee matters of concern to this project. S.B. Rostotsky cited a speech in Moscow by Dr. T. Rosswall, Executive Director of IGBP, in which he stated that man's impact was a matter for the Human Response Programme; in Rostotsky's view, if the Global Change Programme ignored Man and his impact on the environment, it would impoverish itself, a view shared by others at the meeting. It has to be recognised, however, that the Global Database Planning Project is viewed as a contribution by the IGU to IGBP, and this issue can be resolved only by discussion at the highest level.

PRINCIPLES AND PROBLEMS OF DESIGN, IMPLEMENTATION AND UTILISATION

The papers presented in the sessions on principles and problems had been commissioned by the Organising Committee and covered four main themes: the efficient design of spatial databases and appropriate models for them; inputs from remote sensing and cartography and their relationships to GIS; problems of resolution and accuracy; and legal aspects of global databases.

D.F. Marble's contribution on the design of global databases stressed the importance of identifying all significant users and their needs, since an aim must be to maximise the utility of these large databases over as large a number of users as possible. Other important ingredients of the design process were the definition of institutional roles in such a system, resolution of issues of acceptable accuracy and provision for archiving and data dictionaries to preserve the long-term utility of the databases. While design would have to proceed on the basis of existing knowledge, so that - in effect - science would be frozen, the design process would nevertheless provide a flexibility that would allow subsequent changes to be accommodated.

D.J. Peuquet dealt with the selection of appropriate data models and reviewed both general principles and research developments. She concluded that, while tesseral models offered opportunities, vector models would continue to be necessary, and various options were open for combining the two types. A quadtree model represented the limit of what she thought practical today.

In a contribution not included in the papers in this volume, M.J. Jackson noted that it was not possible to lay down a single data structure for organisational reasons and because of fundamental differences in the kinds of spatial data. He outlined a geoschema of data organisation and noted the need for a user interface, since users could not be expected to be confronted with the complexity of a global database. Two key design goals must be a distributed network, involving linked databases and hence interchangeability and standardisation, and high-level graphical interfaces, which would have to be based on general-purpose hardware since the market would not be large enough to support special equipment.

In his review of the integration of remote sensing and geographical information systems, D.S. Simonett expressed considerable concern about the funding available for scientific aspects of the Earth Observing System. Scientific aspects had been underfunded in past satellite programmes and this weakness seemed to be repeated in present plans. He also noted with concern that much historical data form both NASA and NOAA ha been destroyed. He focussed particular attention on the High Resolution Imaging Spectrometer and urged an input from IGBP to specify requirements of data at a level appropriate for geographical databases. He saw a profound interplay between remote sensing and GIS and raised as crucial issues the science questions that should drive the digital databases of the future and the need for connecting database models that would permit the full integration of disparate data sources. His views on funding were challenged, but it was also indicated that the international scientific community could have a major influence on the programme.

In discussing inputs of cartographic data into global databases, D.W. Rhind stressed the complementarity of remote sensing and cartography, with their very different characteristics. Problems of the accuracy of cartographic data had been underplayed in relation to global databases, and he noted other problems associated with poor updating, differences in generalisation and inconsistencies in classification. In view of the ease with which maps could be misused, was it possible for misuse to be limited in some way? He also urged recognition of the role of the military in trying to establish standards and in updating the need to cooperate, but saw problems in achieving this.

In the first of two contributions on accuracy and error, W.R. Tobler stressed that resolution critically affected information content, and raised the question whether data should be stored at very high resolutions and then generalised or stored at different resolutions. M.F. Goodchild reviewed the various kinds of error that might occur in global data and saw the objectives as minimising error and measuring it. Reality was modelled either as a continuous surface or as homogenous areas and it was desirable to put reality into the database and model from that; we had to stop reality being too far removed from the database - the big errors were not in digitising but in the data themselves.

E.V. Epstein's contribution on legal aspects of global databases was very different from that of any other contributors. He noted that both national policy and budgets for staff and resources in support of databases might restrict the flow of data and raised, but did not answer, a number of questions concerning ownership of data and issues of copyright on both data and software. The confidentiality of personal data and definition of international boundaries were issues at either end of the spectrum that might affect the availability of global data.

Three general points were made following these presentations. First, it was suggested that the papers laid great stress on problems and constraints, but that, while these

411

were important, there was too little emphasis on what needed to be done. Second, the temporal dimension had been neglected and we lacked models that integrated the spatial and the temporal; there was often a spatial dimension within time, in that change often implied movement, and we needed to take account of both dimensions. Third, there was a clear need for the measurement, logging and documentation of error, for work on the propagation of error and the creation of artefacts, and for sensitivity testing and the development of robust models that minimised the importance of the many weaknesses of the data, There were also many unanswered questions - whether digitising had ceased to be a constraint and whether computing was in the process of following suit; what were the main constraints on developing global systems; what would be the influence of remote sensing on traditional cartography and what was the role of visualisation?

REVIEW BY WORKING GROUPS AND THE FORMULATION OF RECOMMENDATIONS

The remainder of the meeting was devoted to a review and discussion of written and spoken contributions and to the formulation of recommendations for further action. M.F. Goodchild, as chairman of the Scientific Committee, presented the views of a Committee on the themes that had emerged during the previous three days and identified the issues that might then be further discussed by working groups. Three cross-cutting themes were identified, concerning problems associated with global databases currently under way, interactions with IGBP and Human Response to Global Change (HRGC), which would be major users of global databases, and the need for a research agenda on issues and impediments to the development of useful global databases. From these themes, nine topics had been identified:

1) Scientific uses of global data - the need for a matching of global science and global data, including consideration of the extent to which IGBP-type models needed to be integrated with GIS.

2) Remote sensing as a major source of global data - including issues of volumes, tiling, resolution, error modelling, access, networking, use of spatial statistics and cost.

412

3) Cartographic inputs to global databases - including problems of integrating cartographic sources, handling spatial data in data-poor environments, useful scales of input, priorities of different categories of data, duplication of effort, and the influence of technological changes outside cartography.

4) Database design - including the need for hierarchical data structures, object-orientated and field orientated tiling, thematic division and tagging data to indicate reliability.

5) Networks - the relative influence of likely developments in speed of central processing, communication rates and the ability of databases to handle large volumes, networking of data, software or results, and organisation of networks.

6) Data structures and interchange - the need for standards and formats for interchange, the role of software in generating topology, and the implications for the support of software and hardware and archiving.

7) Copyright and legal issues - the significance of the private and public sectors in respect of access to, and protection of, large databases, issues of litigation and responsibility in the production and use of data.

8) Accuracy and error - establishment of standards for quality statements, research in error modelling, the role of ground truth and the prevention of the misuse of data.

9) Implementation - consideration of the role of the IGU group, the structures, timetables and possible partners for further work.

These topics were then discussed, Among the points raised were the following.

1) It was important, given the timetable of IGBP, not to get involved in long-term research, but rather to consider what could be offered now.

2) It is also necessary to invest time in basic research on the new models that will be needed to characterise the terrestrial surface, on which our attention should be concentrated.

3) Both approaches are possible. In the short term, we need current operational solutions but there are also some long-term issues that require basic research.

4) There are several groups to be influenced, including designers of databases, IGBP and those in research institutes and universities.

5) There are some intractable problems that cannot be solved now and it would be helpful to identify those which can and cannot be solved at this stage and to set priorities.

6) We need to fashion a response to IGBP, to establish their needs and timetables and to identify what we can deliver. We have a special role in respect of the land. Models of the land surface are very difficult and complex, and we should provide models of searching and browsing and system designs for land surface-related information systems.

Following the discussion, it was decided to establish four working groups, to report the following morning. These would investigate:

- Status and needs
- Database design
- Inputs to global databases
- Legal and institutional issues

The group investigating status and needs considered that current archives of global data are more properly regarded as databanks than integrated global GIS. It was suggested that databases should be considered global only if they were concerned with phenomena which were global in nature, origin or effects; and that they satisified the criteria of either being global phenomena that had an impact on the local environment or represented an ensemble of local changes that had an impact on the global environment. The group identified a number of short-term activities, including the compilation of a directory of current and proposed databases, evaluation of the relationship between global databases and GIS and also of the relationship between global databases and the needs for global data. In the medium term, the group proposed that selected databases should be made available for testing and evaluation; that comparisons should be undertaken of datasets that claimed to show the same phenomena; and that a critique of existing databases would be made, with the emphasis on integrated

414

spatial / temporal questions. In the longer term, there would be feedback that would permit the preparation of design standards and, in the light of comments from the scientific community and the emerging needs of IGBP and HRGC, the identification of databases needing enhancement and of new databases that were required.

The group discussing design concluded that in the short-to-medium term, it was unrealistic to think of a fully-integrated global GIS and that the most practical approach was an integration of different databases with global coverages. The technology to handle such databases existed but better data management was needed. There was also a need for explicit data dictionaries to accompany databases and for common exchange formats that would provide gateways between databases. Few examples existed of global databases that had been designed as such from the beginning; an indication was required for each database of the quality of the data and their fitness for use. Although the group regarded a global integrated GIS as unattainable at present, it believed that the aim of such a GIS was necessary to provide the global schema which was essential in order to secure the integrated and consistant development of conceptual models of individual databases. In the short term, the group recommended the preparation of an inventory of existing global databases, which would require considerable resources to complete. Thereafter, a review should be undertaken of the feasibililty of creating a 'Master Extractor' which would not be hardware or software dependent. To assist the transfer of design technology to database builders the group recommended the preparation of a series of pamphlets, the most urgent of which would be one on the creation of the global schema, local schemas and data dictionaries, and a critical review of possible spatial data structures.

The group discussing inputs to global GIS databases recommended that the IGU Project should endorse a proposal of a NASA working party to establish a hierarchical global elevation data model; and that a group be established to study existing and proposed referencing systems, with special reference to their suitability for global databases, and to draft recommendations for review by relevant organisations. It also recommended that global databases would be compatible, in terms of accuracy and information content, with mapping at appropriate scales. The structure of global databases (which would depend primarily on cartographic and remote sensing inputs) whould permit the inclusion and efficient handling of all other spatially-referenced information. Accuracy standards should be developed for global databases and all included data should have qualifiers relating to their origins and accuracy. Producers of remote sensing data should make them available in forms compatible with appropriate spatial referencing systems, Lastly, the IGU should establish an ad hoc advisory group on global data inputs which should include representatives of the main operators and users.

The group on legal and institutional issues (the smallest of the four, perhaps reflecting lack of expertise in this area) reviewed the roles of global data institution, their organisation, support, sources of data and existing and possible future sources of finance, and the possible consequences of distributed networks and a flood of new data. It also considered legal aspects of data control, ownership, responsibility and liability, as well as questions of costs and revenues. Among the issues discussed were the nature of the liability attached to data transferred from other sources, the nature of data as an asset, the mechanisms that existed to control the use of data and the ways in which the nature and the structure of databases might influence control and liability. It also considered the ethical responsibilities of producers of data. A number of short-term recommendations were made: that an inventory of existing world data organisations should be undertaken (including their structure and activities); that expert advice should be sought on international law relating to claims arising from the use of poor data; that an inventory be made of national and international practice relating to copyright, fees and constraints on the release of data; and that a survey be made of the bases for private investment in databases.

CONCLUSIONS AND RECOMMENDATIONS

The chairmen of the four groups reported that evening to the Chairman of the Organising Committee and then to the other groups the following morning. A summary of suggested actions and recommendations was then put to the group and subject to further discussion. Six main conclusions and items for further action were then identified.

1. Establish a working party to investigate the legal issues of control, ownership, liability and copyright as they affect the construction, maintenance and use of global databases.

2. Plan the development of a directory of georeferenced global datasets.

3. Formulate proposals for research in the key areas of accuracy, error and integrity of data. Also to encourage the development of standards of interchange of global databases between scientists and international agencies in respect of data quality and formats.

4. Identify the developments necessary to improve accessibility to global data and their usefulness to scientists working in programmes related to the global environment.

5. Develop guidelines for the creation of a global schema, local subschemas and data dictionaries.

6. Develop mechanisms for continued coordination of global database planning activities.

These results were then communicated to an open meeting at the Royal Society.

REFLECTIONS

This first meeting of the Global Database Planning Project was at once exhausting, frustrating and fascinating. Too much was attempted in too short a time and participants probably suffered from information overload. In an ideal world, the presentations should have been circulated in advance and authors whould have spoken briefly to them in order to allow more time for discussion; but, in the real world, papers were not ready in time for global circulation and few if any of the busy people who participated would have found time to read them. Given the realities, an alternative, not unknown in committee meetings, might have been to provide a period at the beginning of each session when members could at least have browsed through the papers. On the other hand, the format was right, in isolation from a large city and in pleasant surroundings where those informal discussions - which are the life blood of all good meetings - could take place.

Even with the upper limit of fifty, however, a lecture-type presentation allows only a minority to participate in any discussion, especially if time is short. Small group discussions, with clearly defined topics, are likely to be more productive. Timetables were also extremely tight for rapporteurs to produce their reports for distribution the following morning (and possible only through dedicated secretarial work), involving the distillation of many pages produced under pressure in the face of high-speed exchanges. Is there no ready technological solution to such problems?

This paper has been primarilly a summary of what took place at this first meeting. Three majors concerns surface in my mind as I reflect on the week's proceedings. The first, which received increasing attention, was the importance of securing a much better understanding of the needs for global data and the nature of those needs. The second related to the problems, not much discussed except in respect of cartographic data, of assembling global data from a variety of national sources, and particularly those from developing countries which often lack the resources and administrative structure to secure good quality data. Perhaps this is more a problem for HRGC than for IGBP, but I wonder if there is not a need for something in the GIS field analogous to CLICOM, the programme whereby expert meteorological help is provided to meteorological services in developing countries. The third concerns the institutional issues arising from the fact that global data are held both by national and by international bodies. Problems of coordination within national governments and the difficulties of securing a view of data as a national and not a departmental resource pale into insignificance beside those of attempting to achieve similar objectives internationally. The WDCs and GRID both represent mechanisms for acquiring, manipulating and distributing global data that do work, but both are underfunded and vulnerable in that respect. Where national agencies take on international roles, problems also arise, and it significant that no mention has been made at this meeting of the possible contributions of remotely-sensed data from other countries. Can we expect these to be added in due course as a free gift to the holdings of GRID and the WDCs, and will the necessary funding be forthcoming for these agencies to take on a wider role?

This meeting has been of experts, but I also wonder about the demonstration of global GIS on the less expert and the non-expert. We noted earlier how CORINE, although an experimental project, has influenced developments in environmental GIS and in data gathering in constituent countries. May not an international prototype GIS have the same kind of effect? I am attracted by the proposal

418

emanating from the World Data Center for Geophysics at Boulder for the assembly of existing global digital datasets on a CDRom disk, together with user-friendly software to enable the data to be used in an exploratory way. May this and similar developments not help to contribute to the growing awareness of global problems that will also be stimulated by IGBP and HRGC and so provide the constituency of support that will permit the expansion and development of the global databases that we have seen to be desirable?